AN INTRODUCTION TO

ASTRONOMY

THE AURORA BOREALIS

From a painting by Howard Russell Butler at Ogunquit, Maine. (*Courtesy of the American Museum of Natural History, New York*)

AN INTRODUCTION TO
ASTRONOMY

by

ROBERT H. BAKER, Ph.D.

FIFTH EDITION

D. VAN NOSTRAND COMPANY, INC.
PRINCETON, NEW JERSEY

TORONTO   LONDON
NEW YORK

D. VAN NOSTRAND COMPANY, INC.

120 Alexander St., Princeton, New Jersey (*Principal office*)
257 Fourth Avenue, New York 10, New York

D. VAN NOSTRAND COMPANY, LTD.
358, Kensington High Street, London, W.14, England

D. VAN NOSTRAND COMPANY (Canada), LTD.
25 Hollinger Road, Toronto 16, Canada

First Published *March 1957*

Reprinted November 1957

PREFACE TO THE FIFTH EDITION

The thorough rewriting of this book in the new fifth edition to bring it again up to the times has given opportunity for some rearrangement as well. The chapter on the constellations is introduced later than before so as not to break the continuity of the earlier chapters. The description of eclipses now appears at the ends of the chapters on the moon and sun. Star clusters are placed in a separate chapter as their increased importance seems to require. Radio astronomy and the current thinking about cosmic evolution receive more attention.

The general plan and purpose of the book remain the same as in the previous editions. It is a textbook for an introductory course in astronomy without special prerequisites. For this purpose the new edition has the same convenient size as before. Review questions at the ends of the chapters serve to recall what has been read, and lists of references may suggest further reading on the different subjects.

Among the noteworthy advances in this active science since the preparation of the previous edition are the first important results with the 200-inch Hale telescope. The recent enlargement in the values of the distances and sizes of the galaxies has improved our view of the universe. Our own galactic system is still a giant among them, but is no longer considered the largest of all. The first tracings of spiral arms of our galaxy are described. The new activities of radio telescopes in this and other inquiries are noted in various places in the book. The growth of interest in astronomy among the amateurs is recognized by a brief account of some of the larger amateur organizations.

A number of colleagues have contributed suggestions and also material for new illustrations. Dr. Bart J. Bok and Dr. Priscilla F. Bok have given valued advice for the new edition and have critically read the entire manuscript.

ROBERT H. BAKER

Claremont, California,
February, 1957.

CONTENTS

CONTENTS

1

THE EARTH AND THE SKY

THE GLOBULAR EARTH – THE CONVENTIONAL GLOBE
OF THE SKY – EFFECTS OF THE ATMOSPHERE

A small planet attending the sun which is but one of the multitudes of stars, the earth owes its importance to the fact that we live
here. Here we view the celestial scene around us. In order to in-
terpret the scene aright, we first consider the earth that looms large
in the foreground. The science of the stars begins at home. Our
study of astronomy begins with the globe of the earth at the center
of the apparent globe of the heavens and encompassed by the atmosphere through which we look at the celestial bodies.

THE GLOBULAR EARTH

1·1. The Planet Earth. The earth is a planet which revolves
around the sun once in a year, and rotates on its axis once in a day.
It is a dark globe illuminated by the sunlight. The earth's diameter is nearly 8000 miles, and is 27 miles greater at the equator than
from pole to pole. Its mass is 6.6×10^{21} tons, or 66 followed by
20 ciphers, which however is only three millionths of the sun's
mass.

The earth is the only planet known to have large water areas. It
is likewise unique in having an abundance of water vapor and free
oxygen in its atmosphere. With these important features and also
its sufficiently moderate range in surface temperature, it is the only
known planet that seems inviting to life, and particularly to human
life.

1·2. The Texture of the Earth. Aside from its oceans and atmosphere the earth is a globe of rock, which consists essentially of two
parts: the *mantle*, 1800 miles thick, and the *core*. The *crust* is the
outermost 20 miles of the mantle; at least in its outer parts the crust
is composed of igneous rocks, such as granite and basalt, overlain
with sedimentary rocks, such as sandstone and limestone, all to-

1

gether about 3 times as dense as water. The rest of the mantle is composed of heavier silicates of magnesium and iron. Our knowledge of the earth's interior is gained almost entirely from the way it transmits earthquake waves at different depths to distant seismographs.

The core of the earth seems to consist of two parts having different properties. The outer core, more than 1000 miles thick below the mantle, behaves like a liquid; it does not transmit earthquake waves resembling light waves. The inner core, 18 times as dense as water, behaves like a solid, although its temperature may be as high as that at the surface of the sun. Long supposed to be composed of nickel-iron such as is found in many meteorites, this central region by a more recent theory of W. H. Ramsey may consist of the same material as in the higher levels, except that it is more strongly compressed here by the pressure of 60 million pounds to the square inch. There is the idea, too, that the core may be rotating at a different rate from the rest of the earth, and that the interactions may cause the irregularities in the earth's rotation which are troublesome in our timekeeping.

1·3. The Earth's Magnetism has some resemblance to the field of a bar magnet thrust through the earth's center and inclined at a considerable angle to its axis of rotation. The north magnetic pole, toward which the north-seeking end of the compass needle is directed, is in the vicinity of northwest Greenland 1200 miles from the earth's north pole; the south magnetic pole is nearly opposite in Antarctica. The magnetism at a particular place varies in strength and direction and is especially unsteady during a magnetic storm.

Some scientists suppose that the observed magnetic field is a combination of two: (1) the main field lined up with the axis of the earth and caused by its rotation; (2) a residual field caused by motion in the liquid outer core in a way not completely explained. The poles of the field drift westward around the earth once in about 1600 years. Effects of the earth's magnetism are seen in the scarcity of auroral displays and of cosmic rays near the magnetic equator. Magnetic effects are observed in the heavens as well; they are observed in the sun, particularly in sunspots, and in certain stars. They are also inferred in the behavior of the grains of cosmic dust in interstellar space.

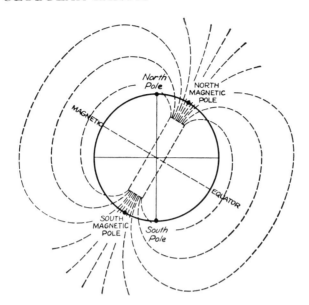

Fig. 1·3. The Earth's Magnetic Field. The magnetic axis is inclined to the axis of the earth's rotation. (*Schematic diagram adapted from* **H. E. White's** Modern College Physics)

1·4. The Earth as a Celestial Body. The photographs of a region of the earth from a rocket at the altitude of 101 miles (Fig. 1·4) give an idea of how the earth would appear from the moon through a telescope magnifying 2400 times. It would appear as a globe, on which its main surface features would be visible. As indicated by the Gulf of California at the upper left in the figure, the water areas would contrast clearly with the land. Bright areas of snow-fields and drifting clouds would add variety to the scene. The works of man would be less clearly revealed. Observed from the moon with the unaided eye (Fig. 1·4A), the earth would appear among the constellations in the lunar sky, nearly 4 times as great in diameter as the moon does in our skies.

From the nearest planets the earth would look like a bright star moving through the constellations. From Mars it would be a fine evening and morning star. From the outermost planets it would be lost in the glare of the sun. From the nearest star the earth and all the other planets would be invisible through the largest telescope, and the sun would be only one of the bright stars.

FIG. 1·4. The Earth from the Altitude of 101 Miles. A mosaic of 4 photographs from a V-2 rocket launched at the Army Ordnance Proving Ground at White Sands, New Mexico. A large area of southwestern United States and northern Mexico is shown. (*Courtesy of Naval Research Laboratory, Washington*)

1·5. Artificial Satellites. The National Academy of Sciences announced in 1955 the decision to launch into space several artificial satellites of the earth. The first launching is scheduled for 1958 from Patrick Air Force Base in Florida. This satellite will be a sphere 30 inches in diameter, weighing $21\frac{1}{2}$ pounds. It will be carried by a multistage rocket and released at a height of 300 miles into very thin air, where it will be given an initial nearly horizontal velocity of about 17,000 miles an hour. Thereafter it will revolve around the earth once in $1\frac{1}{2}$ hours in somewhat eccentric and varying orbits which may range at first between 200 and 800 miles from the ground. Gradually spiraling inward because of air re-

FIG. 1·4A. The Earth as seen from a Crater on the Moon. From a painting by Howard Russell Butler. (*Courtesy of the American Museum of
Natural History, New York*)

sistance, it should finally disintegrate in denser air after an unde-
termined interval.

The artificial satellite may be very faintly visible to the naked eye
in the twilight when it comes near the observer's zenith and is in
the part of its orbit that is nearest the earth. Half its weight will
be that of the apparatus it contains for the recording of physical
measurements and for transmitting them to the ground. It is
expected that the records will add to our information about the
upper atmosphere, the radiations and particles that come in from
outside, and certain properties of the earth that will affect the orbit
of the satellite.

1·6. Positions on the Earth.   One way of denoting positions on the earth's surface is with reference to natural or conventional areas. It is often satisfactory to the inquirer if we say, for example, that Havana is in Cuba or that Cleveland is in Ohio. A second way, especially where positions are required more accurately, is with reference to circles we imagine on the earth and represent on globes and maps. These familiar circles are mentioned here so that we may notice presently their resemblance to circles imagined in the sky.

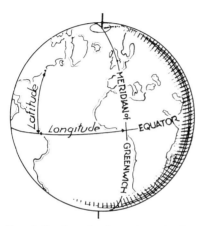

FIG. 1·6.   Longitude and Latitude.

The earth's *equator* is the great circle halfway between its north and south poles. *Parallels of latitude* are parallel to the equator. *Meridians* pass from pole to pole and are, accordingly, at right angles to the equator; they are slightly elliptical but are considered as circles for some purposes. The *prime meridian,* or *meridian of Greenwich,* passes through the original site of the Royal Observatory at Greenwich, England. It crosses the equator in the Gulf of Guinea at the point where the longitude and latitude are zero.

The *longitude* of a place is its angular distance east or west from the prime meridian; it is generally expressed in degrees, from 0° to 180° either way. If the longitude of a place is 60° W, the place is somewhere on the meridian 60° west of the prime meridian. The *latitude* of a place is its angular distance in degrees north or south from the equator, from 0° to 90° either way. If the latitude is 40° N, the place is somewhere on the parallel of latitude 40° north of the equator. Where the longitude and latitude are given, the position of the place is uniquely defined. As an example, the longitude of Yerkes Observatory at Williams Bay, Wisconsin, is 88° 33′ W, and the latitude is 42° 34′ N.

THE CONVENTIONAL GLOBE OF THE SKY

An early picture of the earth and sky represents the appearance so well that we often employ it today, as in Fig. 1·11. Here the earth is a circular plane on which the sky rests like an inverted bowl. A later picture, proposed by Greek scholars as early as the 5th century B.C., is also useful for our descriptions, as in Fig. 2·10. It shows the sky as a spherical shell surrounding a spherical earth at its center. The earth is relatively so very small that it may be only a point in the diagrams at the center of the celestial sphere.

1·7. The Celestial Sphere. Although the stars are scattered through space at various distances from the earth, the difference in their distances is not perceptible to ordinary observation. All the stars seem equally remote. As we view the evening sky, we may imagine that the celestial bodies are set like jewels on the inner surface of a vast spherical shell. This *celestial sphere* survives only as a convenient means of representing the heavens for many purposes. By this convention the stars can be shown on the surface of a globe or in projection on a plane map. Their positions are then denoted in the same ways that places are located on the globe of the earth.

The center of the celestial sphere may be the center of the earth, the observer's place on the earth's surface, the sun, or anywhere else we choose. The size of the sphere is as great as we care to imagine it. Parallel lines, regardless of their distance apart, are directed toward the same point of the sphere, just as the parallel rails of a track seem to converge in the distance.

1·8. Places of the Stars. The *apparent place* of a star is its place on the celestial sphere. It denotes the star's direction, and nothing else about its position in space. Where two stars have nearly the same direction, although one may be more remote than the other, they have nearly the same apparent place. We speak similarly of the apparent places of the sun, moon, and planets. We say that the sun is entering the constellation Leo, and remark on the nearness of the moon to a bright star.

The *apparent distance* between two celestial bodies is accordingly their difference in direction; it is often called the *distance* between them, where there is no chance for ambiguity. Such distances are expressed in degrees or other angular measure. The distance between the Pointers of the Great Dipper is somewhat more than 5°; it is a convenient measuring stick for estimating other distances in the sky.

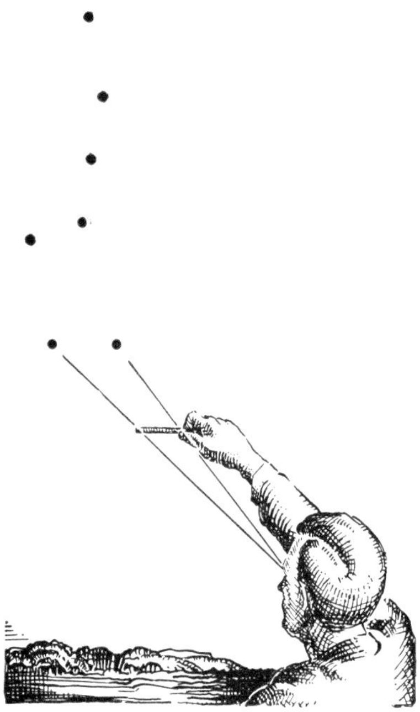

How shall we describe the place of a star so that others will know where to look for it? One way is to specify the constellation in which the star appears. If we say that the star Algol is in the constellation Perseus, anyone who can recognize the different constellations knows about where this star is situated. It is like saying that New Haven is in Connecticut. A second way of denoting the place of a star is with reference to circles of the celestial sphere, such as the horizon.

FIG. 1·8. The Distance Between the Dipper's Pointers Is About 5°.

1·9. The Horizon. Sight along a vertical line. A cord by which a weight is suspended provides such a line when the weight comes to rest. This line leads upward to the *zenith*, the point directly overhead in the sky, and downward through the earth to the *nadir*, the point directly underfoot.

The celestial horizon, or simply the *horizon,* is the great circle of the celestial sphere that is halfway between the zenith and nadir, and therefore 90° from each. The direction of the horizon is observed by sighting along a level surface, perhaps a table top. Because the vertical line is at right angles to the earth's curved surface, the positions of the zenith and nadir among the stars are different at a particular time in different parts of the world.

The *visible horizon,* the line where the earth and sky seem to meet, is rarely the same as the horizon of astronomy. On land it is usually irregular and above the celestial horizon. At sea it is a circle in calm weather, which lies below the celestial horizon; this *dip* of the sea horizon increases with increasing height of the observer's eye above the level of the sea.

1·10. The Celestial Meridian. *Vertical circles* are great circles of the celestial sphere which pass through the zenith and nadir, and accordingly cross the horizon vertically. The most useful of these circles is the observer's *celestial meridian,* the vertical circle that also passes through the north and south poles of the heavens. We consider in the following chapter the locations of the celestial poles, which fix the direction of the celestial meridian. The meridian, in turn, determines the positions of the four *cardinal points* of the horizon: north, east, south, and west.

North and *south* are the opposite points where the celestial meridian crosses the horizon. The *east* and *west* points are midway between them. As we face north, east is to the right and west to the left. When the cardinal points are located, it is proper to define the celestial meridian as the vertical circle that passes through the north and south points.

The north star is almost directly above the north cardinal point, as viewed in north latitudes. The sun is above the south point at noon by the sundial; it rises near the east point and sets near the west point at the beginning of spring or autumn. By such means the directions of the cardinal points are determined.

1·11. Azimuth and Altitude. The *azimuth* of a star is measured in degrees along the horizon from the north point toward the right to the foot of the vertical circle through the star. Thus the azimuth of a star is 0° if it is directly in the north, 90° in the east, 180° in the south, and 270° in the west. Some astronomers prefer to reckon azimuth around from the south point instead.

The *altitude* of a star is its distance in degrees from the horizon, measured along the vertical circle of the star. The altitude is 0° if the star is rising or setting, 45° if it is halfway from the horizon to the zenith, and 90° if it is in the zenith. The *zenith distance,* or the star's distance in degrees from the zenith, is the complement of the altitude.

This is one way of denoting the place of a celestial body. Where, for example, would we look for a star in azimuth 90° and altitude 45°? We would look due east and halfway from the horizon to the zenith; and if the azimuth is 180° and the altitude is 30°, we would find the star due south and a third of the way from horizon to zenith. Certain instruments operate in this system based on the horizon. The engineer's transit is an azimuth-altitude instrument.

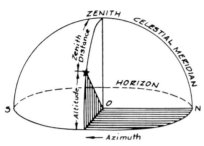

FIG. 1·11. Azimuth and Altitude of a Star. Azimuth is measured along the horizon from the north point around toward the east. Altitude is angular distance above (or below) the horizon. Zenith distance is the complement of altitude.

The navigator's sextant is employed mainly for measuring the altitudes of celestial bodies.

Defining positions in this way has its limitations, because positions so determined are only for a particular instant and place on the earth. The azimuths and altitudes of the celestial bodies are always changing with the daily motion of the heavens, and at the same instant they differ in different parts of the world. We find in the following chapter that more nearly permanent positions can be given relative to the equator rather than the horizon. Meanwhile we turn the attention to the earth's atmosphere and notice particularly how it affects our view of the sky.

EFFECTS OF THE ATMOSPHERE

1·12. The Region of Clouds. The earth's atmosphere is a mixture of gases surrounding the earth's surface to the height of several hundred miles. From its average pressure of 15 pounds to the square inch at sea level, the mass of the entire atmosphere is calculated to be 6×10^{15} tons, or somewhat less than a millionth of the mass of the earth itself. The air becomes rarefied with increasing altitude so rapidly that half of it by weight is within $3\frac{1}{2}$ miles of sea level. The lower atmosphere is divided into two layers, the troposphere and the stratosphere.

The *troposphere* extends to heights ranging from 10 miles at the equator to 5 miles at the poles. Its temperature diminishes upward to the average of −68° F at the top. Consisting chiefly of nitrogen and oxygen in the proportion of 4 parts to 1 by volume, it also contains carbon dioxide, water vapor, and other gases in relatively small amounts, as well as dust in variable quantity. The carbon dioxide is especially serviceable as a blanket to keep us warm at night. Like the glass roof of the greenhouse, it lets the sunlight through to warm the ground, and by its strong absorption of infrared radiations it prevents the rapid escape of the heat.

Fig. 1·12. Cirrus Clouds. (*Photographed at Mount Wilson Observatory*)

The troposphere is the region of rising, falling, and swirling currents, and of clouds which seem too often to interfere with our view of the heavens. Rising air is favorable to the formation of clouds; the moisture it carries is cooled by expansion and by contact with the cooler surroundings. Fog-like *stratus clouds* begin to form at the average elevation of half a mile. *Cumulus clouds* rise from flat bases a mile aloft. The *cirro-cumulus clouds* of the "mackerel sky" have the average altitude of 4 miles. Finally the feathery *cirrus clouds* of ice crystals may be as high as 7 miles or more.

1·13. The Stratosphere extends from the troposphere to a height of 45 miles. Here the currents are chiefly horizontal. The constituents of the air are in about the same proportions as in the region below, with two exceptions. Water vapor is scarce; ozone, having its molecule composed of 3 atoms of oxygen, is formed by action of the sun's ultraviolet radiations on ordinary oxygen molecules mainly in the lower stratosphere.

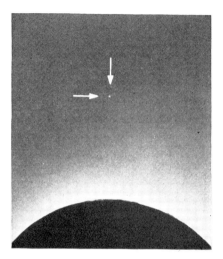

Fig. 1·15. Regulus Near the Uneclipsed Sun. (*Photographed by M. Waldmeier, Arosa, Switzerland*)

Ozone is the most abundant at elevations of from 10 to 20 miles. It helps to protect us from the extreme ultraviolet rays of the sun, which would be injurious to life of all kinds if it could penetrate to the earth's surface. These rays are now being studied in photographs from rockets above the ozone levels to determine what additional information they bring about the sun itself.

The stratosphere contains one fifth of the entire air mass; to its upper limit it is dense enough to make some contribution to twilight, as is known from the duration of this light. Twilight (2·19) is sunlight diffused by the air onto a region of the earth's surface where the sun has already set or has not yet risen.

1·14. The Upper Atmosphere extends from the altitude of 45 miles to at least 500 miles. Here the rare gases are most exposed to the impacts of high-frequency radiations and high-speed particles from outside. The molecules are largely reduced to separate atoms, and the atoms themselves are shattered into electrically charged components.

The *ionosphere,* the region up to the altitude of 200 miles, contains at least 4 fluctuating layers where the ionized gases are concentrated. By successive reflections from these layers and the ground, radio waves can travel long distances before they are dissipated. When the layers are disrupted during a magnetic storm, communication by radio in the higher frequencies is disturbed.

The impacts of particles from the sun on the gases of the upper atmosphere illuminate these gases in the airglow and in the varied colors of the aurora. Auroral streamers reach as far as 500 miles aloft, showing that the atmosphere extends to that height. In the lower ionosphere the resistance of the denser air to the swift flights of meteors heats them to incandescence, so that they make bright trails across the sky.

1·15. The Daytime Sky. The stars are invisible to the unaided eye in the daytime, because the atmosphere diffuses the more intense sunlight down to us from all parts of the sky. The sunlit air also conceals most of the other celestial bodies by outshining them. In addition to the sun, only the moon is conspicuous ordinarily in the daytime. The planet Venus near the times of its greatest brilliancy can be seen without the telescope as a star in the blue sky. The bright planets and stars, however, are easily visible with the telescope in the daytime sky, and with special devices they can be photographed even near the edge of the sun (Fig. 1·15). Why is the clear sky blue, whereas the sunlight itself is yellow?

Sunlight is composed of many colors, as we observe when it passes through a prism, or through raindrops or the spray of the waterfall; it contains all the colors of the rainbow. As the sunlight passes through the atmosphere, the violet and blue light is most scattered by the air molecules, and the red light is least affected. Hence on a clear day the sky takes on the blue color of the light that is scattered down to us most profusely. The blue deepens as we ascend above the humid and dusty lowest layers, and must change to black at a height so great that there is very little air above.

When the sun is near the horizon, most of the blue of its direct light is scattered away before it can reach us through the greater thickness of air that then intervenes. The red light comes through more successfully. Thus the sun is reddened at its rising or setting.

1·16. Apparent Flattening of the Sun. There is another aspect of the sun near the horizon as familiar as its reddened color. There the sun sometimes appears so noticeably flattened at the top and bottom (Fig. 1·16) that it resembles a football. This appearance is caused by refraction of the sunlight in the atmosphere. Refraction of light is the change in the direction of a ray of light when it

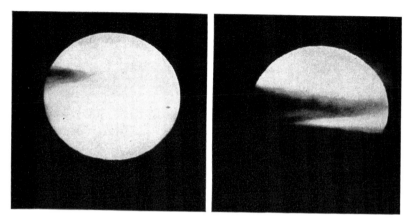

Fig. 1·16. Flattening of the Setting Sun by Refraction. *(Photographed at Yerkes Observatory)*

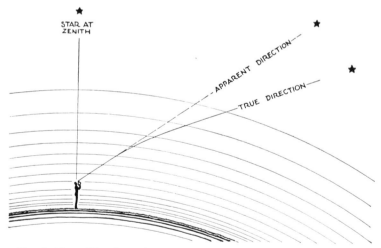

Fig. 1·16A. The Stars Are Elevated by Atmospheric Refraction.

passes from one medium into another, as from airless space into air. The effect is described in Chapter 5 in connection with the operation of the refracting telescope.

As the light of a celestial body comes through the air, it is bent downward by refraction (Fig. 1·16A), so that the object seems to be higher in the sky than its true position. The amount of the apparent elevation increases with the zenith distance of the object, but so gradually at first that for more than halfway to the horizon it is not enough to be detected without the telescope. Near the horizon the increase is rapid, until the effect becomes conspicuous to the naked eye. An object on the horizon is raised above its true place more than half a degree, or more than the apparent diameter of the sun or full moon. Because of the rapid increase in the amount of refraction as the horizon is approached, the circular disk of the sun appears elliptical; the lower edge is raised considerably more than the upper edge.

In addition to its flattened appearance the sun's disk seems to be larger near the horizon than when it is higher in the sky. This is an illusion having nothing to do with refraction. By the same illusion, the moon and the star figures, such as the bowl of the Great Dipper, seem magnified near the horizon.

1·17. Twinkling of the Stars. One of the first things we notice about the stars is their twinkling; their light is unsteady. Especially near the horizon, where a greater thickness of air intervenes, the stars flicker conspicuously at times, and the brightest ones seem to splinter into rainbow hues. The air near the earth's surface is often in commotion; warm currents are rising, cold currents are descending, while horizontal movements of layers of different densities add to the confusion. Viewed through this turmoil the stars twinkle because of the rapidly varying refraction of their light, just as the landscape seems to quiver when we look through the "heat waves" over the highway on a summer day.

The bright planets usually do not twinkle. They are luminous disks instead of points of light, as even a small telescope shows. Each point of the disk may twinkle like a star, but the different points do not do so in unison, because their rays take slightly different paths through the disturbed air. Similarly the moon shines with a steady light.

Through the telescope the images of the stars are blurred when the air is especially turbulent. The rays in each beam of starlight which enters the telescope have been diverted from perfect parallelism and, accordingly, are not brought to the same focus by the lens. Features of the moon and planets also appear blurred in such conditions. The "seeing is bad," and there is not much to be done about it except to wait for better seeing.

FIG. 1·18.   A Solar Halo.   Halo of 22° radius observed at St. Moritz, Switzerland.   (*Photographed by F. Quénisset*)

1·18. Lunar and Solar Halos.   Bright rings which sometimes appear around the moon and sun have no special astronomical significance. They are noticed and commented on by watchers of the skies and are fine examples of refraction effects in the atmosphere. The rings are produced by ice needles and snowflakes in the cirrus and cirro-stratus clouds. These 6-sided crystals refract the moonlight or sunlight, concentrating it in certain directions. Although many effects are possible, the most common one is a single ring having a radius of 22° around the moon or sun. This ring often shows rainbow colors, with the red on the inner, sharper edge the most prominent.

"Moon dogs" and "sun dogs" are two enlargements of the ring on opposite sides of the moon and sun. These appear when many snowflakes in the clouds float with their bases horizontal. A second ring having a radius of 46° and parts of other rings are seen less frequently. The impression that the appearance of a ring around the moon or sun gives warning of an approaching storm has some basis in the fact that the filmy clouds which form the halos are likely to fly ahead of storm clouds.

FIG. 1·19.   The Aurora in Alaska.   (*Photographed by the Geophysical Institute, University of Alaska*)

1·19. The Aurora, or "northern lights" of our hemisphere, is characterized in middle northern latitudes by a luminous arch across the northern sky, its apex in the direction of the magnetic pole. Rays like searchlight beams rise above the arch, drifting, dissolving, and reforming, and draperies may appear in other parts of the sky. Green is the usual color, but red and yellow are often seen as well. Farther north, ribbons spread over the sky. Auroras also appear in the southern hemisphere.

Auroral displays are manifestations of magnetic storms (10·16). They are caused primarily by streams of protons emitted by the sun; these produce the ribbons, according to A. B. Meinel, which are later broken into rays by electron streams. The incoming protons, or hydrogen nuclei, become luminous when they pick up electrons, so that the light, extending from altitudes of 60 to at least 500 miles, is that of glowing hydrogen. They are diverted in the earth's field toward the magnetic poles. The displays are most intense about 23° from those poles, and become less frequent at distances more than twice as far from the poles. South of latitude 35° in our hemisphere, or south of about San Francisco, Memphis, and Atlanta, they do not appear except in magnetic storms of considerable intensity.

1·20. The Airglow is an illumination suffused over the sky, which gives twice as much light as do all the stars. It is faintest overhead and brightest not far from the horizon, which shows that the glow originates in the atmosphere. Invisible to the naked eye, it places a limit on the faintest celestial objects that can be reached in photographs by increasing the exposure times. The longest useful exposure for a direct photograph with the 200-inch telescope and a blue-sensitive plate does not much exceed half an hour before the plate is too hopelessly fogged by the glow to allow any fainter stars to show.

The airglow occurs mainly at altitudes of from 60 to 120 miles. Its light is caused by energy coming from outside and most probably from the sun. First detected in its green light produced by excited oxygen atoms, it was originally known as the "permanent aurora." Red light of oxygen in another state and the yellow of sodium are other prominent colors of the glow. The most intense radiation is in the infrared and is produced by hydroxyl molecules; if this radiation were visible to the eye, the airglow would be as bright as a fine auroral display.

QUESTIONS ON CHAPTER 1

1. If the earth is represented by an 18-inch globe, the polar diameter should be $\frac{1}{16}$ inch less than the equatorial diameter, and the highest mountain should rise $\frac{1}{80}$ inch. Verify this statement.

2. State the longitude and latitude of: (a) the north pole; (b) a point on the equator; (c) the place where you are.

3. Explain that parallel lines regardless of their distance apart are directed toward the same point of the celestial sphere.

4. The moon is much nearer to us than are the stars. What is meant by the statement that the moon is in the constellation Taurus?

5. The moon's apparent diameter is $\frac{1}{2}°$. How many full moons could be placed side by side between the Pointers of the Great Dipper (Fig. 1·8)? What is the Dipper's length in degrees?

6. Compare the visible horizons as seen from an airplane and the ground below it; the celestial horizons.

7. Where in the sky would you look for stars having the following positions: (a) azimuth 90°, altitude 45°? (b) azimuth 180°, altitude 30°? (c) azimuth 270°, altitude 60°?

8. Describe two characteristics of: (a) the troposphere; (b) the stratosphere; (c) the ionosphere.

9. What is the true altitude of a star: (a) when it is rising? (b) when it appears directly overhead? How is the daily duration of sunshine affected by atmospheric refraction?

10. Explain the reddening, flattening, and apparent enlargement of the sun near the horizon.

11. The bright planets generally shine with steady light while the stars around them are twinkling. Explain.

12. Distinguish between the aurora and the airglow. How does the airglow affect astronomical photography?

REFERENCES

Jeffries, Harold, *The Earth.* Its origin, history, and physical constitution. Third edition. Cambridge University Press, 1952.

Kuiper, Gerard P., editor, *The Earth as a Planet.* University of Chicago Press, 1955.

Scientific American devoted its entire issue of September, 1955, to the earth in recognition of the International Geophysical Year, beginning July, 1957.

2

THE EARTH'S DAILY ROTATION

EFFECTS ON THE EARTH — APPARENT ROTATION OF THE HEAVENS

The distinction between rotation and revolution is more definite in astronomy than in some other sciences. *Rotation* is turning on an axis, whereas *revolution* is motion in an orbit. Thus the earth rotates daily and revolves yearly around the sun. In this chapter we consider the earth's rotation and some of its effects.

The earth rotates from west to east on an axis joining its north and south poles. Among the effects of the rotation are the directions of prevailing winds and cyclones, the behavior of the Foucault pendulum, the bulge of the equator, and the apparent rotation of the heavens.

EFFECTS ON THE EARTH

2·1. The Coriolis Effect. The speed of the earth's rotation becomes less with increasing distance from the equator. The speed exceeds 1000 miles an hour at the equator; it is reduced to 800 miles an hour in the latitude of New York, 500 miles an hour in southern Alaska, and so on, until at the pole there is no turning at all.

Consider an air current moving north in the northern hemisphere and carried eastward all the while by the earth's rotation. Because it is going from a latitude of faster rotation to one of slower rotation, the current forges ahead and is accordingly deflected to the right. If the current is moving south instead, it is going from a place of slower to one of faster rotation, and is again deflected to the right. Consider next a current moving either north or south in the southern hemisphere, and we see that it is deflected to the left. Thus we have the following rule which applies to all these horizontal motions.

The earth's rotation deflects moving objects to the right in the northern hemisphere and to the left in the southern hemisphere.

This deflection is known as the *Coriolis acceleration* after the French scientist who demonstrated it more than a century ago.

2·2. Deflection of Surface Winds. The global circulation of the atmosphere is generated by energy in the sunshine which heats the

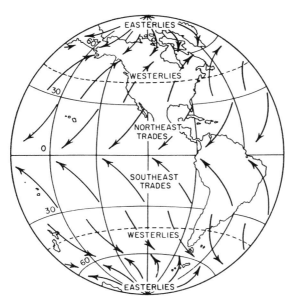

FIG. 2·2. Prevailing Surface Winds. The moving air is deflected to the right in the northern hemisphere and to the left in the southern hemisphere.

air most intensely in the tropics. The warmed air rises there and flows toward the poles. Cooled at high elevations the air descends, notably at latitudes 30° where it flows north and south over the surface. By our rule these surface winds are deflected to the right in the northern hemisphere and to the left in the southern hemisphere (Fig. 2·2). Thus we have the easterly trade winds of the tropics and the prevailing westerly winds of the temperate zones. The easterly winds of the frigid zones are an associated effect.

Ocean currents follow the prevailing winds in a general way, but are complicated by the land barriers. We see the effect of our rule clearly in the Gulf Stream, which flows initially from the southwest.

2·3. Eddies in the Air Circulation, such as cyclones and hurricanes, show the effect of the rule in the directions of their whirling. Consider a cyclone in the northern hemisphere, where the air is locally rising. The surface currents flowing into this area of low pressure are deflected to the right and reach its center indirectly. Thus the whole area, perhaps 1500 miles in diameter, is set whirling in the counterclockwise direction, or contrary to the direction taken by the hands of a clock. In the anticyclones, or "highs" of our hemisphere, the air is descending and flowing out over the surface; these accordingly whirl in the clockwise direction. The directions of cyclones in the southern hemisphere are clockwise, and those of anticyclones are counterclockwise.

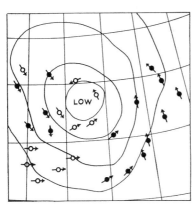

Fig. 2·3. Cyclones in the Northern Hemisphere Whirl Counterclockwise.

The importance of the Coriolis effect extends beyond its meteorological consequences. Correction for the effect is required in long-range artillery fire control and to the altitudes of celestial objects as observed with the bubble octant by the air navigator.

2·4. The Foucault Pendulum. A convincing proof of the earth's rotation was first demonstrated to the public by the French physicist Foucault, in 1851. Under the dome of the Panthéon in Paris, Foucault freely suspended a heavy iron ball by a wire more than 200 feet long and started it swinging. Those who watched the demonstration saw the plane of the oscillation slowly turn in the clockwise direction. They were observing in fact the changing direction of the meridian caused by the earth's rotation relative to the direction of the swing of the pendulum. This celebrated demonstration is often repeated in some of the planetariums and elsewhere.

The rate of change in the direction of the swing of this pendulum depends on the latitude. At the equator, where the direction of the meridian in space is not altered by the earth's rotation, there is no change at all in the direction of the pendulum. In the lati-

inner surface of a rotating hollow globe. This celestial sphere seems to turn daily from east to west around an axis which is the axis of the earth's rotation prolonged to the sky.

The *celestial poles* are the two opposite points on the celestial

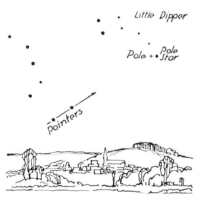

sphere toward which the earth's axis is directed, and around which the stars circle. The north celestial pole is directly in the north, from a third of the way to halfway up in the sky for observers in different parts of the United States. The south celestial pole is similarly depressed below the south horizons of these places.

Fig. 2·8. The Great Dipper's Pointers Show the Way to the Celestial Pole.

The Pointers of the Great Dipper (Fig. 2·8) direct the eye to Polaris, the *pole star,* at the end of the Little Dipper's handle. This moderately bright star is within 1°, or about two moon-breadths, of the pole itself. It is also the *north star* which shows nearly the direction of north. The south celestial pole is not similarly marked by any bright star in its vicinity.

2·9. The Celestial Equator. Just as the earth's equator is halfway between the terrestrial poles, so the *celestial equator* is halfway between the north and south celestial poles. This circle crosses the horizon at its east and west points at an angle which is the complement of the latitude. Thus in latitude 40° N, or the latitude of Philadelphia, the celestial equator is inclined 50° to the horizon and has an altitude of 50° at its highest point in the south.

Hour circles in the sky are like meridians on the earth. They are half circles which connect the celestial poles and are therefore perpendicular to the equator. Unlike the circles of the horizon system which are stationary relative to the observer, these circles are generally considered as sharing in the rotation of the celestial sphere. Where 24 hour circles are imagined equally spaced, they coincide successively with the observer's celestial meridian at intervals of an hour. With reference to the celestial equator and its associated circles, the position of a celestial body is given by its

tude of Chicago the rate of change is 10° an hour. At the pole it is 15° an hour, so that the plane of the oscillation turns completely around in a day.

Another effect of the earth's rotation is seen in the behavior of the gyrocompass, where the rotor automatically brings its axis into

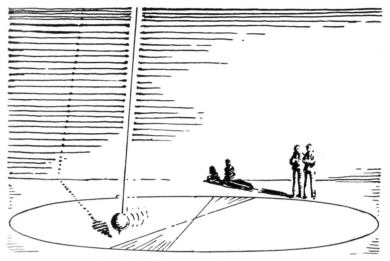

Fig. 2·4. The Foucault Pendulum.

the plane of the geographical meridian, and thus shows the direction of true north. This valuable aid to the navigator would not operate if the earth did not rotate. Still another effect is the bulging of the earth's equator.

2·5. Centrifugal Effect of the Earth's Rotation. The equator is more than 13 miles farther from the earth's center than are the poles; in this sense it is downhill toward the poles. Why then does not all the water of the oceans assemble in these lowest regions around the poles? Why does the Mississippi River flow "uphill" toward the equator? The reason is found in the earth's rotation.

All parts of the rotating earth have a tendency to move away from the axis. It is the same centrifugal effect that urges a stone to fly away when it is whirled around at the end of a cord. Part of the effect of the earth's rotation on an object at its surface is to slide the object toward the equator (Fig. 2·5). The earth has adjusted its form accordingly, so that the upslope toward the equator offsets the tendency to slide toward it.

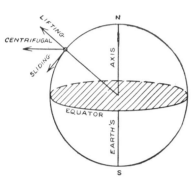

FIG. 2·5. The Earth's Rotation Tends to Propel an Object Toward the Equator and to Diminish Its Weight.

The second component of the centrifugal effect of the earth's rotation lifts the object, so that its weight is diminished. An object weighing 190 pounds at the pole, where there is no centrifugal effect, becomes a pound lighter at the equator, where this effect is greatest, although part of the decrease in weight here is due to the greater distance of the equator from the earth's center. If the period of the rotation should decrease to 1 hour and 24 minutes by our present clocks, an object at the equator would weigh nothing at all. At this excessive rate of rotation the earth would be unstable and liable to disruption.

2·6. Wanderings of the Poles. When the positions of places on the earth are determined repeatedly with high accuracy, it is found that their latitudes do not remain the same. This *variation of latitude* has been observed for many years at a number of international latitude stations distributed over the world, and these results tell us how the equator and therefore the poles have been wandering.

The wanderings of the poles are caused by shiftings of the earth relative to its axis, so that the poles change slightly on the surface. One variation is seasonal, having a period of a year; the other is an oscillation in a period of 14 months. The resulting motion of the poles is irregular and limited. Neither pole is withdrawing much more than 40 feet from its average place; all its wanderings are now confined to an area smaller than that of a baseball diamond. Some scientists suggest the possibility of wider migrations in the past, which might have caused the marked changes in the climates in geological times.

2·7. Changing Period of the Earth's Rotation. The earth's rotation has long set the standard for our timekeeping. The consequent

daily rotation of the heavens has provided the master clock b
which all other clocks have been corrected. The earth-clock w;
formerly considered entirely reliable; the period of the earth
rotation was supposed to be uniform, until it finally proved to
otherwise.

Suppose that someone begins with the idea that his watch is al
right. As the days go by he is surprised to find that everythi
getting ahead of time by his watch. He misses trains that
to depart too early; the sun rises before it should; the town
runs faster and faster. Presently he decides that his watch
be running slow. It is so with the earth's rotation. Peric
currences, such as the revolution of the moon around th
are forging ahead of regular schedules timed by the ear
We conclude that the period of the earth's rotation is in
and also that the increase is not perfectly regular.

By comparing the recorded times of early eclipses wit
culated times when they would have occurred if the earth
rotating uniformly all the while, astronomers have con(
the length of the day is increasing at the rate of $0^s.0016$ i
This would mean that the earth-clock has run slow 3½
ing the past 20 centuries. The tides in the oceans h
garded as the brakes that are so reducing the speed of
They are caused chiefly by the moon's attraction; an
the moon around the earth once in a month, while f
rotates under the tide figure once in a day. Mu(
however, remains in the amount of the increase of th
should be improved with the present more precis
serving the moon's motion (6·8).

There are also sudden and not as yet accurately
tions in the length of the day. The earth's rot
schedule both fast and slow as much as half a m
ance for the tidal retardation is made. A sma'
as well has been ascribed to atmospheric or tid
to effects in the core of the earth.

APPARENT ROTATION OF THE

2·8. The Celestial Poles. The stars rise and
daily and keeping precisely in step as they
terns of stars, such as the Great Dipper, lo
night and year after year. It is as though

right ascension and declination, which resemble terrestrial longitude and latitude.

2·10. Right Ascension and Declination. The *right ascension* of a star is its angular distance measured eastward along the celestial equator from the vernal equinox to the hour circle through the

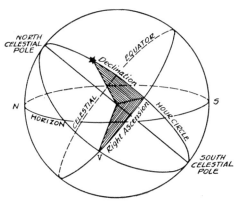

FIG. 2·10. Right Ascension and Declination. Right ascension is measured eastward from the vernal equinox along the celestial equator. Declination is measured north or south from the equator.

star. (The vernal eqinox is the point where the sun's center crosses the celestial equator at the beginning of spring.) Right ascension is expressed in time more often than in angular units. Because a complete rotation of the heavens, through 360°, is made in 24 hours, 15° is equivalent to 1 hour, and 1° to 4 minutes of time. Thus a star's right ascension may be given as 60° or 4 hours.

The *declination* of a star is the star's distance in degrees north or south from the celestial equator, measured along an hour circle through the star. The declination is marked either N or with a plus sign if the star is north of the equator, and S or with a minus sign if it is south.

As an example, the right ascension of the star Arcturus is 14^h 14^m and its declination is 19° 25′ N. The star is accordingly 213° 30′ east of the vernal equinox and 19° 25′ north of the celestial equator. Notice that right ascension is measured only eastward, whereas terrestrial longitude is measured both east and west. The approximate right ascensions and declinations of the brighter stars can be read from the star maps in Chapter 11.

2·11. Hour Angle is often employed in the equator system instead of right ascension. The local *hour angle* of a star is reckoned westward along the equator from the observer's celestial meridian through 360° or 24 hours. Unlike right ascension, which remains nearly unchanged during the day, the hour angle of a star increases at the rate of 15° an hour and, at the same instant, has different values in different longitudes.

Hour angle is frequently used in directing a telescope to a celestial object by means of a graduated circle; the hour angle of the object is found by subtracting its right ascension from the sidereal time (4·2). Hour angle also has much use in celestial navigation. The Greenwich hour angles of celestial bodies are tabulated for this purpose at convenient intervals of the day throughout the year in nautical and air almanacs.

2·12. Latitude Equals Altitude of Celestial Pole. The latitude of a place on the earth is its distance in degrees from the equator. For our present purpose it is more conveniently defined as the number of degrees the vertical line at the place is inclined to the plane of the equator, or to the plane of the celestial equator. This vertical line is directed toward the observer's zenith.

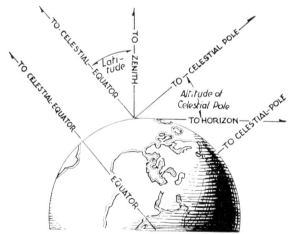

FIG. 2·12. The Latitude of a Place on the Earth Equals the Altitude of the Celestial Pole at That Place. Astronomical latitude is defined as the angle between the vertical line and the equator plane. This angle equals the altitude of the celestial pole because both are complements of the angle between the pole and the zenith.

In Fig. 2·12 we see that the observer's latitude is the same as the declination of his zenith. This angle equals the altitude of the north celestial pole, because both are complements of the same angle between the directions of the zenith and pole. Thus, *the latitude of a place equals the altitude of the celestial pole at that place.* In examining the figure we recall that parallel lines are directed toward the same point of the heavens.

The rule determines the *astronomical latitude*. This observed latitude depends on the vertical line and is affected by anything that alters the vertical. A mountain near the place of observation would cause the plumb line to incline a little in its direction. Such "station errors" may make a difference of nearly a minute of arc in the latitude, although they are usually much smaller. *Geographical latitude* is the observed latitude corrected for station error; it is the latitude that would be observed if the earth were perfectly smooth and uniform.

2·13. The Latitude of a Place on the earth is determined by the rule of the preceding section. If there were a bright star precisely

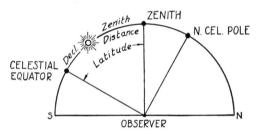

FIG. 2·13. The Latitude of a Place Equals the Sun's Zenith Distance at Its Crossing of the Meridian of the Place Plus Its Declination at That Time.

at the celestial pole, the latitude could be found simply by measuring the altitude of that star. The pole star itself may be employed if correction is made for its distance from the pole. More often the observations are made to determine the declination of the zenith, which we have seen is the same as the latitude. A simple calculation gives the required value when the altitude of a celestial body is observed as it crosses the celestial meridian.

Suppose that a navigator sights the sun at its crossing of the meridian south of the zenith and determines its true altitude as

51° 10′, so that its zenith distance is 38° 50′. Suppose that the sun's declination obtained from an almanac for the time of the sight is 22° 0′ N. The latitude equals the sun's zenith distance plus its declination (Fig. 2·13); it is accordingly 38° 50′ + 22° 0′ = 60° 50′ N. If the sun had crossed the meridian the same distance north of the zenith, the zenith distance would receive the minus sign, and the latitude would have been 16° 50′ S. In operations of the Coast and Geodetic Survey and in some observatories the latitude is obtained very accurately by observing stars with a special instrument, the zenith telescope.

Let us now turn the latitude rule around. When the latitude of a place is given, we know the altitude of the north celestial pole at that place and how the daily courses of the stars are related to the horizon.

2·14. At the Pole the Stars Never Set. At the north pole, latitude 90°, the north celestial pole is in the zenith, and the stars go around

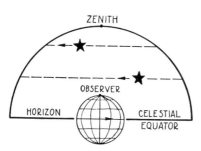

FIG. 2·14. At the Pole the Stars Circle Parallel to the Horizon.

it daily in circles parallel to the horizon. Stars north of the celestial equator never set, while those south of the equator never come into view. In this statement and some others we avoid confusion by referring to the true positions of the stars and not as they are elevated by atmospheric refraction (1·16). The sun, moon, and planets rise and set at the north pole whenever they cross the celestial equator. The sun rises about March 21 and sets about September 23. The moon rises and sets about once a month.

At the south pole everything is reversed. There the south celestial pole stands in the zenith, and the stars of the south celestial hemisphere never set. The long period of sunshine begins with the rising of the sun about September 23.

2·15. At the Equator All Stars Rise and Set. Here, where the latitude is zero, the altitude of the celestial pole is zero by our rule. The north celestial pole is situated at the north point of the horizon, and even the pole star now rises and sets as it circles near this pole. The south celestial pole is at the south point. The celestial equator passes directly overhead from east to west.

At the equator, all parts of the heavens are brought into view by the apparent daily rotation. All stars rise and set. Their courses cross the horizon at right angles and are bisected by it, so that every star is above the horizon 12 hours daily if we neglect refraction. This applies to the sun as well; the duration of sunshine is 12 hours at the equator throughout the year.

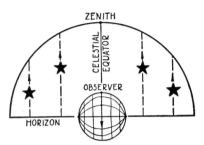

FIG. 2·15. At the Equator the Daily Courses of the Stars Are Perpendicular to the Horizon.

2·16. The Heavens Turn Obliquely for Us who live between the pole and equator. Suppose that we are observing from latitude 40° north. Here the north celestial pole is 40° above the north point of the horizon, and the south pole is the same distance below the south point. The celestial equator arches across from the east point to the west, inclined so that its highest point is 40° south of

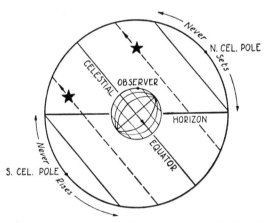

FIG. 2·16. Between the Pole and the Equator the Daily Courses of the Stars Cross the Horizon Obliquely.

the zenith. The daily courses of the stars are likewise inclined toward the south. Half the celestial equator is above the horizon.

Northward from the equator the daily courses of the stars come up more and more above the horizon until they are entirely above it. Southward from the celestial equator they are depressed more and more until they disappear completely.

In this oblique arrangement the celestial sphere is divided into three parts: (1) a circular area around the elevated celestial pole contains the stars that never set; (2) a similar area around the depressed pole contains the stars that never rise; (3) the remaining band of the heavens symmetrical with the celestial equator contains the stars that rise and set. Hence, in latitude 40° N the area of the heavens which is always above the horizon is within a radius of 40° around the north celestial pole, and the area which never comes into view is within a radius of 40° around the south celestial pole. The remainder of the heavens, a band extending 50° on either side of the celestial equator, rises and sets.

If we travel north, the celestial poles move farther from the horizon. The polar areas grow larger until they come together when the pole is reached; there as we have seen no stars rise and set. If we travel south, the celestial poles approach the horizon. The polar areas grow smaller until they disappear when the equator is reached, where all stars rise and set.

2·17. Circumpolar Stars go around the celestial poles without crossing the horizon. These stars either never set or never rise, because they are closer to one of the celestial poles than the distance of that pole from the horizon, a distance that is equal to the observer's latitude. We accordingly make this rule about them for observers in the northern hemisphere:

A star having a distance from the north celestial pole (90° minus the star's declination) less than the latitude of a place never sets at that place. A star having a distance from the south celestial pole less than the latitude never rises.

Suppose that the observer is in latitude 40° N, and consider as an example the bowl of the Great Dipper, declination about 58° N. It never sets here because its north polar distance of 32° is less than the latitude. As a second example, consider the star Canopus, declination 53° S. This brilliant star is not visible in latitude 40° N because its south polar distance of 37° is less than the latitude.

2·18. The Midnight Sun. Consider the sun on June 22; on this date when the sun is farthest north of the equator, the declination

FIG. 2·17. The Heavens Turn Obliquely for Us. Trails of stars approaching their setting. The sky is illuminated with zodiacal light (9·10).

FIG. 2·17A. Circumpolar Star Trails. The exposure time was one hour. The bright trail a little below the pole is that of Polaris

(*Photographed at Yerkes Observatory*)

FIG. 2·18. The Midnight Sun. The exposures were made at intervals of 20 minutes. (*Photographed at Etah, Greenland, by Donald B. MacMillan*)

of its center is $23\frac{1}{2}°$ N, so that its north polar distance is $66\frac{1}{2}°$. How far north must we go on June 22 to see the sun circle around the pole without setting? According to our rule we must go beyond latitude $66\frac{1}{2}°$. When we take into account the refraction effect and the size of the sun's disk, however, we expect to see the sun at midnight on this date as far south as $65\frac{3}{4}°$ N.

The *midnight sun* is seen wherever the sun becomes circumpolar. In far northern latitudes the sun in summer enters the area of the heavens that is always above the horizon; and it becomes circumpolar in far southern latitudes at the opposite season.

2·19. The Duration of Twilight. The gradual transition between daylight and the darkness of night, which we call *twilight,* occurs during the time that the sun, after its setting and before its rising for us, can shine on the atmosphere above us. What is said here about the evening twilight applies in reverse to the morning twilight.

Civil twilight ends when the sun's center has sunk 6° below the horizon. Then it is no longer possible without artificial illumination to continue outdoor operations that require good light. *Nautical twilight* ends when the sun's center is 12° below the horizon. Then the sea horizon is likely to be too dim for the navigator's sextant sights. *Astronomical twilight* ends when the sun's center is 18° below the horizon; by that time the fainter stars have come out overhead. The times of sunset and sunrise and the duration of twilight can be found in some of the almanacs for any date and latitude.

The duration of twilight varies with the time of year and the latitude. Twilight is shortest at the equator where the sun descends vertically and so reaches the limiting distance below the horizon in the shortest time. Astronomical twilight lasts about an hour at the equator, and an hour and a half or more in the latitude of New York. On June 22 it does not end at all north of 48° N, about the latitude of Victoria. Civil twilight persists from sunset to sunrise on this date from latitude 60°, or the latitude of Oslo, Norway, to nearly 66°, where the midnight sun is seen.

QUESTIONS ON CHAPTER 2

1. Explain the deflection of moving objects to the right in the northern hemisphere and to the left in the southern hemisphere. State 3 familiar examples.

2. Show that the behavior of the Foucault pendulum demonstrates the earth's rotation.

3. Why does an object weigh less at the equator than at the poles?

4. How is it possible to determine that the earth's rotation is not quite uniform?

5. Name the celestial circle or coordinate that corresponds to each of the following definitions:

(a) The circle halfway between the celestial poles.
(b) Any circle passing through both celestial poles.
(c) Angular distance north or south from the celestial equator.
(d) Angular distance measured eastward from the vernal equinox along the celestial equator.

6. In what respect does right ascension differ from terrestrial longitude?

7. From what places on the earth would the following situations be true in the absence of atmospheric refraction?

(a) The celestial equator coincides with the horizon.
(b) All parts of the celestial sphere rise and set.
(c) The south celestial pole is in the zenith.
(d) The daily duration of sunshine is 12 hours throughout the year.
(e) The daily circles of the stars are parallel to the horizon.

8. Which of the situations in Question 7 are affected by atmospheric refraction?

9. An observer sights a star at its crossing of the celestial meridian south of the zenith and finds that its altitude is 62° 20′. The star's declination is +12° 10′. Explain that the observer's latitude is 39° 50′ N.

10. In latitude 30° S, what part of the celestial sphere: (a) never sets? (b) never rises?

11. Which of the following stars never set, rise and set, or never rise for an observer in latitude 40° N: Arcturus, declination +19°; Canopus, −53°; Dubhe, +62°; Alpha Crucis, −63°?

12. (a) Distinguish between civil and astronomical twilight. (b) Why is the duration of twilight shortest at the equator?

3

THE EARTH'S ANNUAL REVOLUTION

THE EARTH REVOLVES – THE EARTH'S PRECESSION – THE SEASONS

While the stars are circling westward around us as though they were set on the rotating celestial sphere, the sun gradually lags behind. The sun shifts slowly toward the east against the turning background of the heavens. If we could readily view the stars in the daytime sky, we would then see that the sun moves eastward about twice its breadth in a day, and that it circles completely around the heavens in this direction in the course of a year. Although it is not easily possible to observe the sun's progress directly, this movement was recognized and charted by early watchers of the skies, for it is clearly revealed by the steady procession of the constellations toward the west from night to night at the same hour through the year.

3·1. Annual March of the Constellations. At the same hour from night to night as the seasons go around, the constellations march

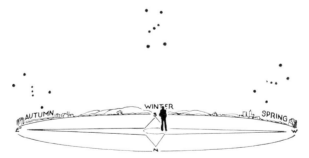

FIG. 3·1. Orion in the Evening at Different Seasons.

slowly across the evening sky and down past the sun's place below the horizon. If we look at a particular group of stars at the same time night after night, we presently observe this westward movement. We notice, for example, Orion's part in the unending parade; it is the brightest and among the most familiar of the constellations.

Orion comes up over the east horizon early in the evening in the late autumn, a tilted oblong figure with three stars in line near its center. At the approach of spring this constellation appears up-ended in the south. As spring advances, Orion comes out in the twilight farther and farther west, its oblong now inclined the other way, until it follows the sun too closely to be visible. Then at dawn in midsummer Orion appears in the east again, on the other side of the sun.

This westward procession of Orion and other constellations past the sun's place shows that the sun is moving toward the east among the stars. Its motion is a consequence but not a proof of the earth's annual revolution around the sun. The same effect would occur if the sun revolved around the earth, as most people before the time of Copernicus supposed that it did.

THE EARTH REVOLVES

Everyone knows today that the earth revolves around the sun. We learn this fact at an early age and accept it as an item of common knowledge. We are told, too, that the sun is something like 93 million miles away, so that the earth must be speeding along at the average rate of $18\frac{1}{2}$ miles a second to go all the way around in a year. There is nothing in our everyday experiences, however, to convince us that the earth is moving in this way. Displacements of the stars that prove the earth's revolution beyond reasonable doubt are too minute to be detected without a telescope. The aberration of starlight is an example.

3·2. Aberration of Starlight. Raindrops fall vertically when there is no wind. Yet they seem to come down slanting to one who walks rapidly through the rain, and still more slanting if he runs instead. As the observer's speed increases, the place from which the raindrops seem to fall shifts farther in the direction he is going. This is the aberration of raindrops.

There is a similar effect on the rays of light from a star. The *aberration of starlight* is the apparent displacement of the star in the direction toward which the observer is moving. It is a much smaller displacement, to be sure; starlight comes down so much faster than the rain that its direction is not appreciably altered by ordinary speeds. Even the earth's swift flight around the sun displaces the stars only 20½" at the most, an amount too slight to be detected by the unaided eye. This displacement of the stars from their true positions is readily observed with the telescope; and here we have convincing evidence of the earth's revolution.

Fig. 3·2. Aberration of Raindrops and Starlight. Just as raindrops come down slanting to one who is running, so the stars are apparently displaced always ahead of us as we go around the sun. Each star seems to describe a little orbit.

If the earth is taking us around the sun, the direction of the revolution must change continuously. The direction of the star's aberration displacement must also change continuously, for it is always in the direction of the observer's motion. If the earth revolves once in a year, the stars must seem to move in small annual orbits around their true places. This is what they seem to be doing, as the telescope shows.

The aberration of starlight was first observed by the English astronomer Bradley who explained its important meaning in 1727, nearly two centuries after the death of Copernicus. Henceforth, there could be no reasonable doubt that the earth revolves around the sun. In a later chapter (12·1) we consider the parallax effect of the earth's revolution.

3·3. The Earth's Distance from the Sun Varies. If the earth's orbit around the sun were a circle with the sun at its center, the earth's distance from the sun would remain the same throughout the year, so that the sun would always appear to be of the same size. Although the difference is not noticeable to the unaided eye, the sun's apparent diameter does vary during the year. Is it greatest early in January and least early in July; the difference between the two is one thirtieth of the average diameter. Thus the earth is nearest the sun about the first of January and farthest from the sun about the first of July, which might seem surprising to anyone who had forgotten that the seasons are not caused by the earth's varying distance from the sun.

The earth's distance from the sun averages 92,900,000 miles; it varies from 91,300,000 to 94,500,000 miles.

3·4. The Earth's Orbit Is an Ellipse of small eccentricity with the sun at one focus. The terms used in this statement are defined as follows:

The *ellipse* is a plane curve such that the sum of the distances from any point on its circumference to two points within, called

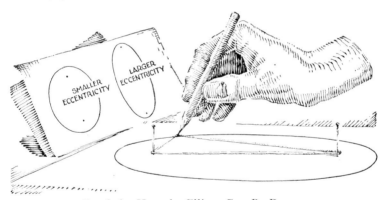

FIG. 3·4.   How the Ellipse Can Be Drawn.

the *foci*, is constant and equal to the longest diameter, or *major axis*, of the ellipse. The definition suggests a way to draw an ellipse (Fig. 3·4); and the drawing of several ellipses in this way makes clear the significance of the eccentricity.

The *eccentricity* of the ellipse denotes its degree of flattening. It is represented by the fraction of the major axis that lies between the two foci. If the eccentricity is zero, the foci are together at the center and the curve is a circle. The ellipse flattens more and more as the eccentricity increases, until at eccentricity 1 the figure becomes a straight line. The earth's orbit is nearly a circle; its eccentricity is .017, or $\frac{1}{60}$. If Fig. 3·4A were drawn to scale, the sun's center would be $\frac{1}{50}$ inch from the center of the ellipse, and the ellipse itself could be scarcely distinguished from a circle.

Perihelion and *aphelion* are the points on the earth's orbit which are respectively nearest and farthest from the sun; they are at opposite ends of the major axis. The earth arrives at perihelion about January 1 and at aphelion about July 1, as we have noticed before. These times move back and forth a little in the calendar and also

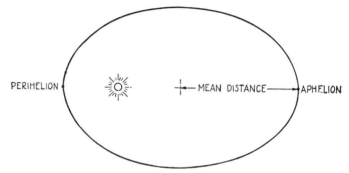

FIG. 3·4A. The Earth's Orbit. It is an ellipse of small eccentricity (much exaggerated in the diagram) having the sun at one focus.

advance an average of 25 minutes a year, because the major axis of the earth's orbit moves slowly around the sun in the direction of the earth's revolution. The earth's *mean distance,* 92,900,000 miles, from the sun is half the length of the major axis, or the average of the perihelion and aphelion distances. The earth is at this distance from the sun in early April and again in early October.

3·5. The Ecliptic. Thus the earth revolves eastward around the sun once in a year and rotates meanwhile on its axis in the same direction once in a day. The earth's axis is inclined $23\frac{1}{2}°$ from the perpendicular to the plane of its orbit, or we may say that the earth's equator is inclined $23\frac{1}{2}°$ to the plane of the orbit. This determines the relation (Fig. 3·5) between the celestial equator and the path the sun seems to describe eastward around the heavens as we revolve around the sun.

The *ecliptic* is the sun's apparent annual path around the celestial sphere; it is a great circle inclined $23\frac{1}{2}°$ to the celestial equator.

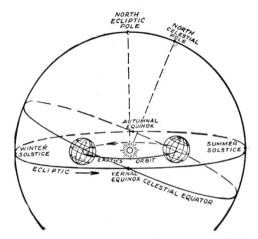

Fig. 3·5. The Celestial Equator Is Inclined to the Ecliptic. It is inclined by the same amount that the earth's equator is inclined to the plane of its orbit around the sun.

The ecliptic is in the plane of the earth's orbit, and the celestial equator is in the plane of the earth's equator. The *north and south ecliptic poles* are 90° from the ecliptic, and are respectively 23½° from the north and south celestial poles. The north ecliptic pole (R.A. 18ʰ, Decl. 66½° N) is in the constellation Draco (Map 1, Chapter 11).

3·6. The Equinoxes and Solstices. The *equinoxes* are the two opposite points of the celestial sphere where the ecliptic crosses the celestial equator. They are so named because days and nights are said to be equal in length when the sun arrives at an equinox, although atmospheric refraction makes the duration of sunlight slightly the longer on such occasions. The *solstices* are the two opposite points midway between the equinoxes, where the ecliptic is farthest north or south from the celestial equator. Here the "sun stands," so far as its north and south motion is concerned, as it turns back toward the equator.

The equinoxes and solstices are points on the celestial sphere; their positions in the constellations are shown in the star maps of Chapter 11. The *vernal equinox* (R.A. 0ʰ, Decl. 0°) is the point where the sun crosses the celestial equator on its way north, about March 21. The *summer solstice* (R.A. 6ʰ, Decl. 23½° N) is the northernmost point of the ecliptic; the sun arrives here about June

22. The *autumnal equinox* (R.A. 12ʰ, Decl. 0°) is the point where the sun crosses the celestial equator on its way south, about September 23. The *winter solstice* (R.A. 18ʰ, Decl. 23½° S) is the southernmost point of the ecliptic; the sun arrives here about December 22. These dates vary a little from year to year owing to the plan of leap years. The positions of the sun refer in each case to the sun's center.

3·7. The Ecliptic in the Evening Sky. The celestial equator keeps the same position in the sky through the year. It is inclined to the horizon at an angle which is the complement of the latitude. Thus

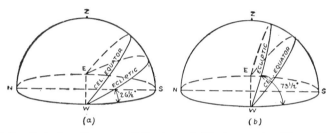

Fɪɢ. 3·7. Relation Between Ecliptic and Horizon. (*a*) The ecliptic is least inclined to the horizon in our latitudes at sunset at the beginning of autumn. (*b*) It is most inclined at sunset at the beginning of spring.

in latitude 40° N the equator crosses the horizon at the east and west points at an angle of 50°, and is 50° above the horizon in the south. The ecliptic, however, takes different positions in the evening sky during the year.

Because the ecliptic is inclined 23½° to the celestial equator, its inclination to the horizon can differ as much as 23½° either way from that of the equator. At sunset at the beginning of autumn (Fig. 3·7) in middle northern latitudes the ecliptic is least inclined to the horizon; the moon and bright planets that may be visible at the time are seen rather low in the south. At sunset at the beginning of spring the ecliptic is most inclined to the horizon; the moon and planets are then crossing more nearly overhead.

The varying angle between the ecliptic and horizon enters in the explanations of a number of features familiar to watchers of the skies. Among these are the harvest moon, the direction of the horns of the crescent moon, the favorable times for seeing the planet Mercury as evening or morning star, and the favorable seasons for viewing the zodiacal light.

3·8. Celestial Longitude and Latitude. The moon and bright planets never depart far from the sun's path around the heavens. For this reason, astronomers of early times, who were especially interested in the motions of the sun, moon, and planets, referred the places of these and other celestial bodies to the ecliptic, and they named the coordinates celestial longitude and latitude. *Celestial longitude* is measured in degrees eastward from the vernal equinox along the ecliptic. *Celestial latitude* is measured north or south from the ecliptic along a circle at right angles to it.

The ecliptic coordinates have only limited use today. The position of a celestial body is now referred more conveniently for most purposes to circles based on the celestial equator by means of right ascension and declination, which closely resemble terrestrial longitude and latitude. These newer coordinates themselves would doubtless have been called celestial longitude and latitude if the terms had not already been appropriated.

THE EARTH'S PRECESSION

3·9. The Earth Resembles a Spinning Top. If a top is spinning with its axis inclined to the vertical, the axis moves around the vertical line in the direction of the spin. The rotation of the top resists the effort of gravity to tip it over; and the conical motion of the axis results, until the spin is so reduced that the top falls over.

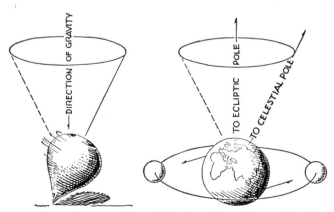

FIG. 3·9. The Earth Resembles a Spinning Top. The pull of the moon on the bulging equator of the rotating earth is the chief cause of the precessional motion.

The earth is rotating similarly on an inclined axis, inclined to the ecliptic plane which is not far from the plane of the moon's motion around us. The attractions of the moon and sun on the earth's bulging equator tend to bring it into the plane with themselves, and thus to straighten up the earth's axis relative to its orbit.

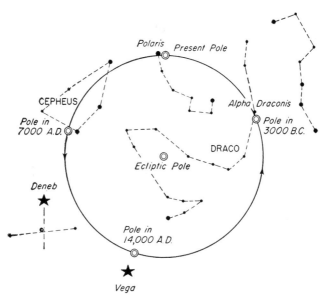

FIG. 3·10. Precessional Path of the North Celestial Pole. The celestial pole describes a circle of 23½° radius around the ecliptic pole.

Their efforts are resisted by the rotation, so that the earth's axis moves slowly instead around the line joining the ecliptic poles in the direction opposite to that of the rotation, once around in 26,000 years at the present rate. This is the *earth's precession*.

3·10. Paths of the Celestial Poles. As the earth's axis goes around in the precessional motion, the celestial poles, toward which the axis is directed, move among the constellations. The poles describe circles 23½° in radius around the ecliptic poles (Fig. 3·10), bringing successively to bright stars along their paths the distinction of being the pole star for a time. Thus Alpha Draconis was the pole star in the north 5000 years ago, the predecessor of our present pole star.

The north celestial pole is now approaching Polaris and will pass

nearest it about the year 2100 at half its present distance. Thereafter, Polaris will describe larger and larger daily circles around
the pole, and its important place will at length be taken by stars
of Cepheus in succession. In the year 7000, Alpha Cephei will
mark the north pole closely. In 14,000, Vega in Lyra will be a
brilliant, although not very close, marker.

In our skies the constellations are slowly shifted by precession
relative to the circumpolar areas, while the poles remain in the
same places at the distance from the horizon equal to the observer's
latitude. Six thousand years ago the Southern Cross rose and set
everywhere in the United States. Now it is invisible from here
except in the southernmost parts of the country.

3·11. Precession of the Equinoxes. The earth's precession, as we
have seen, causes the line joining the celestial poles to describe
the surface of a right cone around the line joining the ecliptic

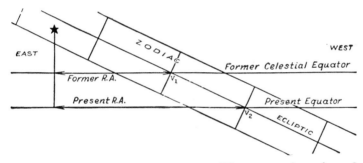

FIG. 3·11. Precession of the Equinoxes. The westward motion of the
vernal equinox, from V_1 to V_2, causes the signs of the zodiac (the 12 equal
divisions marked off from the equinox) to slide westward away from the
corresponding constellations. The right ascensions of the stars are also
altered.

poles. This motion is counterclockwise as we face north. Meanwhile the celestial equator slides westward along the ecliptic, keeping about the same angle between them. The equinoxes, where
the two inclined circles intersect, slide westward along the ecliptic.
This is the *precession of the equinoxes.* Their motion, including
smaller effects of planetary attractions of the earth, is at the rate
of 50″ a year.

The precession of the vernal equinox (Fig. 3·11) causes continuous variations in the right ascensions and declinations of the stars.

It is accountable for the lack of agreement between the constellations and signs of the zodiac, and it makes the year of the seasons shorter than the period of the earth's revolution around the sun (3·13).

3·12. The Zodiac; Its Constellations and Signs. The *zodiac* is the band of the heavens 16° wide, through which the ecliptic runs centrally. It contains the sun, moon, and bright planets at all times, with the occasional exception of the planet Venus. This is the reason for the special importance of the zodiac in the astronomy of early times and in the ancient and now discredited pseudo-science of astrology, in which the places of the planetary bodies had great significance.

Twelve *constellations of the zodiac* lie along this band of the heavens. Because these constellations are of unequal size, the *signs of the zodiac* were introduced in early times in the interest of uniformity; these are 12 equal divisions of the zodiac, each 30° long, marked off eastward from the vernal equinox. Each block, or sign, of the zodiac has the name of the constellation it contained 20 centuries ago.

The names of the 12 constellations and signs of the zodiac are: Aries, Taurus, Gemini, Cancer, Leo, Virgo, Libra, Scorpius, Sagittarius, Capricornus, Aquarius, and Pisces.

In the meantime, the vernal equinox has moved westward among the stars, and the whole train of signs has followed along, because the signs are counted from the equinox. Each sign has shifted out of its constellation and into the adjoining figure to the west. Thus, when the sun arrives on March 21 at the vernal equinox, or "first of Aries," and the almanac says "sun enters Aries," the sun is entering the zodiacal sign Aries. The sun is then in the constellation Pisces, however, and will not enter the constellation Aries itself for another month.

3·13. The Year of the Seasons is about 20 minutes shorter than the true period of the earth's revolution. The difference is caused by the precession of the equinox.

The *sidereal year* is the interval of time in which the sun appears to perform a complete revolution around the heavens with respect to the stars. This is the true period of the earth's revolution. The length of the sidereal year is $365^d\ 6^h\ 9^m\ 10^s$ of mean solar time.

The *tropical year* is the interval between two successive arrivals of the sun's center at the vernal equinox. Because the equinox is shifting westward to meet the sun, this *year of the seasons*, from the beginning of spring to the beginning of spring again, is shortened. The length of the tropical year is 365^d 5^h 48^m 46^s. This is nearly the average length of the present calendar year.

THE SEASONS

3·14. Cause of the Seasons. Why is the weather warmer in summer than in winter? It is not because we are nearer the sun in summer; for we have seen that the earth is more than 3 million miles farther

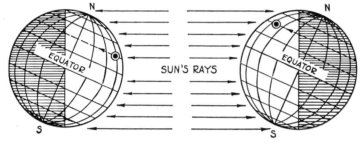

FIG. 3·14. Summer and Winter in the Northern Hemisphere. The weather is warmer in summer because the daily duration of sunshine is greater and the sun's rays are more nearly direct.

from the sun in summer than in winter. The cause of the seasons is found in the inclination of the earth's equator to the plane of its orbit.

In summer the northern end of the earth's axis is inclined toward the sun. Not only is the daily duration of sunshine longer at any place in our northern latitudes than it is in winter, but the sun also climbs higher, so that its rays are more nearly vertical and more concentrated on our part of the world. In winter the northern end of the axis is inclined away from the sun. The daily duration of sunshine is then shorter for us and the sun is lower at noon. The sun's rays come down more slanting in the winter, so that they are more spread out over the ground and are also obstructed more by the greater thickness of the intervening air. Thus the weather is warmer in summer than in winter because the sun shines for a longer time each day and reaches a greater height in the sky.

3·15. The Lag of the Seasons. Summer in our northern latitudes begins about June 22, when the sun arrives at the summer solstice and turns back toward the south. The duration of sunshine is longest on that day, and the sun climbs highest in the sky. Yet the hottest part of the summer is likely to be delayed several weeks

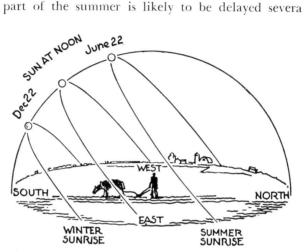

FIG. 3·15. Daily Circles of the Sun in Summer and Winter.

until the sun is well on its way south. Why does the peak of the summer come after the time of the solstice?

As the sun goes south, its rays bring less and less heat to our part of the world from day to day. For some time, however, the diminishing receipts still exceed the amounts of heat we are losing by the earth's radiation into space. Summer does not reach its peak until the rate of heating is reduced to the rate of cooling. Similarly our winter weather is likely to be more severe several weeks after the time of the winter solstice. After the sun turns north, about December 22, the temperature continues to fall generally until the amount of heat we receive from the sun becomes as great as the daily loss.

3·16. The Seasons in the Two Hemispheres. Although the seasons are not caused by the earth's varying distance from the sun, the earth is farther from the sun in our summer and nearer the sun in our winter than at similar seasons in the southern hemisphere. Summers in the northern hemisphere might well be a little cooler than southern summers, and northern winters might be milder than southern winters. Thus the northern hemisphere might seem to have the more agreeable climates. Yet the variation in the earth's distance from the sun is only 3 per cent of the distance itself, and there is more water in the southern hemisphere to modify extremes of temperature.

It would be unsafe to make a general comparison of the weather in corresponding latitudes north and south of the equator. Dif-

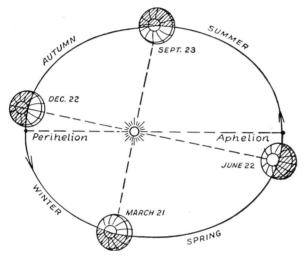

Fig. 3·16. The Seasons in the Northern Hemisphere. The earth arrives at perihelion soon after the time of the winter solstice.

ferences in elevation and in the effects of air and ocean currents would have to be taken into account. Consider, for example, the climates near the two poles. There is mainly water around the north pole; on the other hand, a great expanse of land surrounds the south pole, and high land too, so that the winter there is the more severe.

3·17. The Climatic Zones. The positions and widths of the climatic zones are determined by the inclination of the earth's equator to the plane of its orbit. Because this inclination is $23\frac{1}{2}°$, the *torrid* zone extends $23\frac{1}{2}°$ north and south from the equator; everywhere in this region the sun is directly overhead on some days of the year. The *tropic of Cancer*, $23\frac{1}{2}°$ north of the equator, forms the northern boundary of the torrid zone. Here the sun is overhead at noon on June 22, when it arrives at the summer solstice and enters the sign Cancer of the zodiac. The *tropic of Capricorn,* $23\frac{1}{2}°$ south of the equator, is the southern boundary of the torrid zone. Here the sun is overhead at noon on December 22, when it enters the sign Capricornus.

Similarly, the north and south *frigid zones* extend $23\frac{1}{2}°$ from the poles and are bounded by the arctic and antarctic circles, respectively. Although they are modified a little by the effect of refraction near their borders, the frigid zones are the regions where the sun may become visible at midnight during part of the year, and may not appear even at noon at the opposite time of the year. The extreme conditions obtain at the poles themselves, where the sun shines continuously for 6 months and remains out of sight for the following 6 months.

The north and south *temperate zones* lie between the torrid and frigid zones. Here the sun never reaches the point overhead, nor does it ever fail to appear above the horizon at noon.

QUESTIONS ON CHAPTER 3

1. Explain that the sun's annual eastward motion becomes evident when we observe what constellations appear successively in the south at the same hour of the evening during the year.

2. How do the annual aberration orbits of the stars demonstrate the earth's revolution around the sun?

3. What information about the earth's revolution is given by the statement that the orbit is an ellipse of small eccentricity having the sun at one focus?

4. Explain that the ecliptic unlike the celestial equator does not keep the same position in the sky of a particular place. Show that it passes nearest the zenith in middle northern latitudes at sunset at the beginning of spring.

5. Name the celestial points or coordinates which are defined as follows:

(a) The northernmost point of the ecliptic.
(b) The intersection of ecliptic and celestial equator where the sun is going north.
(c) The two points 90° from the ecliptic.
(d) Angular distance along the ecliptic measured eastward from the vernal equinox.

6. The precession of a top is in the direction of its rotation, whereas that of the earth is in the opposite direction. Explain this difference as a consequence of the difference in one of the factors producing the precessions.

7. Explain the effect of the earth's precession on the celestial poles. Show that when Vega becomes the pole star (Fig. 3·10) our present pole star will rise and set in latitude 40° N.

8. Explain the effect of the precession on the vernal equinox; on the right ascensions of the stars.

9. Distinguish between the signs and constellations of the zodiac. Explain the displacement of the signs caused by precession.

10. State and explain the difference in length between the tropical and the sidereal year.

11. Why is the weather warmer in summer? Why are the warmest days in middle northern latitudes likely to come considerably later than June 22?

12. Show that the boundaries of the climatic zones are determined by the inclination of the ecliptic and celestial equator.

Mount Wilson Observatory from the Northwest.

4

TIMEKEEPING

THE TIME OF DAY — THE CALENDAR

We often compare our watches with clocks and radio signals which are regulated by a clock in the Naval Observatory. The observatory clock is kept right by frequent comparisons with the master clock in the sky, which itself is operated by the daily rotation of the earth. The standard time of day we commonly use will be more clearly explained if we first consider the kinds of time astronomers read from the celestial clock in order to derive the correct standard time.

THE TIME OF DAY

4·1. The Clock in the Sky. Any one of the stars or any chosen point of the celestial sphere can serve as the end of the hour hand of the clock in the sky. The hour hand is that part of an hour circle which connects our time reckoner with the celestial pole. This hour hand goes around once a day, telling the time to those who read it. The following definitions hold for whatever point is selected as the time reckoner.

A *day* is the interval between two successive transits of the time reckoner over the same branch of the celestial meridian. A star *transits* when it crosses the meridian; and since a star does so twice a day, we distinguish between *upper transit* above the celestial pole and *lower transit* below the pole. It is *noon* when the time reckoner is at upper transit. Local *time of day* is the hour angle of the time reckoner if the day begins at noon, or 12 hours plus the hour angle if the day begins at midnight. The hour angle of the time reckoner is the angle at the pole between our hour hand and the upper branch of the meridian; it is measured for this purpose in hours westward from the meridian.

4·2. Time by the Stars. Instead of selecting one of the stars as the time reckoner for star time, or *sidereal time,* astronomers

52

choose the vernal equinox. By our definitions, the *sidereal day* is the interval between two successive upper transits of the vernal equinox. *Sidereal time* is the hour angle of the vernal equinox; it is reckoned from sidereal noon through 24 hours to the next noon.

Sidereal time is kept by special clocks in the observatories, which are set directly from the clock in the sky. The principle, illustrated in Fig. 4·2, is as follows: The sidereal time at any instant is the same as the right ascension of a star which is at upper transit at that instant. Evidently what is needed is something to show the place of the celestial meridian precisely, so that the instant of the star's crossing can be correctly observed. The transit instrument will serve to explain how it is done.

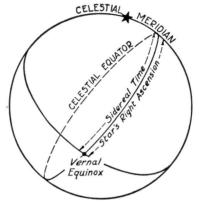

Fig. 4·2. Sidereal Time Equals the Right Ascension of a Star at Upper Transit.

4·3. Determining the Sidereal Time. The astronomical transit instrument is a small telescope which can be rotated on a single axis set in the east and west direction. As the telescope is turned, it points always toward the celestial meridian which is represented by a vertical thread in front of the eyepiece. The observer directs the telescope to the place where a star is about to pass. He can watch the star as it moves across the field of view until it reaches the meridian line.

Suppose that the sidereal clock reads $3^h 42^m 22^s.7$ at the instant the star is transiting, and that the star's right ascension as given in a catalog is $3^h 42^m 26^s.2$, which by our rule is the correct sidereal time at that instant. The sidereal clock is therefore 3.5 seconds slow. Now by comparison and a simple calculation the solar time can be found as well.

Recording devices are employed to time the transits of stars more accurately than can the direct visual observations. The photographic zenith tube has replaced the simple transit instrument at the Naval Observatory and elsewhere. This is a fixed vertical telescope for photographing stars as they cross the meridian nearly

FIG. 4·3.   Transit Instrument at the Naval Observatory.

overhead.   With this device an error of only three thousandths of a second is expected in a time determination from a set of 18 stars.

4·4.   The Solar Day Is Longer than the Sidereal Day.   Suppose that the sun is just now at the vernal equinox and that the two are at upper transit on the celestial meridian of the observer, at O (Fig. 4·4).   It is sidereal noon and also solar noon—noon by the sun. The sidereal day will end when the earth has made a complete rotation, bringing the vernal equinox again to upper transit.   We recall that parallel lines are directed toward the same point on the remote celestial sphere.

Meanwhile the earth will have advanced in its orbit around the sun so that, after the ending of the sidereal day, it must rotate still farther to bring the sun again to the meridian.   Since the earth revolves nearly a degree in a day and rotates through one degree in 4 minutes, the solar day is nearly 4 minutes longer than the sidereal day; the difference is about $3^m 56^s$.

Thus the earth rotates once in a sidereal day, not once in a day by a watch that keeps sun time. Because the apparent rotation of the celestial sphere is completed in a sidereal day, a star rises at the same sidereal time throughout the year. By solar time, however, it rises 4 minutes earlier from night to night, or 2 hours earlier from month to month. On successive nights at the same time by our watches the stars appear a little farther toward the west than

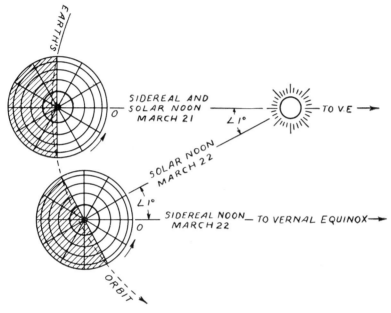

FIG. 4·4. The Solar Day Is Longer than the Sidereal Day.

they did before. As the seasons advance the constellations march slowly across the evening sky (3·1). Each season brings its own display of stars.

4·5. Apparent Solar Days Vary in Length. Because our activities are regulated by the sun and not by the stars, we prefer to keep solar time rather than sidereal time. Sidereal noon, for example, comes at night during part of the year. Yet the apparent sun, that is to say, the sun we see, is not a uniform timekeeper. This is so for two principal reasons.

1. *The earth's revolution around the sun is not uniform.* The earth revolves in its elliptical orbit in accordance with the *law of equal areas:* the line joining the earth to the sun sweeps over equal

areas in equal times. Because we are nearer the sun in winter than in summer (Fig. 4·5), the shorter line joining the earth and sun in winter must go around farther than the longer line in summer to sweep over the same area. The earth revolves farther in a day in winter and must rotate farther after the ending of the sidereal day to bring the sun again to the meridian. Thus apparent solar days (days by the sundial) are longer in winter than in summer.

2. *The ecliptic is inclined to the celestial equator.* When the sun is near a solstice, where the ecliptic is parallel to the celestial equator, its daily displacement by the earth's revolution has its

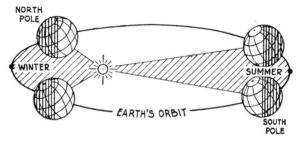

Fig. 4·5. The Earth Revolves Faster in Winter Because It Is Then Nearer the Sun.

full effect in delaying the sun's return to the meridian. When it is near an equinox, part of the sun's displacement is north or south, which does not delay its return. For this reason the apparent solar day is longer in summer and winter than in spring and fall. Both effects conspire to make this day longer in winter in the northern hemisphere.

4·6. The Mean Sun, or average sun, is employed for the keeping of ordinary time. This conventional sun would be a smooth-running timekeeper if the rotation of the earth were precisely uniform; its day, which is the average of all the apparent solar days through the year, would then be constant. *Mean solar time* is time by the mean sun. Its difference from apparent solar time at any instant, known as the *equation of time,* can be found from tables in the astronomical almanacs. Table 4·I shows how much the apparent time is fast or slow with respect to local time by the mean sun on the first of each month. These values for the equation of time are for midnight at Greenwich during 1955; they are correct within a few seconds for any other place or year.

TABLE 4·I.   EQUATION OF TIME

(Apparent time faster or slower than local civil time)

Jan. 1	3^m 8^s	slow	July 1	3^m 30^s	slow
Feb. 1	13 32	slow	Aug. 1	6 18	slow
Mar. 1	12 40	slow	Sept. 1	0 20	slow
Apr. 1	4 16	slow	Oct. 1	9 57	fast
May 1	2 48	fast	Nov. 1	16 20	fast
June 1	2 28	fast	Dec. 1	11 21	fast

The rapid change in the equation of time near the beginning of the year has an effect which is noticed by everyone. At this time of year the earth is nearest the sun and is accordingly revolving fastest. The sun is then moving fastest eastward along the ecliptic, delaying its rising and setting as timed by the mean sun. For this reason the sun does not begin to rise earlier in the morning by our watches until about 2 weeks after the date of the winter solstice, although it begins to set later in the evening about 2 weeks before that date.

4·7. Universal Time and Ephemeris Time. *Civil time* is the specific reckoning of mean solar time, in which the day begins at midnight. The local civil time at a particular place is accordingly 12 hours plus the local hour angle of the mean sun. Greenwich civil time, the local time at the meridian of Greenwich, is known as *universal time;* it is employed for the tabulation of data in present almanacs and will continue to be until 1960.

Civil time would be adequate for all purposes if the earth's rotation were uniform. It will indeed remain satisfactory for all ordinary purposes, because the master clocks will continue to be kept right by frequent sights on the stars, and most people will not be concerned with any other kind of time. For the foretelling of astronomical events, however, the irregular rotation of the earth (2·7) makes it hazardous to predict precisely what the universal time will be. Beginning with the year 1960, the American and British almanacs, which will then conform in other respects as well, will tabulate their data for intervals of ephemeris time.

Ephemeris time will run on uniformly; its constant unit will equal the length of the tropical year at the beginning of 1900 divided by the number of seconds and fraction in that year. The corrections of these predicted times to universal times will be determined later from observed positions of the moon (6·8).

Although sidereal time and apparent solar time are always local times, civil time is most often employed in the conventional forms of zone time and standard time.

4·8. The Difference Between the Local Times of two places at the same instant is the difference between their longitudes expressed in time. This is true because the earth makes a complete rota-

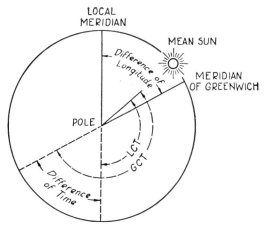

Fig. 4·8. Difference of Longitude Equals Difference of Local Time.

tion with respect to a celestial time reckoner in 24 hours of its kind of time; and there are 360° or 24 hours of longitude around the world. The rule applies to any kind of local time, whether it is sidereal, apparent solar, or civil, where the same kind of time is denoted at the two places. When the local time at one place is given, and the corresponding local time at another place is required, add the difference of their longitudes if the second place is east of the first; subtract if it is west.

In the time diagram of Fig. 4·8, we are looking at the earth from above its pole and are projecting the sun onto the equator in the longitude where it is overhead; the east to west direction is counterclockwise. The observer on the earth is in longitude 60° W, or 4^h W. The local civil time (LCT) there is 9^h, and the Greenwich civil time (GCT), or universal time, is 13^h, so that the difference of 4 hours in the local times of the two places is the difference of their longitudes. Here and in other places the time of day is counted through 24 hours continuously; 9^h is 9 A.M. and 13^h is 1 P.M.

This is also the basic rule for determining longitudes. When the local times at two places are known at the same instant, the difference in hours multiplied by 15 is the difference in degrees of longitude between the places.

4·9. The Time Zones. The local civil times at a particular instant are the same only for places on the same meridian. They become progressively later toward the east and earlier toward the west; the

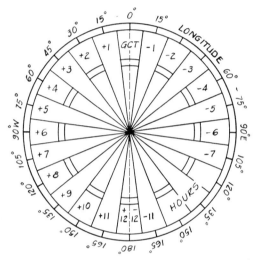

FIG. 4·9. Time Zone Diagram. The earth is viewed from above the south pole. The numbers outside the circle are the longitudes of the standard meridians. The numbers inside are corrections in hours to universal time.

rate of change in latitude 40° is one minute of time for a distance of a little more than 13 miles. The confusion that would ensue if every place kept its own local time is avoided by the use of time zones and belts. In its simplest form the plan is as follows:

Standard meridians are marked off around the world 15° or one hour apart both east and west from the meridian of Greenwich. The local times of these meridians accordingly differ successively by whole hours. The time to be kept at any place is the local civil time of the standard meridian nearest the place. Thus the world is divided by boundary meridians into 24 equal time zones, each

15° wide and having one of the standard meridians running centrally through it. The time is the same throughout each zone; it is one hour earlier than the time in the adjacent zone to the east, and one hour later than the time in the zone to the west. The rule to be followed when crossing a boundary between two zones on an eastward voyage is to set the watch ahead one hour, the minutes and seconds remaining as before; and on a westward voyage to set the watch back one hour.

Zone time is employed in the operations of ships at sea and of many aircraft over the sea. This uniform plan is occasionally modified near land, where it is shown by the charts, so that the ship's clock may agree with the standard time kept ashore.

4·10. Standard Time divisions on land follow in a general way the pattern of the time zones at sea. Their boundaries are often irregular; these are affected by local preference and are subject to change. In some areas the legal time differs from the times in adjacent belts by a fraction of an hour. There is also the arbitrary and not uniform practice of setting the clocks ahead of the accepted standard time for part of the year.

Four standard times are employed mainly in the United States and Canada; they are Eastern, Central, Mountain, and Pacific standard times. These are, respectively, the local civil times at the standard meridians 75°, 90°, 105°, and 120° west of the Greenwich meridian and are, accordingly, 5, 6, 7, and 8 hours earlier than universal time.

4·11. Where the Date Changes. Suppose that an airplane leaves San Francisco at noon on Monday, and proceeds due west around the world with the speed of the earth's rotation relative to the sun in that latitude. The sun accordingly remains practically stationary in the sky during the voyage, and the watches aboard are set back to noon whenever a boundary between time divisions is crossed. When the plane comes around again to San Francisco, the crew might be surprised to find that it is now Tuesday noon if they had forgotten the rule for the change of date.

The rule is generally to change the date at the 180° meridian. When this meridian is crossed on a westward voyage, as in going from San Francisco to Manila, the date is advanced; if the line is crossed on Monday noon, it is then Tuesday noon. At the eastward crossing the date is set back. Where the 180° meridian

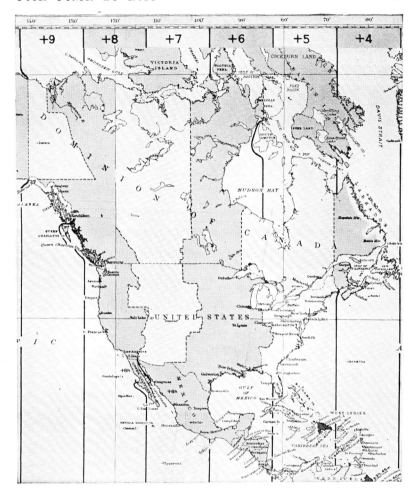

FIG. 4·10. Time Zone Chart of North America. The large numbers at the top are corrections in hours to universal time. (*Adapted from H.O. 5192 by permission of U.S. Navy Hydrographic Office*)

traverses land areas, the *international date line* may depart from the meridian so as not to divide a politically associated region. Thus it bends to the east around Siberia and to the west around the Aleutian Islands.

4·12. Radio Time Signals. The beats of a clock in the U.S. Naval Observatory, kept accurate by frequent observations of the stars, are sent out from naval radio stations and stations of the National

Bureau of Standards. The naval radio stations at Annapolis and elsewhere transmit the signals during the last 5 minutes of scheduled hours. They are dash signals on a variety of frequencies representing the seconds beats of a crystal-controlled standard time clock. These are transmitted on continuous waves and can be heard only with receivers suited to code reception. The dashes are omitted at certain seconds (Fig. 4·12) so that the listener can readily identify the minute and second of each signal. A long

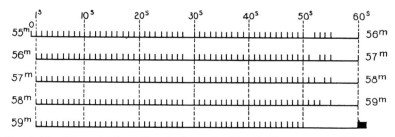

Fig. 4·12. Plan of Time Signals from the Naval Observatory. The short lines represent dot signals; these are omitted at the 29th second and before the beginning of each minute, where the number of signals immediately preceding the long breaks denotes the number of minutes before the beginning of the hour. The longest break of all comes before the long dash that announces the beginning of the hour.

dash following the longest break announces the beginning of the hour.

The seconds time signals from the standard frequency station WWV of the National Bureau of Standards at Beltsville, Maryland, are transmitted continuously day and night on 5, 10, 15 Mc/sec and other frequencies. They are heard as clicks which are superposed on standard audio frequencies. These employ modulated waves and may therefore be heard with ordinary radiophone receivers. The seconds clicks are interrupted at the 59th second of each minute. At 1 minute before the beginning of the hour and at every multiple of 5 minutes thereafter, the audio tone is interrupted for exactly a minute for the purpose of making announcements. These are examples of the distribution of the correct time by observatories in various parts of the world.

4·13. Conversion of Time. Given the time at one place, it is frequently desired to know the corresponding time at another place. The conversion is often to or from universal time, for which present almanacs are likely to tabulate their data. In passing from zone time to universal time, the correction is found by dividing the longitude of the place in degrees by 15 and taking the nearest whole number. In passing from the standard time of a place to universal time, the correction may not be the same as from zone time in the same longitude, because of irregularities in the standard time belts. The following examples illustrate such conversions:

1. The zone time is $21^h 22^m$, May 25, at a place in longitude 103° W. Required the corresponding universal time and date.
Answer: The UT is $4^h 22^m$, May 26.

2. *The American Ephemeris and Nautical Almanac* gives the time of the beginning of autumn in 1956 as September 23 at $1^h 36^m$, universal time. Required the corresponding Central standard time and date.
Answer: The CST is $19^h 36^m$ (7:36 P.M.), September 22.

3. The "daylight saving time" in San Francisco is 7:30 P.M. Required the time at Galveston, Texas, which remains on standard time.
Answer: The CST is 8:30 P.M.

THE CALENDAR

Calendars have been in use since the beginnings of civilizations. They have tried to combine natural measures of time, the solar day, the lunar month, and the year of the seasons, in the most convenient ways, and have encountered difficulties because these measures do not fit evenly one into another. Calendars have been of three types: the lunar, the lunisolar, and the solar calendar.

4·14. Calendars of Three Types. (1) *The lunar calendar* is the simplest of the three types, and it was the earliest to be used by almost all nations. Each month began originally with the "new moon," the first appearance for the month of the crescent moon after sunset. Long controlled only by observation of the crescent, this calendar was eventually operated by fixed rules. In the fixed lunar calendar the 12 months of the common lunar year are alternately 30 and 29 days long, making 354 days in all. The Mohammedan calendar is a survivor of this type.

(2) *The lunisolar calendar* tries to keep in step with both the moon's phases and the seasons, and is the most complex of the three types. It began by occasionally adding a 13th month to the short lunar year to round out the year of the seasons. The extra

month was later inserted by fixed rules. The Jewish calendar is the principal survivor of the lunisolar type.

(3) *The solar calendar* makes the year conform as nearly as possible to the year of the seasons, and neglects the moon's phases; its 12 months are generally longer than the lunar month. Only a few early nations, notably the Egyptians and eventually the Romans, adopted this simple type.

4·15. The Early Roman Calendar dates formally from the founding of Rome in 753 B.C. It was originally a lunar calendar of a sort, beginning in the spring and having 10 months. The names of the months, if we use mainly our own style instead of the Latin, were: March, April, May, June, Quintilis, Sextilis, September, October, November, and December. The years for many centuries thereafter were counted from 753 and were designated A.U.C., in the year of the founding of the City. Two months, January and February, were added later and were eventually placed at the beginning, so that the number months have ever since then appeared in the calendar out of their proper order.

In its 12-month form the Roman calendar was of the lunisolar type. The day began at midnight instead of at sunset as with most early people. An occasional extra month was added to keep the calendar in step with the seasons. The calendar was managed so unwisely, however, that it fell into confusion; its dates drifted back into different seasons from the ones they were supposed to represent.

When Julius Caesar became the ruler of Rome, he was disturbed by the bad condition of the calendar and took steps to correct it. He particularly wished to discard the lunisolar form with its troublesome extra months. Caesar was impressed with the simplicity of the solar calendar the Egyptians were using, and he knew of their discovery that the length of the tropical year is very nearly $365\frac{1}{4}$ days. He accordingly formulated his reform with the advice of the astronomer Sosigenes of Alexandria. In preparation for the new calendar the "last year of confusion," 46 B.C., was made 445 days long in order to correct the accumulated error of the old one. The date of the vernal equinox was thereby brought to March 25. The Julian calendar began on January 1, 45 B.C.

4·16. The Julian Calendar was of the solar type, and so neglected the moon's phases. Its chief feature was the adoption of $365\frac{1}{4}$

days as the average length of the calendar year. This was accomplished conveniently by the plan of leap years. Three common years of 365 days are followed by a fourth year containing 366 days; this *leap year* in our era has a number evenly divisible by 4.

In lengthening the calendar year from the 355 days of the old lunisolar plan to the common year of 365 days, Caesar distributed the additional 10 days among the months. With further changes made in the reign of Augustus, the months assumed their present lengths. After Caesar's death in 44 B.C., the month Quintilis was renamed July in honor of the founder of the new calendar. The month Sextilis was later renamed August in honor of Augustus.

Because its average year of $365^d 6^h$ was $11^m 14^s$ longer than the tropical year, the Julian calendar fell behind with respect to the seasons about 3 days in 400 years. When the council of churchmen convened at Nicaea in A.D. 325, the vernal equinox had fallen back to about March 21. It was at that convention that previous confusion about the date of Easter was ended.

4·17. Easter was originally celebrated by some early churches on whatever day the Passover began, and by others on the Sunday included in the Passover week. The Council of Nicaea decided in favor of the Sunday observance and left it to the church at Alexandria to formulate the rule, which is as follows:

Easter is the first Sunday after the 14th day of the moon (nearly the full moon) which occurs on or immediately after March 21. Thus if the 14th day of the moon occurs on Sunday, Easter is observed one week later. Unlike Christmas, Easter is a movable feast because it depends on the moon's phases; its date can range from March 22 to April 25.

DATES OF EASTER SUNDAY

1956, Apr. 1	1961, Apr. 2	1966, Apr. 10
1957, Apr. 21	1962, Apr. 22	1967, Mar. 26
1958, Apr. 6	1963, Apr. 14	1968, Apr. 14
1959, Mar. 29	1964, Mar. 29	1969, Apr. 6
1960, Apr. 17	1965, Apr. 18	1970, Mar. 29

4·18. The Gregorian Calendar. As the date of the vernal equinox fell back in the calendar, March 21 and Easter which is reckoned from it came later and later in the season. Toward the end of the 16th century the equinox had retreated to March 11. Another reform of the calendar was proposed by Pope Gregory XIII.

Two rather obvious corrections were made in the Gregorian reform. First, ten days were suppressed from the calendar of that year; the day following October 4, 1582, became October 15 for those who wished to adopt the new plan. The date of the vernal equinox was restored in this way to March 21. The second correction made the average length of the calendar year more nearly equal to the tropical year, so that the calendar would not again get so quickly out of step with the seasons. Evidently the thing to do was to omit the 3 days in 400 years by which the Julian calendar year was too long. This was done conveniently by making common years of the century years having numbers not evenly divisible by 400. Thus the years 1700, 1800, and 1900 became common years of 365 days instead of leap years of 366 days, whereas the year 2000 remained a leap year as in the former calendar. The average year of the new calendar is still too long by 26 seconds, which is hardly enough to be troublesome for a long time to come.

The Gregorian calendar was gradually adopted, until it is now in use, at least for civil purposes, in practically all nations. England and its colonies including America made the change in 1752. By that time there were 11 days to be suppressed; for that century year was a leap year in the old calendar and a common year in the new one. September 2, 1752, was followed by September 14. The countries of eastern Europe were the latest to make the change, when the difference had become 13 days.

4·19. Suggested Calendar Reform. Irregularities in our present calendar are frequently cited as reason for reforming it. The calendar year is not evenly divisible into quarters; the months range in length from 28 to 31 days, and their beginnings and endings occur on all days of the week; the weeks are split between months. Some people say that the irregularities should be corrected. Others are not sure that the improvement would be great enough to offset the confusion in our records that the change might bring.

Recent proposals for calendar reform are based on the period of 364 days, a number evenly divisible by 4, 7, and also 13. An extra day is added each year in such a way as not to disturb the sequence of weekdays, and another is added every 4 years in the same manner, except in the century years not evenly divisible by 400. Two proposed calendars are the 13-month perpetual calendar and the 12-month perpetual calendar known as the world calendar.

The first plan divides the year into 13 months of 28 days each. In this plan a calendar for one month would serve for every other month forever if it is remembered when to add the two stabilizing days. This proposal met with approval for a time, but lost favor because it seemed too drastic a change from the present calendar.

The second plan divides the 364-day period into 12 months. The four equal quarters of the year remain the same forever. Each quarter begins on Sunday and ends on Saturday. Its first month has 31 days, and its second and third months have 30 days each. One stabilizing day is added each year at the end of the fourth quarter; it is called Year-End Day, December Y, and is an extra Saturday. The second extra day is added every fourth year, with the usual exceptions, at the end of the second quarter; it is called Leap-Year Day, June L, and is also an extra Saturday. This plan is a more moderate change from the present calendar; it was disapproved, however, by the United Nations in 1956.

QUESTIONS ON CHAPTER 4

1. Suppose that the star Arcturus is selected as our time reckoner for ordinary purposes instead of the sun. What would then be the definitions of noon, day, and time of day? Why would this plan be inconvenient?

2. A certain star rises tonight at 10 o'clock standard time. State the time of its rising tomorrow night; a month from now.

3. Give two reasons why apparent solar days are longest near the beginning of winter.

4. State the difference between the standard time belts and the time zones employed at sea, and the reason for the difference.

5. At noon universal time, what are the corresponding standard times at New York, Chicago, and San Francisco?

6. The total eclipse of the moon on November 7, 1957, begins at 2:12 P.M. universal time. At what standard time does it begin at Denver?

7. At 2:00 A.M. universal time, May 10, the local civil time at a certain place is 9:40 P.M., May 9. Explain that the longitude of the place is 65° W.

8. At 11:55 P.M. on Tuesday an airplane flying west over the ocean is about to cross the 180° meridian. State the time and date for the plane 10 minutes later.

9. Name the terms which are defined as follows:

(a) Hour angle of the vernal equinox.
(b) Hour angle of the mean sun plus 12 hours.
(c) Time by the sundial.
(d) Standard time near the meridian 90° west of Greenwich.

10. Distinguish between the lunar, lunisolar, and solar calendars.

11. State the two chief changes in our calendar made in the Gregorian reform, and the reasons for the changes.

12. Give some reasons for a reform of our present calendar, and an argument against it.

REFERENCES

The American Ephemeris and Nautical Almanac. Published yearly. Superintendent of Public Documents, U.S. Government Printing Office, Washington 25, D. C.

Nassau, J. J., *Practical Astronomy.* Second edition. McGraw-Hill Book Company, New York, 1948.

Shaw, R. William, and Samuel L. Boothroyd, *Manual of Astronomy.* A guide to observation and laboratory interpretation in elementary astronomy. Third edition. F. S. Crofts and Co., New York, 1947.

The 26-inch Refracting Telescope of the U.S. Naval Observatory.
(*Photograph by Underwood and Underwood*)

5

TELESCOPES AND THEIR USES

REFRACTING TELESCOPES — REFLECTING TELESCOPES
— THE SPECTROSCOPE — RADIO TELESCOPES

The chief optical feature of the telescope is its *objective*, which receives the light of a celestial object and focuses the light to form an image of the object. The image may be formed either by refraction of the light by a lens or by reflection from a curved mirror. Optical telescopes are accordingly of two general types: *refracting telescopes* and *reflecting telescopes*. Schmidt telescopes are modifications of the reflecting type. In the *radio telescopes* the radio radiations from a celestial source are received by an antenna which concentrates them on receiving and recording apparatus.

REFRACTING TELESCOPES

5·1. Light Comes to Us in Waves which spread from a source, such as the sun, in something like the way that ripples spread over the surface of a pond when a stone is dropped into the water. *Light* may be defined as the sensation that is produced when waves of appropriate lengths enter the eye, or more generally in terms of the wave motion itself.

The *wave length* is the distance from crest to crest of successive waves. In the limited range which causes the sensation of light, the wave lengths vary from 1/70,000 inch for violet light to nearly twice that length for the reddest light we can see. The total *radiation* from a source has a far greater range of wave length than the eye can detect, from gamma rays of the order of a billion waves to the inch to radio waves which may be many miles long. The *frequency* of the radiation is the number of waves emitted by the source in a second; it equals the velocity of light divided by the wave length.

The *velocity of light* is about 186,300 miles a second; it is the speed of all the radiation in a vacuum. The speed is reduced in a medium, such as air or glass, depending on the density of the me-

69

dium and the wave length. This is the reason for the refraction of light.

5·2. Refraction of Light is the change in the direction of a ray of light when it passes obliquely from one medium into another of

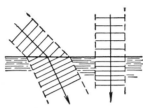

different density, as from air into glass. A "ray" of light denotes the direction in which a narrow section of the wave system is moving.

When a ray of light obliquely enters a denser medium, where its speed is reduced (Fig. 5·2), one side is retarded before the other. The wave crests are accordingly swung around, and the ray becomes more nearly perpendicular to the boundary between the two media. When the oblique ray enters a rarer medium instead, it is refracted away from the perpendicular. Evidently the direction of the ray is not altered if it is originally perpendicular to the boundary.

FIG. 5·2. Refraction of Light. A ray of light passing obliquely from one medium into another is changed in direction.

Fig. 5·2A shows how a double convex lens forms by refraction a real inverted image of an object which is farther from the lens than is the focal point, *F*, the point where rays parallel to the axis of the lens are focused. Rays which pass through the center of the lens are unchanged in direction. When the image formed by this

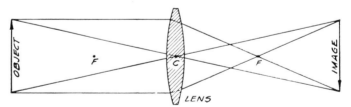

FIG. 5·2A.   A Simple Convex Lens Forms an Inverted Real Image of a Celestial Object.

lens is brought within the focal distance of a similar lens, the second lens serves as an eyepiece with which to view and magnify the image, leaving it inverted. A single lens, however, does not give a sharp image, mainly because it refracts shorter waves more than longer ones, violet light more than red, so that it does not bring them together at the same focus. This confusion of colors is partly corrected by the use of a compound lens.

5·3. The Refracting Telescope. The objective of a refracting telescope is generally a combination of two lenses. Its *aperture,* or clear diameter, is given in denoting the size of the telescope. The *focal length,* or distance from the objective to its focus, is often about 15 times the aperture. Thus a 12-inch telescope has an aperture of 12 inches and may be about 15 feet long. For visual use the inverted image formed by the objective is viewed with an *eyepiece,* a magnifier of small lenses set in a sliding tube. The objective of a visual refractor focuses together the yellow and adjacent colors of the spectrum, to which the eye is especially sensitive, but not the blue and violet light which most affects the ordinary photographic plate. Without a correcting device it does not serve well for photography.

Where a telescope intended for visual purposes is used as a camera, a plate holder replaces the eyepiece. A yellow filter and a yellow-sensitive plate may be combined to utilize the light that is sharply focused, or a correcting lens may be introduced for a particular kind of plate. Refracting telescopes intended only for photography often have more than two lenses in the objective; they generally have shorter focal lengths and give clear pictures of greater areas of the sky.

5·4. The 40-inch Telescope of Yerkes Observatory at Williams Bay, Wisconsin, is the largest refracting telescope; its focal length is 63 feet. It has about the greatest permissible aperture for an instrument of this kind, where the objective can be supported only at the edge. A larger lens might sag seriously under its own weight.

The *equatorial mounting* of the 40-inch telescope (Fig. 5·4) is an example of the type generally used for the larger refracting telescopes. The *polar axis* is parallel to the earth's axis; around it the telescope is turned parallel to the celestial equator. The *declination axis* is supported by the polar axis; around it the telescope is turned along an hour circle, from one declination to another.

The polar axis carries a graduated circle showing the hour angle of the star toward which the telescope is pointing. There is also a dial on the pier, which indicates the star's right ascension. A

FIG. 5·4. The 40-inch Telescope, Yerkes Observatory. This is an equatorial telescope; it can be moved parallel and perpendicular to the celestial equator.

circle on the declination axis shows the declination of the star. By the use of these circles the telescopes can be pointed toward a celestial object of known right ascension and declination; it is then kept pointing at the object by mechanism in the pier. The dome is turned by motor, so that the telescope may look out in any direction through the opened slit.

The 36-inch telescope of Lick Observatory on Mount Hamilton in California is second in size among refracting telescopes. About 40 refracting telescopes have apertures of 20 inches or more.

REFLECTING TELESCOPES

5·5. Reflection from a Concave Mirror. The concave spherical mirror represented in Fig. 5·5 has its center of curvature at C and its focal point at F, to which rays parallel to the axis of the mirror are reflected. Rays passing through the center strike the mirror normally and return without change in direction. The mirror forms an inverted real image of a distant object.

All mirrors are achromatic, because reflection does not disperse the light acording to wave length, as does refraction. The spheri-

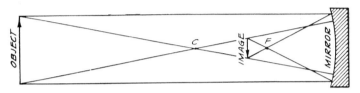

Fig. 5·5. A Concave Mirror Forms an Inverted Real Image of a Celestial Object.

cal mirror, however, does not form a clear image; its focal points are not the same for its inner and outer parts. A remedy is to make the mirror paraboloidal instead of spherical. A good image is then formed, which may be viewed with an eyepiece or photographed. Thus a concave mirror can serve as the objective of a telescope.

5·6. The Reflecting Telescope has as its objective a concave mirror at the lower end of the tube; this is a circular disk of glass having its upper surface ground to suitable curvature and coated with a film of metal, such as aluminum. The glass serves only to give the desired form to the metal surface, and it need not have the high optical quality required for a lens. The entire back of the disk may be supported. The focal length of the mirror is often about 5 times its aperture; sometimes it is less. Because the reflecting telescope is shorter than the ordinary refractor of the same diameter, it is less costly to construct and to house. These are reasons why very large telescopes are of the reflecting type.

The large mirror reflects the light of the celestial object to the *prime focus* in the middle of the tube near the upper end, where the image is accessible to the observer only in the very largest telescopes. In the *Newtonian form* a small plane mirror at an angle of 45° near the top of the tube reflects the converging beam from the large mirror to focus at the side of the tube. In the *Cassegrainian form* a small convex mirror replaces the plane mirror; it reflects the beam back through an opening in the large mirror to focus below it. Where the large mirror has no opening, which is the case with the 100-inch Mount Wilson telescope, the returning beam is reflected to focus at the side by a plane mirror in

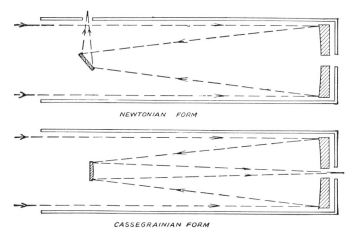

NEWTONIAN FORM

CASSEGRAINIAN FORM

FIG. 5·6. The Reflecting Telescope in Two Forms. In the Newtonian form the converging beam from the large mirror is diverted to the side by a small diagonal plane mirror. In the Cassegrainian form the beam is reflected back to focus behind the large mirror.

front of the large one. This and some other large telescopes provide another place of observation, the *coudé focus*, by reflection of the beam through the polar axis to a laboratory below.

5·7. The 200-inch Hale Telescope on Palomar Mountain in southern California, completed in 1948, is the largest optical telescope. Its large mirror is a disk of pyrex glass nearly 17 feet in diameter and 27 inches thick, having its upper, concave surface coated with aluminum. At the prime focus 55 feet above the mirror the observer is carried in a cage 5 feet in diameter, which obstructs less than 10 per cent of the incoming light. Here a 5 × 7 inch photographic plate records an area of the sky 26' × 36½', or about the apparent area of the full moon. Stars of the 19th magnitude can be detected with an eyepiece, and stars as faint as the 24th magnitude can be photographed or measured photoelectrically.

When the 41-inch convex mirror is set in the converging beam, it reflects the light through the 40-inch opening in the large mirror to focus below it. The effective focal length is 267 feet at the Cassegrainian focus and 510 feet at the coudé focus in the laboratory.

Fig. 5·7. The 200-inch Hale Telescope, Palomar Observatory. View from the east.

The telescope tube of skeleton construction moves in declination within the yoke which forms the polar axis. The tube, together with the mirror and observer's cage, weighs 140 tons. The dome is 137 feet in diameter.

5·8. Other Large Reflecting Telescopes. The 120-inch telescope of the Lick Observatory on Mount Hamilton, California, is the second largest telescope; its mirror has a focal length of 50 feet. This telescope also has an observer's cage at the prime focus. Next in order are the 100-inch telescope of the Mount Wilson Observatory in California, the 98-inch telescope of the Royal Greenwich Observatory in England, when it is in operation, and the 82-inch telescope of the McDonald Observatory on Mount Locke, Texas. Four others complete for the moment the list of optical telescopes 6 feet or more in diameter.

These telescopes are often employed as cameras; the photographic place replaces the eyepiece at the focus. The photographs provide permanent records of the heavens, which can be studied deliberately. By cumulative effect of the light with prolonged

FIG. 5·8.   Dome of the 120-inch Telescope, Lick Observatory.

exposure they show features invisible to the eye at the same telescope. The telescopes are also employed to concentrate the light of celestial objects on auxiliary apparatus, such as the spectroscope and photoelectric photometer.

The type of reflecting telescope thus far described is admirable for photographing limited areas of the heavens. Another type is more effective for recording larger areas distinctly.

5·9. The Schmidt Telescope is named after its designer, Bernhard Schmidt, an optical worker at the Hamburg Observatory in Germany. Its objective is a spherical mirror, which is easy to make but is not by itself suitable for a telescope. Parallel rays reflected by the central part of such a mirror are focused farther away from it than are those reflected from its outer zones. The appropriate correction is effected by a special type of thin lens, the correcting plate, at the center of curvature of the mirror. The lens slightly diverges the outer parts of the entering beam with respect to the

Fig. 5·9. The 48-inch Schmidt Telescope. Palomar Observatory.

middle, so that the entire beam is focused on a slightly curved surface. The photographic plate, suitably curved by springs in the plate holder, faces the mirror between it and the correcting plate. The size of this type of telescope is denoted by the diameter of the correcting plate. The Schmidt telescope can photograph rapidly and clearly a considerable area of the heavens, for example, a large part of the Milky Way.

The largest telescope of this kind is the 48-inch Schmidt telescope of the Palomar Observatory. Its 72-inch mirror has a radius of curvature of 20 feet, which is about the length of the tube. The focal length is 10 feet. An important achievement of this telescope is the National Geographic Society–Palomar Observatory Sky Survey, a photographic atlas of the heavens north of declination 27° S. The atlas consists of 879 pairs of negative prints from blue- and red-sensitive plates, each print 14 inches square and covering an area 7° on a side. The survey reaches stars of the 20th magnitude and exterior galaxies of the 19.5 magnitude.

Other examples of this newer type are the 24-inch Schmidt telescope of the Warner and Swasey Observatory in Cleveland, the similar Curtis Memorial telescope of the University of Michigan Observatory, and the 31½-inch Schmidt telescope of the Hamburg Observatory, dedicated in 1955. The 33-inch Baker-Schmidt telescope of the Boyden Station near Bloemfontein, South Africa, is a modified type.

5·10. Advantages of a Large Telescope. (1) A larger telescope has greater light-gathering power, which increases the depth of space to be explored. (2) It is likely to permit greater magnifying power. (3) It has greater resolving power, so that it reveals finer detail than can be observed with a smaller telescope.

The *light-gathering power* of a telescope increases in direct proportion to the area of the objective, or the square of its diameter. A particular star is accordingly 400 times as bright with the 200-inch telescope as with a 10-inch telescope. Thus stars can be observed with the former that are too faint to be detected with the latter.

The *magnifying power* of a telescope used as a camera increases with the length of the telescope. The diameter of a celestial object in the photograph equals the focal length of the telescope times the angular diameter of the object in degrees divided by 57°.3. Thus the moon, having an angular diameter of about ½°, appears 5¾ inches in diameter in a photograph at the prime focus of the 200-inch telescope, and about 1¼ inches with a 10-inch refracting telescope of the usual type. In either case, the size can, of course, be increased by enlargement of the photograph.

The *resolving power* of a telescope is the angular distance between two stars that can be just separated with the telescope in the best conditions. This least distance, d in seconds of arc, is related to the wave length, λ, and the aperture, a, in the same units by the formula: $d'' = 1.03 \times 206{,}265'' \times \lambda/a$. For visual telescopes the formula becomes: $d'' = 4''.56/a$, where the aperture is expressed in inches; the value is $0''.023$ for the 200-inch telescope, and $0''.46$ for a 10-inch telescope. We notice presently how the much greater wave lengths employed in radio telescopes make them less effective in separating fine detail.

THE SPECTROSCOPE

5·11. Dispersion of Light.   When a beam of light passes obliquely from one medium to another, as from air into glass, its direction is altered (5·2). Because the amount of the change in direction in-

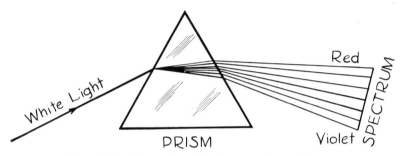

Fig. 5·11.   Formation of a Spectrum by a Prism.

creases progressively with decrease in wave length of the light, from red to violet, the beam is *dispersed* by refraction into a *spectrum*. Thus the rainbow is produced when sunlight is dispersed by raindrops. The spectrum is often obtained by passing the light through a glass prism (Fig. 5·11). It goes on beyond the visible range into the ultraviolet in one direction and the infrared in the other, where it may be recorded by photography and other means.

5·12. The Spectroscope.   A familiar type of spectroscope consists of a glass prism, toward which a collimator and view telescope are directed. The light enters the tube of the collimator through a narrow slit between the sharpened edges of two metal plates. The slit is at the focal point of the collimator lens. After passing through the lens, the rays are accordingly parallel as they enter the prism. The light is refracted by the prism and dispersed into a spectrum which is brought to focus by the objective of the view telescope and magnified by its eyepiece. For purposes of astronomy the spectroscope is attached to the telescope which serves to concentrate the light of the celestial body and to focus it on the slit. Here, and in the laboratory as well, the eyepiece is generally replaced by a plate holder.

FIG. 5·12. The Spectroscope. (*Courtesy of Adam Hilger, Ltd.*)

5·13. Three Kinds of Spectra. When the spectroscope is directed successively toward a variety of luminous objects in the heavens and in the laboratory, it is found that spectra are of three kinds.

The *bright-line spectrum* is an array of bright lines on a dark background. The source of the light is a glowing gas which radiates in a limited number of wave lengths. Each gaseous chemical

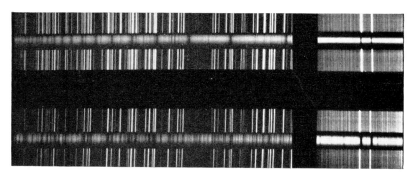

FIG. 5·13. Dark-Line and Bright-Line Spectra. At the left are the ultraviolet dark-line spectra of Alpha Cygni (above) and Betelgeuse (below). They are photographed between bright lines of the iron spectrum. At the right the dark D lines of sodium in the yellow region of the stars' spectra appear between bright comparison lines of sodium. Here the Doppler displacements are clearly shown. (*Photographed at Mount Wilson Observatory*)

element emits its particular selection of wave lengths and can, therefore, be identified by the pattern of lines of its spectrum. A glowing neon tube, for example, produces a bright-line spectrum.

The *continuous spectrum* is an unbroken band of light. The source of the light is a luminous solid, liquid, or opaque gas, which emits all wave lengths. The chemical composition of the source is not revealed. The glowing filament of a lamp and the surface of the sun produce continuous spectra.

The *dark-line spectrum* is an array of dark lines on a bright background. Gas intervenes between the observer and the source, which by itself may produce a continuous spectrum. The gas abstracts from the light the particular wave lengths that it emits itself, and thus tells its own chemical composition. The spectrum of the sun (10·9) is a dark-line spectrum, because the sunlight filters through the atmospheres of the sun and earth before reaching us.

Where the gases consist of molecules, such as carbon dioxide and methane, they produce their characteristic *bands* of bright or dark lines. It will be understood that these descriptions apply to regions of the spectrum invisible to the eye as well as the visible ones.

5·14. The Doppler Effect. The lines in the spectrum of a celestial source inform us not only of its chemical composition, but also of its velocity in the line of sight. Where the source from which the waves are spreading is approaching the observer, the waves are crowded together, so that the wave lengths are diminished. Where the source is receding, the waves are spread farther apart, so that their lengths are increased. This effect was explained long ago by the Austrian physicist Doppler for the case of sound waves; a familiar example is the lowered pitch of the whistle as the locomotive passes us. The effect in the spectrum is as follows:

Where the source of light is relatively approaching or receding from the observer, the lines in its spectrum are displaced respectively to shorter or longer wave lengths by an amount that is directly proportional to the speed of approach or recession.

The shift of the spectrum lines from their normal positions is often our only means of observing the motion of a celestial body relative to the earth. We notice later some applications of this useful effect.

RADIO TELESCOPES

Radiations from the heavens at radio frequencies were first detected, in 1931, by K. G. Jansky of the Bell Telephone Laboratories. In 1936, Grote Reber at his home in Wheaton, Illinois, built a fixed paraboloidal antenna 31 feet in diameter for his pioneer recordings of areas of the Milky Way as they passed his meridian. Radio radiations from the sun were first reported in 1942. The tracing of the spiral structure of our galaxy with radio telescopes began very recently. Progress is rapid in these new fields, in which physicists and radio engineers as well as astronomers are engaged.

5·15. The Radio Telescope in its simplest form bears some resemblance to the optical telescope of the reflecting type, but it does

FIG. 5·15. The 50-foot Radio Telescope at the Naval Research Laboratory, Washington.

not, of course, form an image of the celestial object. Its antenna
is a paraboloidal "dish" of metal sheet or wire mesh. The antenna
collects the radio beam from the part of the heavens toward which
it is directed and focuses it on a short rod, whence it is conveyed
to a sensitive receiver. The strength of the signal is then recorded
in a selected wave length by a registering meter. The telescope in
this form is now generally steerable; it can be turned like the optical telescope to different parts of the heavens.

Various other types of antennas are in use, many of them designed to improve the resolving power. J. D. Kraus at Ohio State
University employs a line of wire helices. B. Y. Mills in Australia
has a 1500-foot flat cross of dipoles mounted above a horizontal
reflector of chicken wire.

The radio telescope is as effective by day as by night. It can
operate through a cloudy sky and through cosmic dust. It can
locate the otherwise dark hydrogen clouds along the spiral arms of
our galaxy by being tuned to the wave length of 21 cm ($16 \cdot 9$) in
which they radiate, and may be capable of recording strong radio
sources at distances beyond the reach of optical telescopes.

5·16. The Fineness of Detail that can be distinguished with the
radio telescope is denoted by the same formula we have given
($5 \cdot 10$) for the optical telescope. It is the angular distance between
two radio point sources that can be barely separated. This critical
angle is proportional directly to the wave length of the radiation
and inversely to the size of the antenna. Because it operates with
the longer wave lengths, the radio telescope is much less effective
in separating fine detail than is an optical telescope of the same
size.

In order to improve the resolving power and also to increase the
gathering power, radio telescopes are being constructed with larger
and larger antennas. Among the newer telescopes having dishes
for antennas are the 50-foot radio telescope of the Naval Research
Laboratory in Washington, the 60-foot telescope at the Agassiz
Station of Harvard Observatory, the 75-foot telescope at Kootwijk,
Netherlands, the 250-foot telescope at the Jodrell Bank Station
of the University of Manchester in England, and one of the same
size to be constructed near Sydney, Australia. An 84-foot radio
telescope is planned for the Naval Research Laboratory, twin
100-inch telescopes for the California Institute of Technology to be

installed in the vicinity of Mount Whitney, and a 140-foot telescope for a site in the Appalachian Mountains.

5·17. The 60-foot Radio Telescope of Harvard Observatory is for the moment the largest telescope of this type in America. The paraboloidal antenna has a diameter of 60 feet and a focal length of 21 feet. The antenna is made of expanded aluminum mesh, each opening $\frac{3}{8}$ inch wide, and is supported by tubing. It is carried by a motor-driven equatorial mounting, and can be directed toward any part of the sky. The antenna is connected with an electronic

FIG. 5·17. The 60-foot Radio Telescope at the Agassiz Station, Harvard Observatory. (*Photograph by Robert E. Cox*)

receiver especially designed for recordings of the 21-cm line. Simultaneous recordings are possible in 20 channels around this wave length.

QUESTIONS ON CHAPTER 5

1. Distinguish between the refracting and the reflecting telescope. State the size and location of the largest telescope of each kind.

2. Give reasons why very large telescopes are all reflecting telescopes.

3. Mention some advantages of the equatorial mounting for a telescope.

4. Distinguish between the Newtonian and Cassegrainian forms of the reflecting telescope.

5. Describe the Schmidt telescope. What are some of its advantages over the type of reflecting telescope considered in Question 4?

6. State 3 advantages of a larger telescope as compared with a smaller one.

7. Explain how a spectrum is produced when a beam of light is passed through a glass prism. What is the purpose of the slit before the prism?

8. Describe the appearance of: (a) the bright-line spectrum; (b) the continuous spectrum; (c) the dark-line spectrum.

9. What is the physical nature of the source producing each kind of spectrum? What can be learned about the chemical composition of the source in each case?

10. State and explain the effect in the spectrum when the source of light is approaching or receding from the observer.

11. Explain that a radio telescope is less effective in separating fine detail than an optical telescope of the same size.

12. State some advantages of a radio telescope as compared with an optical telescope.

REFERENCES

Dimitroff. George Z., and James G. Baker, *Telescopes and Accessories.* Harvard University Press, Cambridge, 1945.

Ingalls, Albert G., editor, "Amateur Telescope Making, Book 1," "Amateur Telescope Making, Advanced," and "Amateur Telescope Making, Book 3." *Scientific American*, New York.

King, Henry C., *The History of the Telescope.* Sky Publishing Corporation, Harvard Observatory, Cambridge, 1955.

Lovell, A. C. B., and J. A. Clegg, *Radio Astronomy.* John Wiley and Sons, New York. 1952.

Mount Wilson and Palomar Observatories, *Frontiers in Space.* The Bookstore, California Institute of Technology, Pasadena.

Wright, Helen, *Palomar.* The Macmillan Company, New York, 1952.

6

THE MOON IN ITS PHASES

MOTIONS OF THE MOON — THE MOON'S SURFACE
FEATURES — ECLIPSES OF THE MOON

The moon is the earth's *satellite,* or attendant. Next to the sun, it is the most conspicuous in our skies, because it is the nearest celestial body to the earth. The moon and the earth revolve together around the sun, and mutually revolve meanwhile around a point between their centers. Some satellites of other planets are larger than the moon, but none of these reflects as much sunlight to its planet as does the moon to the earth. In this chapter we consider the moon's motion relative to the sun and to the earth, its surface features which are in marked contrast with those of the earth, and its eclipses when it enters the earth's shadow.

MOTIONS OF THE MOON

6·1. The Earth and Moon Are Like a Double Planet. Although the moon is not the largest of the satellites, it has the distinction of being the one most nearly comparable with its primary in size and

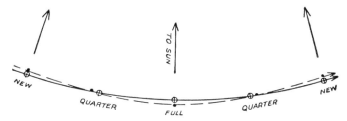

FIG. 6·1. Orbits of the Earth and Moon Around the Sun.

mass. The moon's diameter of 2160 miles is more than a quarter of the earth's diameter, and its mass is $\frac{1}{82}$ as much as the earth's mass.

Imagine the centers of the earth and moon joined by a stout rod.

The point of support at which the two bodies would balance is the *center of mass* of the earth-moon system. It is this point around which the earth and the moon mutually revolve monthly; and it is the elliptical path of this point around the sun that we have hitherto called the "earth's orbit." The center of mass of the earth-moon system is only 2900 miles from the earth's center and is therefore within the earth. Thus the moon revolves around the earth, although not around its center. In the descriptions that follow it is convenient to consider the moon's revolution relative to the earth's center.

6·2. The Moon's Distance from the Earth. The direct way of measuring the distance of a celestial body is by observing its parallax. *Parallax* is the difference between the directions of an object when it is viewed from two different places. Notice how a

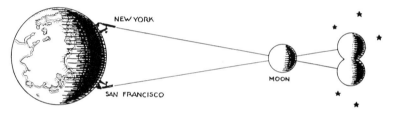

FIG. 6·2. The Moon's Directions Differ by Nearly Its Breadth as Viewed from New York and San Francisco.

near-by object seems to jump back and forth against a distant background when it is viewed alternately with the two eyes. The nearer the object, the greater is its change in direction; and the amount of the parallax would be greater, of course, if our eyes were farther apart. Where the parallax has been measured and the distance between the two points of observation is known, the distance of the object is readily calculated.

The difference in the moon's directions from two widely separated places on the earth is so great that the parallax can be accurately measured. Observed at the same instant from New York and San Francisco, the moon's positions among the stars differ by nearly the full breadth of the moon, or nearly half a degree. When we speak of the moon's parallax ordinarily, it is as though one observer were at the center of the earth and the other at the equator with the moon on his horizon. It is this equatorial horizontal parallax that is given for the sake of uniformity.

The moon's parallax at its average distance from the earth is nearly 1°. The average distance of the moon from the center of the earth is 238,857 miles, which is only about 60 times the radius of the earth, or less than 10 times its circumference.

The distances which separate the celestial bodies are so great in comparison with the sizes of the bodies that it is often impractical to represent the two on the same scale in the diagrams. In Fig. 6·2, for example, the moon should be placed 2½ feet from the 1-inch earth. The distance has been reduced here much more than the sizes of the earth and moon in order to keep the diagram within the page and also to show these bodies clearly.

6·3. The Moon's Orbit Relative to the Earth is an ellipse of small eccentricity, having the earth at one focus. At *perigee,* where the moon is nearest us, the distance between the centers of the moon and earth may be as small as 221,463 miles. At *apogee,* where the moon is farthest from us, the distance may be as great as 252,710 miles. The resulting variation of more than 10 per cent in the moon's apparent diameter is still not enough to be conspicuous to the unaided eye.

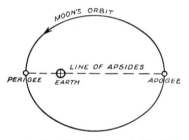

Fig. 6·3. The Moon's Orbit Relative to the Earth. The orbit is an ellipse of small eccentricity (much exaggerated in the diagram) with the earth at one focus.

The moon's orbit around us is changing continually, mainly because of unequal effects of the sun's attraction for the moon and earth. For example, the major axis of the orbit rotates eastward in a period of about 9 years. This is one of the many variations which make the determination of the moon's motion an intricate problem, but a problem now being so well solved that the moon's course in the heavens is soon likely to be predictable with high accuracy.

6·4. The Moon's Phases are the different shapes it shows. The moon is a dark globe like the earth; one half is in the sunlight, while the other half turned away from the sun is in the darkness of night. The phases are the varying amounts of the moon's sunlit hemisphere that are turned toward us successively in the course of the month.

It is the *new moon* that passes the sun; the dark hemisphere is toward us. The moon is invisible at this phase unless it happens to pass directly across the sun's disk, causing an eclipse of the sun. On the second evening after the new phase the thin *crescent* moon is likely to be seen in the west after sundown. The crescent grows thicker night after night, until the sunrise line runs straight across the disk at the *first quarter*. Then comes the *gibbous* phase as the bulging sunrise line gives the moon a lopsided appearance. Finally,

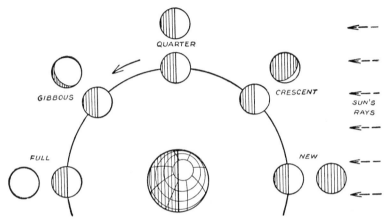

Fig. 6·4. The Phases of the Moon. The outer figures show the phases as seen from the earth.

a round *full moon* is seen rising at about nightfall. The phases are repeated thereafter in reverse order as the sunset line advances over the disk; they are gibbous, *last quarter,* crescent, and new again.

The horns, or *cusps,* of the crescent moon point away from the sun's place, and nearly in the direction of the moon's path among the stars. They are more nearly vertical in the evenings of spring, and more nearly horizontal in the autumn. Their direction in the sky follows the changing direction of the ecliptic with respect to the horizon during the year.

6·5. Earthlight on the Moon. Often when the moon is in the crescent phase we see the rest of the moon dimly illuminated. This appearance has been called "the old moon in the new moon's arms," for the bright crescent seems to be wrapped around the faintly lighted part (Fig. 6·5).

The thin crescent is in the sunlight. The rest of the moon's

disk is made visible by sunlight reflected from the earth. Just as the moon tempers the darkness of night for us, so the earth shines on the moon. If anyone lived on the earthward side of the moon, he would see the earth up among the stars in his sky (Fig. 1·4A) going through all the phases that the moon shows to us. They are, of course, supplementary; full earth occurs at new moon. The full earth would look 4 times as great in diameter as the full moon appears to us, and something like 60 times as bright; for the earth is not only a larger mirror to reflect the sunshine but, owing to

Fig. 6·5. Earthlight on the Moon at the Crescent Phase in the Morning Sky. The planet Saturn had emerged from behind the moon half an hour before. (Photographed at Yerkes Observatory)

the atmosphere, it is a better reflector as well; it returns a third of the light it receives from the sun.

Earthlight is plainest when the moon is a thin crescent, for the earth is then near its full in the lunar sky. It is a bluer light than that of the sunlit moon, because a considerable part of it is sunlight reflected by our atmosphere. The air around us scatters the shorter wave lengths more effectively, as the blue sky shows.

6·6. The Month of the Phases,

from new moon to new again, averages slightly more than 29½ days, and varies in length more than half a day. It is the *synodic month,* and the lunar month of the calendars. Because it is shorter than our calendar months, with a single

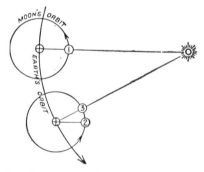

Fig. 6·6. The Month of the Phases Is Longer than the Sidereal Month. Between positions 1 and 2 the moon has made one revolution, completing the sidereal month. The synodic month does not end until the moon has reached the position 3.

exception, the dates of the different phases are generally earlier in successive months.

The length of the *sidereal month* averages 27⅓ days. It is the true period of the moon's revolution around the earth. At the end of this interval the moon has returned to nearly the same place among the stars. In the meantime the sun has been moving eastward as well, so that more than two days elapse after the end of the sidereal month (Fig. 6·6) before the synodic month is completed.

6·7. The Moon's Path Among the Stars. Two apparent motions of the moon are observed by everyone. First, the moon rises and sets daily; it circles westward around us along with the rest of the celestial scenery, because the earth is rotating from west to east. Second, the moon moves eastward against the turning background of the stars, because it is revolving in this direction around the earth. In the course of a day the moon revolves $360°/27.3$, or about 13°, moving slightly more than its own diameter in an hour.

The moon's apparent path among the stars is nearly a great circle of the celestial sphere, which is inclined about 5° to the ecliptic. It therefore crosses the ecliptic at two opposite *nodes*. The *ascending node* is the point where the moon's center crosses the ecliptic going north; the *descending node* is where it crosses going south. The nodes *regress,* or slide westward along the ecliptic. Regression of the nodes goes on at a much faster rate than does precession of the equinoxes (3·11). In only 18.6 years the nodes shift completely around the ecliptic. The moon's path through the constellations of the zodiac is considerably different from month to month.

6·8. The Moon-Clock. The moon's revolution around the earth, at the rate of about ½° an hour, provides an independent clock for correcting the inaccuracies of other clocks operated by the earth's variable rotation (2·7). Stars of the zodiac appear profusely on the dial of the moon-clock; the problem has been to determine accurately the place of the center of the moon's large disk among them at a particular instant.

In its eastward movement the moon frequently passes over, or *occults*, a star. The star disappears almost instantly at the moon's eastern edge and as abruptly reappears at the western edge. Occultations of the brighter stars and planets are predicted for each year in *The American Ephemeris and Nautical Almanac* for various longitudes across the country. These occurrences have been used for determining the places of the moon. They are interesting to watch with the telescope, or with the naked eye where the star is bright enough. The photograph of Jupiter and its satellites emerging from behind the moon (Fig. 6·8) provides a spectacular example.

FIG. 6·8.   Jupiter and Its Satellites Emerging from Behind the Moon.
(Photographed by Paul E. Roques, Griffith Observatory)

A recent device, known as the dual-rate moon position camera, is employed at the Naval Observatory for more accurate reading of the moon-clock, and will soon be adopted in other places as well. Attached to a telescope of moderate size, it holds the moon fixed relative to the stars during the exposure. In the photographs the positions of 30 or 40 points on the bright edge of the moon are measured in relation to about 10 neighboring stars. This method is expected not only to control better our timekeeping but also to improve our knowledge of the moon's orbit and its variations.

6·9. The Moon Rises Later from Day to Day. We have seen that the solar day is about 4 minutes longer than the sidereal day because the sun moves eastward relative to the stars. Due to the fact that the moon moves eastward still faster than the sun, the "lunar day" is longer than the solar day. The interval from upper transit of the moon to its next upper transit averages 24^h 50^m of solar time, varying as much as 15 minutes either way; it is of special importance to those who live beside the ocean, for it is twice the interval between high tides.

Not only its crossing of the meridian but also the rising and setting of the moon are delayed an average of 50 minutes from day to day. The variation from regularity in the moonrise is even more marked, and we notice it particularly in the rising of the moon near its full phase.

The *harvest moon* is the full moon that occurs nearest the time of the autumnal equinox. Then the moon near its full rises from night to night with the least delay as observed in our northern latitudes. In the latitude of New York the least delay is shorter by an hour than the greatest delay. Thus the harvest moon lingers longer in our early evening skies than does the nearly full moon of other seasons, giving more light after sundown for harvesting. It can be shown that the least delay in the moonrise on successive nights occurs when the moon's path among the stars is least inclined to the east horizon, as it is at sunset at the time of the autumnal equinox.

6·10. The Moon Moves North and South during the month, just as the sun does during the year and for the same reason. The moon's path among the stars is nearly the same as the ecliptic and is, therefore, similarly inclined to the celestial equator.

Consider the full moon. Opposite the sun at this phase, the full moon is farthest north when the sun is farthest south of the equator. The full moon near the time of the winter solstice rises in the northeast, climbs high in the sky, and sets in the northwest, as observed in middle northern latitudes; it is above the horizon for a longer time than are the full moons of other seasons. In summer it is the other way around. The full moon of June rises in the southeast, transits low in the south, and soon sets in the southwest, like the winter sun.

In some years the moon ranges farther north and south than in other years. The greatest range in its movement in declination occurs at intervals of 18.6 years. This was the case in 1950, when the moon was going fully 5° farther than the sun both north and south from the celestial equator, and many people remarked on it

at the time. This variation in the range of the moon's north and
south motion is a consequence of the regression of the nodes of its
path (6·7).

FIG. 6·12. The Moon at First Quarter. The moon is inverted and reversed, as it appears ordinarily through the telescope. The mountains
are plainest near the sunrise line, at the right, where the shadows are
longest. (*Photographed at Yerkes Observatory*)

6·11. The Moon's Rotation; Its Librations. As often as it is revealed in the changing phases, the face of the "man in the moon"
is always toward us; no one has seen the back of his head. This
means that the moon rotates on its axis once in a sidereal month,
while it is revolving once around the earth. Although the statement is true in the long run, anyone who watches the moon care-

fully during the month can see that the same hemisphere is not turned precisely toward us at all times. Spots near the moon's edge are sometimes in view and at other times turned out of sight,

FIG. 6·12A. The Gibbous Moon About Two Days After First Quarter. The group of seas which form the "girl reading" is nearer the moon's western edge than in Fig. 6·12. The crater Copernicus is a little more than halfway down along the bulging sunrise line. (*Photographed at Yerkes Observatory*)

as Figs. 6·12 and 6·12A clearly show. The moon seems to rock as it goes around us. These apparent oscillations, or *librations*, arise chiefly from two causes.

1. The moon's equator is inclined about $6\frac{1}{2}°$ to the plane of its orbit. Thus its north pole is brought toward us at one time and its

south pole is toward us two weeks later, just as the earth's poles are presented alternately to the sun during the year.

2. The moon's revolution is not uniform. In its elliptical orbit around us, the law of equal areas (4·5) applies; the nearer the moon to the earth, the faster is its revolution. Meanwhile the rotation of the moon is practically uniform. Thus the two motions do not keep perfectly in step, although they come out together at the end of the month. The moon rocks in the east and west direction, allowing us to see farther around it in longitude at each edge than we could otherwise.

Fully 59 per cent of the moon's surface has faced the earth when the month is completed. The remaining 41 per cent is never seen; and if anyone lived in that region of the moon, he could never see the earth.

THE MOON'S SURFACE FEATURES

6·12. The Lunar Seas. Two features of the moon are plainly visible to the unaided eye. First, the changing phases are among the most conspicuous sights in the heavens and were the first to be correctly explained. Second, the large dark areas we see on the disk of the moon were as well known in early times, although they were not as well interpreted, as they are today.

The dark areas form the eyes, nose, and mouth of the familiar "man in the moon" and the profile of the "girl in the moon," which is easily seen when Fig. 6·12A is turned around to represent the view of the moon without the telescope. The "girl reading," the "hare," and the "frog" are all formed by the same group of seas in the telescopic aspect of the moon.

Formerly supposed to be water areas, the lunar seas were given fanciful watery Latin names that have now survived their original meanings. One is Mare Serenitatis (Sea of Serenity); others are Mare Imbrium (Sea of Storms) and Sinus Iridum (Bay of Rainbows). The seas cover half the moon's visible surface and are especially prominent in its northern hemisphere. Roughly circular, they are mostly connected, with the conspicuous exception of Mare Crisium (Fig. 6·13). Although we still call them "seas," the dark spots are relatively smooth plains which are not all at the same level. A frequent explanation is that they are hardened pools of lava, resembling the great basaltic plateaus of the earth.

6·13. The Moon Through the Telescope. There is still another feature of the moon's surface to be detected occasionally with the naked eye; the sunrise and sunset lines are not perfectly smooth.

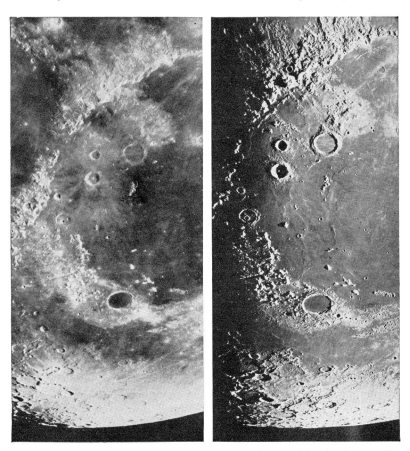

Fig. 6·13. Region of Mare Imbrium Under Different Illuminations. The lunar Apennines appear at the top, the Alps and the crater Plato below the center. (*Photographed at Mount Wilson Observatory*)

Bright projections into the dark hemisphere show where the sunlight illuminates lofty peaks before the sun has risen or after it has set on the plains around them. The moon is mountainous, a feature that was verified as soon as the telescope came into use.

It was in 1609 that the Italian scientist Galileo heard of the discovery by a Dutch spectacle maker that two lenses held at suitable distances before the eye gave a clearer view of the landscape.

Galileo fitted two small lenses into a tube and went out to view the heavens; he directed this telescope toward the moon first of all. Galileo observed the lunar mountains and estimated that they are comparable in height with terrestrial mountains. This he could do by noticing how far from the sunrise line into the darkness the peaks first catch the rays of the sun. Like little stars they appear at first, growing larger until they join the sunlit hemisphere. The heights of the lunar mountains may also be calculated from the lengths of their shadows and the altitude of the sun in their sky at that time.

The mountains on the moon are most distinct when they are near the sunrise or the sunset line. There the shadows are long, as they are with us in the early morning or late afternoon, so that the sunlit peaks stand out in bold relief among the shadows. The view of the mountains is especially good within about two days of the quarter phases.

Compare the two photographs (Fig. 6·13) of the same region at different phases of the moon. In the view at the left the sun is shining more directly on the region; the shadows are shorter, and the surface seems rather flat. In the photograph at the right the region is near the sunset line; the shadows are longer, and the mountains are more conspicuous.

6·14. The Lunar Mountains. There are only a few irregularities of the moon's surface that remind us at all of our own mountain ranges. Best known of these are the three ridges which form the curving western border of Mare Imbrium, the right eye of the "man in the moon" as we view the moon without the telescope, and which separate it from Mare Serenitatis. These are the Apennines, Caucasus, and Alps; their names are among the few that have survived from Hevelius' map of the moon of 1647, in which the lunar formations have the names of terrestrial ones. With a few exceptions the prominent mountains on the moon bear the names of scholars of former times, according to the system introduced by Riccioli in 1651. Examples are the Leibnitz and Doerfel mountains near the moon's south pole; some of their peaks rise as much as 26,000 feet above the plains.

The mountains around Mare Imbrium slope abruptly toward it and more gradually outward. It is as though they were all that remain of a nearly circular rampart 700 miles across which surrounded the great sea.

Fig. 6·14. The Moon Shortly After the Full Phase. The sunset line is appearing at the left. The longest ray system radiates from the crater Tycho near the moon's south pole. Shorter ray systems surround Copernicus and some other craters. (*Photographed at Yerkes Observatory*)

6·15. The Lunar Craters have nearly circular walls, steep and often shelving on the inside and sloping more gradually to the plain outside. Lofty peaks surmount some of the walls, and peaks also appear near the centers of many craters. Some craters have floors depressed several thousand feet below the plain. In others the floors are elevated; the inside of the crater Wargentin is nearly as high as the top of the wall itself. Some craters have rough, bright floors; Aristarchus is the brightest of these. Others, such as Plato in the lunar Alpine region, are as dark inside as the seas.

More than 30,000 craters are recognized. They range in size

FIG. 6·15. Lunar Landscape at Last Quarter. The crater Tycho is at the right of the center. The walled plain Clavius is near the top. (*Photographed at Lick Observatory*)

from pits a few hundred feet across, which can be seen only with large telescopes, to "walled plains," such as Clavius (Fig. 6·15), about 150 miles in diameter, near the moon's south pole.

Two versions of the origins of the lunar craters and the other formations have long received attention, but without a firm decision as yet between them. One opinion is that the moon's surface features are mainly of igneous origin, having been formed during the cooling of the moon. The earliest and largest of the mountain rings provided the basins of the later lunar seas. As the moon's crust thickened, conditions became favorable for the forming of the smaller rings of the craters.

The second opinion is that the irregularities of the moon's surface were caused mainly by the fall of meteoritic masses. These blasted out the basins of the seas, scattering debris over the moonscape and perhaps producing great lava pools as well by the heat of their impacts.

6·16. Lunar Rays and Rills. The lunar *rays* are bright streaks often as wide as 5 or 10 miles and up to 1500 miles long, which radiate from points near a few of the craters and pass over mountain and plain alike without much regard for the topography. The longest and most conspicuous ray system radiates from the crater Tycho near the moon's south pole; it is a prominent feature of the full moon as viewed with any telescope. A system of shorter and more crooked rays is centered near the crater Copernicus.

The lunar *rills* are clefts as wide as half a mile and of unknown depth. Some are irregular, whereas others run nearly straight for many miles. They are generally not conspicuous through small telescopes. The rills might seem to have been caused by the parting of the crust as it cooled.

6·17. The Absence of Atmosphere. We can readily see that the moon has no perceptible amount of atmosphere around it. There is no twilight on the moon; the sunrise and sunset lines form a perfectly sharp division between day and night. The moon's disk is undimmed near the edge, where a greater thickness of atmosphere would intervene. When the moon occults a star, there is no dimming or reddening of the star before its abrupt disappearance behind the moon.

Two neighboring worlds share the sunshine together. One, the earth, has air around it and is the abode of life and activity. The other, the moon, is airless and therefore lifeless, a dead world where practically nothing happens. Why does the earth have an abundance of air, while the moon has none to speak of? The answer is found in the feebler surface gravity of the moon. The moon's attraction for objects near its surface is only one sixth the corre-

sponding attraction of the earth; it is not effective enough to hold
an atmosphere around the moon.

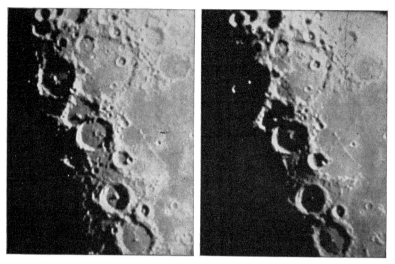

FIG. 6·17. Sunset on the Moon. The sunset line is moving toward the
right. No twilight intervenes between day and night as it does on the
earth. (*Photographed at McMath-Hulbert Observatory*)

6·18. The Escape of Atmospheres. The molecules of a gas dart
about incessantly. Their speeds increase as the temperature is
raised, and at the same temperature are greater for lighter gases
than for heavier ones. The molecules of hydrogen, the lightest
gas, are moving as fast as a mile a second at the freezing temperature of water. The molecules of our air at ordinary room temperatures have speeds somewhat greater than half a mile a second.

These are averages. At the same temperature and for a particular
kind of gas the speeds vary. Collisions between the molecules bring
some of them momentarily almost to rest and propel others much
faster than the average. Whether the molecules at their highest
speeds can fly away into space depends on the strength of the re-
straining pull of gravity.

The *velocity of escape* is the speed that a molecule or anything
else must attain to escape from a specified body. If a ball is thrown
upward, it is soon brought down by the earth's attraction. Given
a greater initial speed, the ball goes higher and returns to the
ground after a longer time. With what speed must a ball be started
so that it will never return? This critical speed is the velocity of

escape. Its value at the earth's surface is nearly 7 miles a second, without allowance for air resistance. The molecules in our air do not ordinarily have speeds as great as this; hence, the earth has retained its atmosphere, except some of the very lightest gases. The velocity of escape at the moon's surface, however, is only $1\frac{1}{2}$ miles a second. An atmosphere could not remain there for a long time.

6·19. An Expedition to the Moon is considered by some people a possibility before the end of the century. There is already a pro-

FIG. 6·19. The Lunar Apennines. (*Photographed at Lick Observatory*)

posal to launch, by rocket propulsion, a small unmanned satellite above the earth's atmosphere. Given a suitable initial horizontal speed up there, this satellite could revolve indefinitely around us. If this project is successful, the next one might be to send up crews to assemble a similarly revolving space station. The following step might be an expedition from that station to the moon.

Conditions the voyagers would find on the moon are quite well known to us. Some of them would differ drastically enough from conditions at home to threaten the survival of the party. The glaring sunlight during the long day on the moon heats its surface to the ordinary boiling point of water, and includes deadly ultraviolet rays. The temperature at nightfall drops abruptly, and at midnight is 500° F lower than at noon. The absence of air and water of course presents a difficult problem. The bare, lifeless landscape is not inviting. The moon is a perfect and dangerous desert.

ECLIPSES OF THE MOON

6·20. The Earth's Shadow. Like any other opaque object in the sunshine, the earth casts a shadow in the direction away from the sun. The *umbra* of the shadow is the part from which the sun-

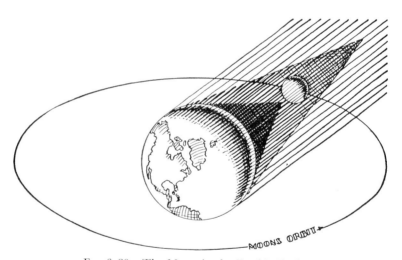

FIG. 6·20. The Moon in the Earth's Shadow.

light would be completely excluded if some light were not scattered into it by the earth's atmosphere. The umbra is a long, thin cone reaching an average of 859,000 miles into space before it tapers to a point. This darker part of the shadow is often meant when we speak of the *shadow*. It is surrounded by the *penumbra*, from which the direct sunlight is only partly excluded.

Suppose that a large screen is held at right angles to the direction of the shadow, and that it is moved out into space in that direction. The umbra of the earth's shadow would fall on this screen as a dark circle growing smaller with increasing distance of the screen, until at the moon's distance the diameter of the shadow would be 5700 miles, or nearly 3 times the moon's diameter of 2160 miles.

Because the earth's shadow points away from the sun, it sweeps eastward around the ecliptic once in a year as the earth revolves. At intervals of a synodic month, the faster-moving moon overtakes the shadow and sometimes passes through it.

6·21. The Moon in the Earth's Shadow. *Umbral eclipses* occur when the moon passes through the umbra of the earth's shadow.

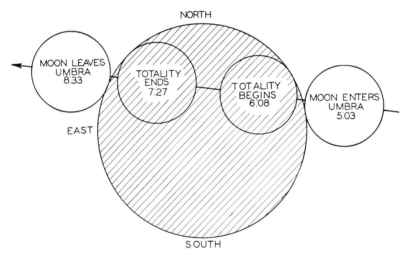

FIG. 6·21. Path of the Moon Through the Umbra of the Earth's Shadow During the Eclipse of the Moon, November 18, 1956. Universal times are given.

The longest eclipses, when the moon goes centrally through the shadow, last about $3^h\,40^m$; this duration is counted from the first contact with the umbra until the moon leaves the umbra completely. Total eclipse can last as long as $1^h\,40^m$, preceded and followed by partial phases, each of about an hour's duration. Usually the eclipse is not central (Fig. 6·21), so that its duration is shorter. Often the moon passes so far from the center of the shadow

that it is never completely immersed in the umbra, and the eclipse
is partial throughout.

Penumbral eclipses occur when the moon passes through the
penumbra of the earth's shadow without entering the umbra. The
weakened light of the part of the moon that is in the penumbra
is visible to the eye when the least distance of the edge of the moon

FIG. 6·21A. The Moon in the Penumbra of the Earth's Shadow, March
23, 1951. The weakening of the light of the northern (lower) part of the
moon was not visible to the eye. (*Photographed by Paul E. Roques,
Griffith Observatory*)

from the umbra does not exceed one third of the moon's diameter;
it is detected in the photograph (Fig. 6·21A) when the least distance
does not exceed two thirds of the moon's diameter.

A lunar eclipse is visible wherever the moon is above the horizon
during its occurrence, that is, over more than half the earth, count-
ing the region that is rotated into view of the moon while the
eclipse is going on. The universal times when the moon enters
and leaves the penumbra and umbra and of the beginning and end
of totality are published in advance in various almanacs for all
umbral eclipses.

Eleven umbral lunar eclipses are scheduled in the interval from

1957 to 1965 inclusive as visible, at least in part, in a considerable
area of the United States and Canada. Eight of these are total.

UMBRAL LUNAR ECLIPSES VISIBLE IN THE UNITED STATES AND CANADA

| | Middle of Eclipse | Duration of | |
Date	Universal Time	Umbral Phase	Totality
1957, May 13	22^h 32^m	3^h 34^m	1^h 20^m
1957, Nov. 7	14 28	3 20	0 32
1958, May 3	12 11	0 42	. . . .
1960, Mar. 13	8 30	3 40	1 36
1960, Sept. 5	11 23	3 38	1 30
1961, Mar. 2	13 32	3 4	. . . .
1961, Aug. 26	3 8	3 18	0 14
1963, Dec. 30	11 7	3 34	1 24
1964, June 25	1 7	3 40	1 38
1964, Dec. 19	2 35	3 28	1 4
1965, June 14	1 51	1 40	. . . .

6·22. The Moon Is Visible in Total Eclipse. The first conspicuous
effect of the lunar eclipse is seen soon after the moon enters the
umbra. A dark notch appears at the eastern edge of the moon and

FIG. 6·22. Partial Eclipse of the Moon. Progress of the eclipse as the
moon entered the earth's shadow until it became nearly total. The moon
is not inverted. (*Photographed by Albert W. Recht, Chamberlin Observatory*)

slowly overspreads the disk. The shadow is so dark in comparison with the unshaded part (Fig. 6·22) that the moon might be expected to disappear in total eclipse. As totality comes on, however, the moon usually becomes plainly visible.

The moon in total eclipse is still illuminated by sunlight which filters through the earth's atmosphere around the base of the shadow. The light is diffused by the air into the shadow and onto the moon. It is redder than ordinary sunlight for the same reason that the sunset is red, so that the totally eclipsed moon has an unfamiliar hue. The brightness of the moon then depends on the transparency of the atmosphere around the base of the shadow. Enough light usually sifts through to show the surface features clearly. On rare occasions the moon becomes very dim.

QUESTIONS ON CHAPTER 6

1. How would the moon's parallax compare with its present value (a) if the moon's distance were twice as great? (b) if the earth's radius were twice as great?

2. Describe the moon's orbit relative to the sun; relative to the earth.

3. Where is the moon in the sky at sunset when its phase is new? first quarter? full?

4. Explain why the cycle of the moon's phases is longer than the period of the moon's revolution around the earth.

5. Show that the interval between upper transits of the moon is about 50 minutes longer than the solar day.

6. At what time of year does the full moon pass nearest the zenith in middle northern latitudes? State its least possible distance from your zenith.

7. Explain the causes of two librations of the moon.

8. Name the terms which are defined as follows:

(a) The moon's phase between first quarter and full.
(b) The point of the moon's orbit which is nearest the earth.
(c) The true period of the moon's revolution around the earth.
(d) The interval between successive new moons.
(e) The moon near its full which rises with the least delay on successive nights.

9. Describe each of the following features of the lunar surface and state your idea of the origin of each: (a) the seas; (b) mountains; (c) craters; (d) rays.

10. If a manned rocket succeeds in reaching the moon, what conditions will the crew find there different from those at home?

11. Why does the moon remain visible in total eclipse?

12. When will the next umbral eclipse of the moon be visible in the United States and Canada? At what time will the middle of the eclipse occur where you are?

REFERENCES

Baldwin, Ralph B., *The Face of the Moon*. University of Chicago Press, 1949.

Haber, Heinz, *Man in Space*. The Bobbs-Merrill Company, New York, 1953.

Moore, Patrick, *A Guide to the Moon*. W. W. Norton and Company, New York, 1954.

Ryan, Cornelius, editor, *Conquest of the Moon*. The Viking Press, New York, 1953.

The 16-inch Coronagraph Dome, Sacramento Peak Observatory, New Mexico.

7

THE PATHS OF THE PLANETS

MOTIONS OF THE PLANETS — THE LAW OF GRAVITATION — THE PLANETARY SYSTEM

Seven bright celestial bodies move about among the "fixed stars" that form the constellations. They are the sun, the moon, and the five planets—Mercury, Venus, Mars, Jupiter, and Saturn, which have the appearance of stars to the unaided eye. These were the *planeta,* or "wanderers," of the ancients. These 7 bodies are among our nearest neighbors in space. In the foreground of the starry scene they are conspicuous in our skies. Their brightness and their complex movements against the background of the stars have made them objects of special interest through the ages.

MOTIONS OF THE PLANETS

7·1. The Planets Move in Loops. Anyone who has viewed the spectacle of the heavens that is displayed in one of the larger planetariums knows how the planets swing back and forth in their courses among the stars. Celestial movements of a year can be represented in a short time in the sky of the planetarium. The looped paths of the planets are shown very clearly there.

For the most part, the planets move eastward through the constellations. This is their *direct* motion; for it is in this direction that they revolve around the sun. At intervals, which are not the same for the different planets, they turn and move backward, toward the west; they *retrograde* for a while before resuming the eastward motion. They are said to be *stationary* at the turns. Thus the planets seem to march and countermarch among the stars, progressing toward the east around the heavens in series of loops.

These apparent movements of the planets are readily observed in the sky itself. Watch the red planet Mars from week to week, for example, beginning as soon as it rises at a convenient hour of the evening. Notice the planet's position among the stars on each occasion, and mark the place and date on a star map. The line of dots will show presently, as it does in Fig. 7·1, that Mars steers a devious course.

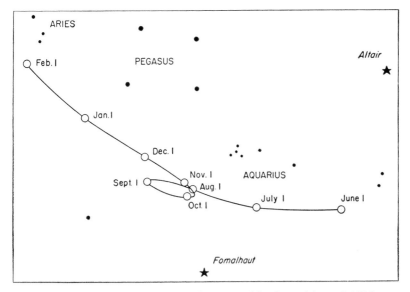

FIG. 7·1. · Path of Mars Near the Favorable Opposition of 1956.

7·2. The Problem of the Planetary Motions. Just how do the planets move around the earth so as to proceed in loops among the constellations? By what combinations of uniform circular motions centered in the earth can their observed movements be represented? This was the problem the early scholars wished to solve. Intuitively they agreed that celestial motions ought to be uniform and in circles; then, too, the circle is an easy figure for calculations.

The globe of the earth was stationary at the center of their universe. The sphere of the stars turned daily around it. Within that sphere the 7 wanderers shared its daily turning, and also moved eastward around the earth at various distances from it.

7·3. The Geocentric System. The most enduring early plan for solving the problem of the planetary motions was developed by Ptolemy at Alexandria in the 2nd century and is, accordingly, known as the *Ptolemaic system.* It was a plan of epicycles. In the simplest form of the system (Fig. 7·3) each planet was supposed to move on the circumference of a circle, the *epicycle,* while the center of that circle revolved around the earth on a second circle, the *deferent.* By such combinations the attempt was made to represent the observed movements of the planets. The Ptolemaic plan became more complex as time went on. During many centuries that intervened between the decline of Greek culture and the revival of learning in Europe, Arabian astronomers undertook to improve the system so that it would more nearly represent the planetary movements. They tried to get a better fit by adding more epicycles and by other devices. Each planet was eventually provided with

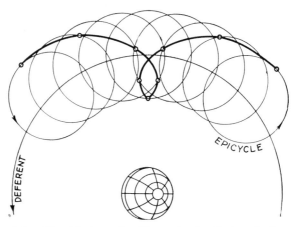

FIG. 7·3.   The Motion of a Planet in the Ptolemaic System.

from 40 to 60 epicycles turning one upon another. It was then that King Alphonso of Castile remarked that had he been present at the Creation he might have given excellent advice. The theory of the central earth had begun to seem unreasonable.

7·4. The Earth in Motion. From the times of the early Greek scholars there was an undercurrent of opinion that the earth is not stationary. The followers of Pythagoras, who taught that the earth is a globe, supposed that it is moving. Aristarchus of Samos, in the 3rd century B.C., is said to have been convinced that the earth rotates daily on its axis and revolves yearly around the sun. There were others who caught glimpses of the truth. Such ideas, however, then seemed unbelievable to almost everyone and received little attention.

By the time that Columbus sailed west on his famous voyage, there was growing dissatisfaction with the theory of the central, stationary earth. Before the companions of Magellan had returned from the first trip around the world, a European scholar had reached the conclusion anew that the earth is in motion. His name, as we say it, was Nicholas Copernicus. His theory of the moving earth was published in 1543.

The *Copernican system* set the sun in the center instead of the earth which now took its rightful place as one of the planets revolving around the sun. It retained the original idea that the planets moved uniformly in circles, and accordingly remained a system of epicycles. Copernicus could offer no convincing proof of either the earth's revolution or daily rotation which he also advocated.

7·5. Tycho's Observations.   Tycho Brahe greatly improved the instruments and methods of observing the positions of the celestial bodies. He saw clearly that an improvement in the theory of the motions of the planets required more reliable data on their apparent movements among the stars. Born in 1546, the most fruitful years of his life were spent in his observatory on the formerly Danish island of Hven, 20 miles northeast of Copenhagen. He died in Prague in 1601.

It was before the invention of the telescope. Tycho's chief instruments were large quadrants and sextants having plain sights. With these, he and his assistants observed the planets night after night and determined their right ascensions and declinations with a degree of accuracy never before attained. He gave special attention to the planet Mars, a fortunate choice because its orbit is not as nearly circular as are the orbits of some of the other bright planets.

7·6. The Planets Move in Ellipses Around the Sun.   John Kepler was Tycho's assistant in his last years in Prague. He inherited the records of the positions of the planets, which his master had kept for many years. Kepler studied the records patiently in the hope of determining the actual motions of the planets. In 1609 he announced two important conclusions, and in 1618 he discovered the third. They are known to us as *Kepler's laws:*

1. *The planets move around the sun in ellipses having the sun at one of the foci.* Thus the planets do not go around the earth, and their orbits are not circles.

2. *Each planet revolves in such a way that the line joining it to*

the sun sweeps over equal areas in equal intervals of time. The nearer the planet comes to the sun, the faster it moves, as we have already noticed (4·5) in the case of the earth.

3. *The squares of the periods of revolution of any two planets are in the same ratio as the cubes of their mean distances from the sun.* This useful relation is called the *harmonic law.*

Here ended the attempts to represent the movements of the planets by uniform circular motions centered in the earth. There was still no evidence, however, that the earth itself revolves around the sun.

THE LAW OF GRAVITATION

While Kepler was deriving his laws which describe how the planets go around the sun, his contemporary, Galileo Galilei in Italy, was laying the foundations of mechanics. He questioned the traditional ideas about the motions of things and set out to determine for himself how they really move. It remained for Isaac Newton in England to formulate clearly the new laws of motion and to show that they apply not merely to objects immediately around us but to the celestial bodies as well. The principal feature of the new mechanics was the concept of an attractive force which operates under the same rules everywhere in the universe.

7·7. Force Equals Mass Times Acceleration. Before the time of Galileo, an undisturbed body was supposed to remain at rest. Hence, it seemed appropriate that the earth should be stationary. Anyone who asserted that the earth is moving might well be asked to explain by what process it is kept in motion.

Galileo's experiments led him to the new idea that uniform motion in a straight line is the natural state. An object will go on forever in the same direction with the same speed unless it is disturbed. Rest is the special case where the initial speed happens to be zero. Uniform motion in a straight line, therefore, demands no explanation. It is only when the motion is changing either in direction or in speed that an accounting is required. We say then that a force is acting on the body, and inquire where the force originates.

The strength of the *force* is measured by its effect on the body on which it acts; it equals the mass of the body multiplied by its *acceleration,* or the rate of change of its velocity (directed speed). The acceleration may appear as increasing or diminishing speed, or changing direction, or both. A stone falling vertically faster and faster is accelerated. An object moving in a circle with constant speed is accelerated. In both cases a force is acting.

7·8. The Laws of Motion were formulated by Newton in his *Principia* (1687) substantially as follows:

1. *Every body persists in its state of rest or of uniform motion in a straight line unless it is compelled to change that state by a force impressed upon it.* Where a force is applied:

2. *The acceleration is directly proportional to the force and inversely to the mass of the body, and it takes place in the direction of the straight line in which the force acts.*

3. *To every action there is always an equal and contrary reaction.*

The second law defines force in the usual way. The first law states that there is no acceleration where no force is acting; the motion of the body remains unchanged. The third law asserts that the force between two bodies is the same in the two directions. A bat exerts no greater force on the ball than the ball exerts on the bat; but the lighter ball experiences a greater acceleration than the heavier bat and batter combined.

Armed with these laws of motion, Newton succeeded in reducing Kepler's three laws of the planetary movements to a single universal law. It is said that the fall of an apple one day as Newton sat in his garden started the great mathematician to thinking of this problem. Does the attractive force that brings down the apple also control the moon's revolution around the earth? Does a similar force directed toward the sun cause the planets to revolve around it?

7·9. The Law of Gravitation. A force is continuously acting on the planets, because their courses around the sun are always curving. It is an attractive force directed toward the sun; this fact can be deduced from Kepler's law of equal areas, although we shall not stop to do so. From further studies of Kepler's laws, Newton discovered the law of the sun's attraction. He found that the force between the sun and a planet is proportional directly to the product of their masses, and inversely as the square of the distance between their centers.

Newton next calculated the law of the earth's attraction. An apple falls 16 feet in the first second. The moon, averaging 60

times as far from the earth's center, is drawn in from a straight-
line course $\frac{1}{20}$ inch in a second, which is about 16 feet divided
by the square of 60. Using more exact values than these, he showed
that the force of the earth's attraction for objects around it is
inversely proportional to the squares of their distances from its
center. Although his studies could not extend beyond the planetary system, Newton concluded that he had discovered a universal
law and so announced it in his *law of gravitation:*

*Every particle of matter in the universe attracts every other par-
ticle with a force that varies directly as the product of their masses
and inversely as the square of the distance between them.*

7·10. How the Planets Revolve. Consider the earth as an example.
By Newton's law there is an attractive force between the earth and
the sun, which is the same in the two directions. Started from rest
they would eventually come together. The earth is moving, however, nearly at right angles to the sun's direction at the rate of
$18\frac{1}{2}$ miles a second, and in one second it is attracted less than an
eighth of an inch toward the sun. It is this deviation from a
straight line course second after second
through the year that causes the earth
to revolve around the sun.

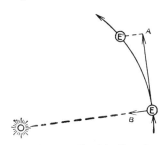

Fig. 7·10. Earth's Revolution Explained by the Laws
of Motion. At the position
E the earth, if undisturbed,
would continue on to A, by
the first law of motion. It
arrives at E' instead, having
been attracted in the meantime toward the sun the
distance EB.

Properly speaking, the earth and sun
mutually revolve around a point between their centers. The ancient problem of whether the sun or the earth
revolves was not well stated. Both revolve. If the earth and sun were
equally massive, the point around
which they wheel yearly would be halfway between their centers. Because
the sun is a third of a million times as
massive as the earth, this center of mass
is only 280 miles from the sun's center;
and it is not far from the center for all
the other planets.

Thus the planets revolve around the
sun, although not precisely around its center. The first law of
motion explains their continued progress, and the force of gravitation causes them to revolve around the sun instead of going away
into space.

7·11. The Orbits of the Planets relative to the sun are ellipses having the sun's center at one of the foci. These *relative orbits* are the ones we employ for the planets generally, and similarly for the satellites revolving around their planets. They are the same in form as the actual orbits and differ from them only slightly in size.

Newton showed from his law of gravitation that the orbits of revolving bodies in general may be any one of the three *conics*. These are the ellipse, parabola, and hyperbola. The ellipse includes the circle, where the eccentricity is zero. The parabola, eccentricity 1, is open at one end, and the hyperbola is wider open. Evidently the permanent members of the sun's family have closed, elliptical orbits.

If the earth, now revolving in nearly a circle at the rate of 18½ miles a second, could be speeded up, its orbit would become larger and more eccentric. At the speed of 26 miles a second the orbit would become a parabola, and the earth would depart from the sun. This is the velocity of escape from the sun at the earth's distance.

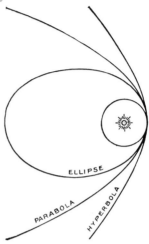

Fig. 7·11.   Different Shapes of Orbits.

7·12. The Masses of the Planets. The law of gravitation views the physical universe as a scheme of masses and distances. It is, therefore, of considerable interest to inquire how the masses are measured. The *masses* of some planets, that is, the quantities of material they contain, can be found by Kepler's harmonic law (7·6) as Newton restated it more precisely:

The squares of the periods of *any two pairs* of mutually revolving celestial bodies, *each multiplied by the combined mass of the pair*, are in the same proportion as the cubes of the mean distances that separate the pairs.

Suppose that we wish to find the mass of the planet Saturn. We write this proportion, taking Saturn and one of its satellites as one pair and the earth and sun as the second pair. Let the unit of mass be the combined mass of the earth and sun, the unit of distance the mean distance between the earth and sun, and the unit of time the period of the earth's revolution around the sun. The relation becomes simply: The mass of Saturn and its satellite, which may be neglected, equals the cube of the mean distance of the satellite from Saturn divided by the square of its period of revolution around Saturn.

The masses of planets having satellites have been found in this way. It is more difficult to weigh planets, such as Mercury, Venus, and Pluto, which have no satellites; their masses are determined by their disturbing effects on the motions of neighboring bodies.

7·13. Courses and Forces. Early astronomers tried to represent the planetary movements by combinations of circular motions centered in the earth. Copernicus set the sun in the center instead of the earth. Kepler discovered that the planets revolve around the sun in ellipses instead of circles and epicycles. So far the interest was confined to the courses themselves.

Newton's law of gravitation directed the attention to mighty forces controlling the courses of the planets. This law has made possible the present accurate predictions of the planetary movements. It has promoted the discoveries of celestial bodies hitherto unknown, from their effects on the motions of known bodies. It applies equally well to mutually revolving stars.

For most purposes astronomers make their calculations on the basis of the law of gravitation. It is only rarely that the newer theory of relativity predicts celestial events with appreciably greater accuracy. The advance of Mercury's perihelion around the sun at a faster rate than is predicted by the law of gravitation is a well-known example. The apparent displacements of stars away from the sun's place in the sky at total eclipses of the sun is another example of the occasionally greater merit of relativity in representing what goes on.

THE PLANETARY SYSTEM

The meaning of the word *planet* as a body revolving around the sun began with the acceptance of the Copernican system which added the earth to the list of planets, subtracted the sun from the original list, and reduced the moon to its proper place as a satellite of the earth.

The known membership of the planetary system has increased greatly since Copernicus' time. Knowledge of satellites attending other planets began with Galileo's discovery, in 1610, of the four bright satellites of Jupiter. The planet Uranus, barely visible to the naked eye, was discovered in 1781. Neptune, which is always too faint to be seen without the telescope, was found in 1846. The discovery of the still fainter and more remote Pluto in 1930 completed the list of the 9 known *principal planets*. Ceres, the largest of the *asteroids,* or *minor planets,* was the first of these to be discovered, in 1801.

The earth is one of the principal planets. The moon is one of 31 satellites which accompany 6 of these planets. Thousands of asteroids and great numbers of comets and meteor swarms are also members of this large family which, including the sun itself, is known as the *solar system.*

7·14. The Planets Named and Classified. The names of the planets in order of mean distance from the sun are:

Inferior planets { Mercury } Inner planets
Venus
Earth

Superior planets {
Mars
The Asteroids or Minor planets
Jupiter
Saturn
Uranus } Outer planets
Neptune
Pluto

They are classified as inferior and superior planets, and also as inner and outer planets. The *inferior planets* are nearer the sun than the earth's distance, and the *superior planets* revolve outside the earth's orbit. The *inner planets* revolve inside the main zone of the asteroids, whereas the outer planets have their orbits outside this zone. The 4 inner planets and Pluto as well are sometimes known as the *terrestrial planets,* because they are small as compared with the *major planets:* Jupiter, Saturn, Uranus, and Neptune.

Not all the asteroids are confined to the main zone; some of them invade the regions of the principal planets. A part of the orbit of Pluto (Fig. 7·21) is nearer the sun than is Neptune's orbit.

7·15. Aspects and Phases of Inferior Planets. The *elongation* of a planet at a particular time is its angular distance from the sun.

Certain positions of the planet relative to the sun's place in the
sky have distinctive names and are known as the *aspects* of the
planet. The planet is in *conjunction* with the sun when the two
bodies have the same celestial longitude, so that the planet's elongation is not far from 0°. It is in *quadrature* when the elongation is

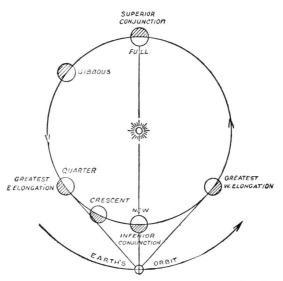

Fig. 7·15. Aspects and Phases of an Inferior Planet. The elongations are
limited; the phases are like those of the moon.

90°, and is in *opposition* when its celestial longitude differs by 180°
from the sun's, so that its elongation is near 180°.

The times of the aspects of the principal planets are predicted
in *The American Ephemeris and Nautical Almanac*. For the conjunctions of the planets with one another and with the moon, the
times predicted there are the instants when the two bodies have
the same right ascension.

The inferior planets, Mercury and Venus, have limited elongations; they appear to us to oscillate to the east and west of the sun's
place. From superior conjunction, beyond the sun, they move
out to *greatest eastern elongation,* which does not exceed 28° from
the sun for Mercury and 48° for Venus. Here they turn westward
relative to the sun, pass between the sun and the earth at *inferior
conjunction,* then move out to *greatest western elongation,* and

finally return toward the east behind the sun. As Fig. 7·15 shows, the inferior planets go through the complete cycle of phases, just as the moon does. Their phases are full at superior conjunction, quarter at the greatest elongations, and new at inferior conjunction.

7·16. Aspects and Phases of Superior Planets. The superior planets, such as Mars and Jupiter, revolve around the sun in periods longer than a year. They accordingly move eastward through the constellations more slowly than the sun appears to do. With respect to the sun's place in the sky, they seem to move westward (clockwise in Fig. 7·16), and attain all values of elongation in that direction from 0° to 180°. At *conjunction* they pass behind the sun to presently appear in the east before sunrise. At *western quadrature* they are near the celestial meridian at sunrise. At *opposition* they rise around the time of sunset, and at *eastern quadrature* they are near the meridian at sunset.

From Fig. 7·16 we also see that the superior planets show the full or nearly full phase at

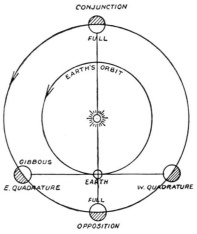

Fig. 7·16. Aspects and Phases of a Superior Planet. The aspects are similar to those of the moon. The only phases are full and gibbous.

all times to the earth. Mars near its quadrature appears conspicuously gibbous, because it is the nearest of these planets to the earth, so that its hemispheres turned toward the sun and earth are considerably different.

7·17. The Places of the Planets among the stars do not appear in the star maps, of course, because they are continually changing. Their right ascensions and declinations for a particular date can be found in an almanac and can then be marked in the maps. The positions of Jupiter and Saturn when they are opposite the sun's place are given in Table 7·I. The dates of oppositions of Mars and the constellations in which it is then situated are in Section 8·6.

TABLE 7·I. Oppositions of Jupiter and Saturn

Year	Jupiter			Saturn		
	UT	R.A.	Decl.	UT	R.A.	Decl.
1957	Mar. 17^d 18^h	11^h 51^m	$+ 2°.7$	June 1^d 19^h	16^h 39^m	$-20°.3$
1958	Apr. 17 7	13 42	$- 8 .9$	June 13 23	17 27	$-21 .8$
1959	May 18 20	15 40	$-18 .4$	June 26 2	18 16	$-22 .5$
1960	June 20 2	17 55	$-23 .7$	July 7 6	19 05	$-22 .2$
1961	July 25 10	20 18	$-20 .1$	July 19 11	19 54	$-21 .0$
1962	Aug. 31 15	22 39	$- 9 .7$	July 31 19	20 43	$-18 .9$
1963	Oct. 8 11	0 55	$+ 4 .5$	Aug. 13 5	21 30	$-16 .0$
1964	Nov. 13 9	3 16	$+17 .0$	Aug. 24 20	22 17	$-12 .3$
1965	Dec. 18 9	5 43	$+23 .1$	Sept. 6 15	23 03	$- 8 .1$

The dates of conjunctions and greatest elongations of Venus are in Section 8·2.

7·18. Retrograde Motions of the Planets. Consider again the loops in the planets' movements among the stars, which mystified the early astronomers and promoted the complex machinery of the Ptolemaic system. At intervals the planets interrupt their motions toward the east, and retrograde, or move back toward the west, for a while. The retrograde motions occur because we are observing from a planet that is revolving at a different rate from the others.

A superior planet, such as Mars, retrogrades near the time of its opposition; for the faster-moving earth then overtakes it and leaves it behind. On the other hand, Mars has its fastest direct motion near its conjunction with the sun, where its own motion and its displacement by ours are in the same direction. The inferior planets retrograde near inferior conjunction. In general, a planet retrogrades when it is nearest the earth.

7·19. The Distances of the Planets from the sun are given in Table 7·II, where other information about the planets and their orbits appears as well. These are mean distances; the distances vary because the orbits are ellipses with the sun at one focus. To find the greatest amount that a planet's distance departs from the mean, multiply the mean distance by the fraction representing the eccentricity of the planet's orbit. Thus the mean distance of Mercury from the sun is 36 million miles, and the eccentricity of its orbit is 0.206; the greatest variation from the mean is therefore $7\frac{1}{2}$ million miles. Mercury is $28\frac{1}{2}$ million miles from the sun at perihelion and $43\frac{1}{2}$ million miles at aphelion.

A relation known as *Bode's law* is an easy way to remember the relative distances from the sun of all except the most remote planets. Write in a line the numbers: 0, 3, 6, 12, and so on, doubling the number each time to obtain the next one. Add 4 to each number, and divide the sums by 10. The resulting series of numbers: 0.4, 0.7, 1.0, 1.6, 2.8. . . . represents the mean distances of the planets expressed in astronomical units. The *astronomical unit* is the earth's mean distance from the sun.

Compare the distances found by this rule with the actual mean distances in astronomical units given in Table 7·II. The agreement is quite close except for Neptune and Pluto, although it would be less impressive for Mercury if the rule of doubling the number had been followed from the start.

7·20. The Scale of the Solar System. When the distance of one planet from the sun is given, the distances of the others can be calculated from their periods of revolution by Kepler's harmonic law (7·6). The earth's mean distance from the sun is taken as the yardstick which sets the scale for the distances of planets from the sun, of satellites from their planets (Table 7·III), and of the stars as well. This is the reason for calling it the astronomical unit and for wishing to determine its value as accurately as possible.

We have seen (6·2) that the moon's distance is found by observing its parallax from two stations on the earth. The distance of the sun is measured less reliably in this way, because its parallax is much smaller, and also because the stars are less available as reference points in the daytime. More dependable values of the astronomical unit have been derived by observing the larger parallaxes of the nearer planets, particularly of the asteroid Eros at its closest approaches to the earth.

The value of the solar parallax adopted in the astronomical almanacs by international agreement is 8″.80; this is the difference in the direction of the sun's center as it would be viewed from the center and equator of the earth, when the sun is on the horizon and

TABLE 7·II. THE PLANETS

Name		Symbol	Mean Distance from Sun		Period of Revolution		Eccentricity of Orbit	Inclination to Ecliptic
			Astron. Units	Million Miles	Sidereal	Synodic		
Inner	Mercury	☿	0.3871	35.96	days 87.969	days 115.88	0.206	7° 0′
	Venus	♀	0.7233	67.20	224.701	583.92	0.007	3 24
	Earth	⊕	1.0000	92.90	365.256	. . . . . .	0.017	0 0
	Mars	♂	1.5237	141.6	686.980	779.94	0.093	1 51
	Ceres	①	2.7673	257.1	years 4.604	466.60	0.077	10 37
Outer	Jupiter	♃	5.2028	483.3	11.862	398.88	0.048	1 18
	Saturn	♄	9.5388	886.2	29.458	378.09	0.056	2 29
	Uranus	♅	19.1820	1783	84.015	369.66	0.047	0 46
	Neptune	♆	30.0577	2794	164.788	367.49	0.009	1 46
	Pluto	♇	39.5177	3670	247.697	366.74	0.249	17 9

Name	Mean Diameter in Miles	Mass ⊕ = 1	Density Water = 1	Period of Rotation	Inclination of Equator to Orbit	Oblateness	Stellar Magnitude at Greatest Brilliancy
Sun ☉	864,000	331,950	1.41	24^d.65	7° 10′	0	−26.8
Moon ☾	2,160	0.012	3.33	27 .32	6 41	0	−12.6
Mercury	2,900	0.05	6.1	88	7?	0	−1.9
Venus	7,600	0.81	5.06	30?	23?	0	−4.4
Earth	7,913	1.00	5.52	23^h 56^m	23 27	1/296	. . . . . .
Mars	4,200	0.11	4.12	24 37	24	1/192	−2.8
Jupiter	86,800	318.4	1.35	9 50	3 7	1/15	−2.5
Saturn	71,500	95.3	0.71	10 02	26 45	1/9.5	−0.4
Uranus	29,400	14.5	1.56	10 45	98	1/14	+5.7
Neptune	28,000	17.2	2.29	15 48?	29	1/40	+7.6

$\dfrac{m}{m}$ $\dfrac{1}{1-1}$ = ⚬ ∞

$\dfrac{V}{m}$ $\dfrac{2.583333}{1.583333} = 1.631578948$

$\dfrac{E}{m}$ $\dfrac{4.166666}{3.166666} = 1.315789474$

$\dfrac{m}{m}$ $\dfrac{7.833333}{6.833333} = 1.146341463$

$\dfrac{J}{m}$ $\dfrac{49.4166666}{48.4166666} = 1.020654045$

$\dfrac{S}{m}$ $\dfrac{101.9166666}{100.9166666} = 1.009909166$

$\dfrac{U}{m}$ $\dfrac{350}{349} = 1.00286533$

$\dfrac{N}{m}$ $\dfrac{686.66666}{685.66666} = 1.00145843 5$

$\dfrac{P}{m} =$ $\dfrac{1032.08333}{1031.08333} = 1.000969854$

$+360° =$
227.368 $(\tfrac{1}{x}°)$
226.5° = 586.
.001705
113.684
113.7° 473.

52.683°
51.6° 411.

7.435
7.45° 367.

3.567
3.598 363

1.0315
1.032°
361.0

.5250
0.526°
360.9

0.349°
360.5

.24084
.75916

TABLE 7·III. THE SATELLITES

Name	Discovery		Mean Distance in Miles	Period of Revolution	Diameter in Miles	Stellar Magnitude at Mean Opposition
Moon			238,857	27^d 7^h 43	2160	−12
SATELLITES OF MARS						
Phobos	Hall,	1877	5,800	0 7 39	10?	+12
Deimos	Hall,	1877	14,600	1 6 18	5?	13
SATELLITES OF JUPITER						
Fifth	Barnard,	1892	113,000	0 11 53	150?	13
I Io	Galileo,	1610	262,000	1 18 28	2000	5
II Europa	Galileo,	1610	417,000	3 13 14	1800	6
III Ganymede	Galileo,	1610	666,000	7 3 43	3100	5
IV Callisto	Galileo,	1610	1,170,000	16 16 32	2800	6
Sixth	Perrine,	1904	7,120,000	250 14	100?	14
Seventh	Perrine,	1905	7,290,000	259 14	35?	17
Tenth	Nicholson,	1938	7,300,000	260 12	15?	19
Eighth	Melotte,	1908	14,600,000	739	35?	17
Ninth	Nicholson,	1914	14,700,000	758	17?	19
Eleventh	Nicholson,	1938	14,000,000	700	19?	18
Twelfth	Nicholson,	1951	13,000,000	625	14?	19
SATELLITES OF SATURN						
Mimas	Herschel,	1789	115,000	0 22 37	300?	12
Enceladus	Herschel,	1789	148,000	1 8 53	350	12
Tethys	Cassini,	1684	183,000	1 21 18	500	11
Dione	Cassini,	1684	234,000	2 17 41	500	11
Rhea	Cassini,	1672	327,000	4 12 25	1000	10
Titan	Huygens,	1655	759,000	15 22 41	2850	8
Hyperion	Bond,	1848	920,000	21 6 38	300?	13
Iapetus	Cassini,	1671	2,210,000	79 7 56	800	11
Phoebe	Pickering,	1898	8,034,000	550	200?	14
SATELLITES OF URANUS						
Miranda	Kuiper,	1948	81,000	1 9 56	.....	17
Ariel	Lassell,	1851	119,000	2 12 29	600?	15
Umbriel	Lassell,	1851	166,000	4 3 28	400?	15
Titania	Herschel,	1787	272,000	8 16 56	1000?	14
Oberon	Herschel,	1787	364,000	13 11 7	900?	14
SATELLITES OF NEPTUNE						
Triton	Lassell,	1846	220,000	5 21 3	2350	13
Nereid	Kuiper,	1949	3,440,000	359 10	200?	19

at its average distance from us. The corresponding mean distance of the earth from the sun is 92,900,000 miles.

7·21. The Revolutions of the Planets around the sun and of the satellites around their planets exhibit some striking regularities, which apply more generally to the larger ones. These and the

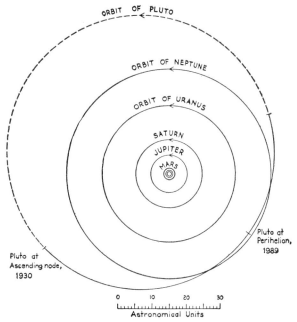

FIG. 7·21. Approximate Orbits of the Principal Planets. They are in general nearly circles around the sun, and are nearly in the same plane. The part of Pluto's orbit south of the ecliptic is indicated by the broken line.

exceptions in the cases of the less massive members provide important clues concerning the origin of the solar system (9·17).

1. *All the planets revolve from west to east.* This includes all the asteroids. Most satellites revolve in this direction, which is also the favored direction of all rotations in the system.

2. *The orbits of the planets and satellites are nearly circles,* as a general thing. The orbits of the smallest principal planets, Mercury and Pluto, are considerably eccentric. Among the still smaller asteroids some orbits are even more eccentric.

3. *The orbits of most planets and satellites lie nearly in the same*

plane. With the exception of Pluto's orbit, the orbits of the principal planets are inclined less than 8° to the ecliptic plane, so that these planets are observed always near the ecliptic, and mostly within the boundaries of the zodiac. These three regularities do not apply to many comets and meteor swarms, especially to those having the longer periods of revolution.

The true periods of revolution of the planets, or their *sidereal periods,* increase with distance from the sun in accordance with Kepler's harmonic law, from 88 days for Mercury to nearly 250 years for Pluto. The *synodic periods* are also given in Table 7·II. They are the intervals between two successive conjunctions of the planet with the sun, as seen from the earth; for the inferior planets the conjunctions must both be either inferior or superior. In other words, the synodic period is the interval in which the faster-moving inferior planet gains a lap on the earth, or in which the earth gains a lap on the slower superior planet. Mars and Venus have the longest synodic periods because they are nearest the earth and run it the closest race around the sun.

QUESTIONS ON CHAPTER 7

1. In what respects did the Copernican system of the planetary motions differ from the Ptolemaic system? from the present view?

2. Suppose that a planet revolves around the sun in the period of 8 years. Show by Kepler's third law that its distance from the sun is 4 times the earth's distance.

3. Explain that an object moving in a circle with constant speed is continuously accelerated.

4. State the law of gravitation. How is the force between two bodies affected: (a) if the original distance between them is doubled? (b) if the distance is unaltered but the mass of one body is doubled?

5. Explain the revolution of a planet around the sun, employing the first law of motion and the law of gravitation.

6. Show that the mass of a planet is readily determined if the planet has a satellite.

7. Name: (a) an inferior planet; (b) a superior planet; (c) an inner planet; (d) a major planet; (e) a minor planet.

8. State the earth's average distance from the sun. Why is it called the astronomical unit?

9. Why cannot the sun's distance from us be dependably measured by observing its parallax from two stations on the earth, as the moon's distance is determined?

10. Associate the appropriate term with each of the following definitions:

(a) The angular distance of a planet from the sun.
(b) The aspect of an inferior planet when it is between the sun and the earth.
(c) The aspect of a superior planet when it is opposite the sun's place in the sky.
(d) The motion of a planet from east to west among the stars.
(e) The interval of time between two successive conjunctions of a planet with a star as seen from the sun.

11. Why does Mars near its quadrature show the gibbous phase more noticeably than do the other superior planets?

12. Venus and Mars have the longest synodic periods (Table 7·II) of the principal planets. Explain.

REFERENCES

Abetti, Giorgio, *The History of Astronomy*. Henry Schuman, New York, 1952.

Dreyer. J. L. E., *History of the Planetary Systems from Thales to Kepler*. Photo-offset edition. Dover Publications, New York, 1953.

Yerkes Observatory, Williams Bay. Wisconsin.

8

PLANETS AND THEIR SATELLITES

MERCURY AND VENUS – MARS, THE RED PLANET – THE
ASTEROIDS – JUPITER, THE GIANT PLANET – SATURN,
THE RINGED PLANET – URANUS AND NEPTUNE – PLUTO,
THE MOST REMOTE PLANET

MERCURY AND VENUS

These two planets revolve inside the earth's orbit, Mercury once
in 88 days, Venus in 225 days. They accordingly oscillate to the
east and west of the sun's place in the sky and are never very far
from it. At times they come out in the west at nightfall as evening
stars; at other times they rise before the sun as morning stars. Both
planets, as we view them with the telescope, show the whole cycle
of phases (7·15) just as the moon does. Neither planet has a
satellite.

Mercury is the nearest to the sun and the smallest of the principal
planets. Its diameter, 2900 miles, is less than half again as great
as the moon's diameter. Venus, the brightest planet, outshines
all the celestial bodies except the sun and moon. Its diameter,
7600 miles, is only slightly less than the earth's diameter. Our
nearest neighbor among the principal planets, it comes within an
average of 26 million miles of the earth.

8·1. Mercury as Evening and Morning Star. The terms "evening
star" and "morning star" are applied more often to the appearances
of the inferior planets in the west after sunset and in the east before
sunrise. They are employed for the superior planets as well, to
signify that they set after or rise before the sun.

Mercury is occasionally visible to the naked eye for a few days
near the times of its greatest elongations. It then appears in the
twilight near the horizon as a bright star, sometimes even a little
brighter than Sirius, and twinkling like a star because of its small
disk and low altitude. The elongations occur about 22 days before

and after inferior conjunction. Because the synodic period is only 116 days, several greatest elongations occur in the course of a year; they are, however, not equally favorable.

Mercury's altitude above the horizon at sunset and sunrise varies considerably on these occasions, in our latitudes. The altitude is greatest, and the planet is therefore most easily visible, when the ecliptic is most inclined to the horizon (3·7). On this account the most favorable times to see Mercury as evening star are at its greatest eastern elongations in the early spring, and as morning star at its greatest western elongations in the early autumn. Such occasions are especially favorable when the planet is then near its greatest distance from the sun. In its rather eccentric orbit Mercury's distance from the sun's place in the sky at its greatest elongations varies from 28° at its aphelion to as little as 18° at its perihelion.

8·2. Venus as Evening and Morning Star. Venus emerges slowly from superior conjunction, behind the sun, to appear as evening star, requiring 220 days to reach greatest eastern elongation. Then in only 72 days it moves back to inferior conjunction, this time between us and the sun, presently to become the morning star. In 72 days more it reaches greatest western elongation, where it turns again to begin the 220-day return to superior conjunction. Thus the entire synodic period is 584 days.

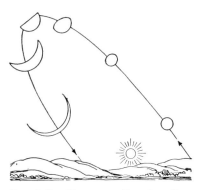

Fig. 8·2. Venus as Evening Star. Changing phase and apparent size of the planet as viewed with the telescope.

The greatest brilliancy of Venus as evening and morning star occurs about 36 days before and after inferior conjunction. On these occasions it appears 15 times as bright as Sirius, the brightest star, and 6 times as bright as the planet Jupiter. Then the planet appears through the telescope in the crescent phase, a crescent between 5 and 6 times as great from horn to horn as the apparent diameter of the fully lighted disk it shows over beyond the sun. Around the times of greatest brilliancy, Venus becomes visible in full daylight, like a star in the blue sky to the naked eye.

DATES OF CONJUNCTIONS AND ELONGATIONS OF VENUS

Superior Conjunction	Greatest Elongation East (Evening Star)	Inferior Conjunction	Greatest Elongation West (Morning Star)
1957, Apr. 14	1957, Nov. 18	1958, Jan. 28	1958, Apr. 9
1958, Nov. 11	1959, June 23	1959, Sept. 1	1959, Nov. 11
1960, June 22	1961, Jan. 29	1961, Apr. 10	1961, June 20
1962, Jan. 27	1962, Sept. 3	1962, Nov. 12	1963, Jan. 23
1963, Aug. 29	1964, Apr. 10	1964, June 19	1964, Aug. 29

8·3. Mercury Resembles the Moon. The best views of Mercury with the telescope are obtained in the daytime when the planet is well above the horizon. In addition to the phases, some dark markings are glimpsed and are also recorded in photographs, which are remindful of the lunar seas. The great increase in the planet's brightness from the quarter to the full phase, as the shadows become shorter, indicates that its surface is as mountainous as the surface of the moon. Like the moon, too, Mercury has no atmosphere, and would not be expected to have any because of its small size and surface gravity. It is the only principal planet where atmosphere is certainly absent.

Just as the moon rotates in the period of its revolution around us, so Mercury rotates once in 88 days while it is going once around the sun; the equality of the periods is verified by Dollfus in France, who finds that the equator is inclined about 7° to the ecliptic. Because of the considerable eccentricity of its orbit, the librations of Mercury leave only 30 per cent of the surface in permanent darkness. That part of the planet has a temperature not far above absolute zero, whereas the rocks on the sunward side are hot enough to melt lead; such extremes of temperature are unique in the planitary system. For these reasons we conclude that Mercury is a lifeless world.

8·4. Cloudy Atmosphere of Venus. The surface of Venus is so concealed by the atmosphere around it that it has not been observed even in infrared photographs. Photographs of the planet through violet filters reveal a variety of atmospheric markings which were studied by F. E. Ross as early as 1928. The markings are ascribed to clouds of yellowish dust that is abundant there because of the lack of water. They frequently appear as alternate bright and dark bands which are presumably parallel to the equator. These bands inform us that the rotation period must be considerably less than the period of the planet's revolution around the sun. Yet the period cannot be as short as a day, because the spectrum lines are not noticeably slanting, as they are in the swiftly rotating Saturn (Fig. 8·24). Ross estimated that the rotation period of Venus may be about 30 days.

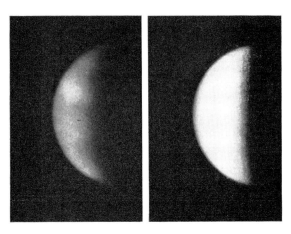

Fig. 8·4. Venus Near the Quarter Phase. In violet light (left) and red light (right). (*Photographed, April 8, 1950, by Gerard P. Kuiper at McDonald Observatory*)

More recently, Kuiper at McDonald Observatory and Richardson at Mount Wilson measured the directions of the cloud bands in their photographs of Venus. From the average of the two results, we conclude that the equator may be inclined to the ecliptic about as much as are the equators of the earth and Mars.

The spectrum of Venus also gives no evidence of water vapor or of free oxygen in its atmosphere. It reveals instead a surprising amount of carbon dioxide, many times as much in the available upper levels as in the entire atmosphere of the earth. Although Venus resembles the earth in size, mass, and distance from the sun, and has sometimes been called the "earth's twin sister," it seems unlikely that we would find this dust bowl of the planetary system a desirable place in which to live.

8·5. Transits of Mercury and Venus. The inferior planets occasionally *transit*, or cross directly in front of the sun at inferior conjunction. They then appear as dark dots against the sun's disk. About 13 transits of Mercury occur in the course of a century; they are possible only within 3 days before or after May 8, and also within 5 days of November 10, when the sun passes the nodes of

Fig. 8·5. Transit of Mercury, November 14, 1953. (*Photographed by J. L. Gossner at the Naval Observatory. U.S. Navy photograph*)

the planet's path. The latest one, on November 14, 1953 (Fig. 8·5), was observed in the United States, and the following one, on May 6, 1957, will also be visible here. Transits are scheduled for the remainder of the century on November 7, 1960, May 9, 1970, November 10, 1973, November 13, 1986, November 6, 1993, and November 15, 1999, a grazing transit. Transits of Mercury are not visible without the telescope.

These transits, which can be timed rather accurately, have been useful for improving our knowledge of the planet's motions. A century ago, the French mathematician Leverrier discovered from records of many transits that the perihelion of Mercury's orbit is advancing faster than would be predicted by the law of gravitation. The major axis of the planet's orbit is turning eastward, mainly because of the attractions of other planets. The observed excess in its turning has now been explained by the theory of relativity.

Transits of Venus are less frequent; they are possible only when

the planet arrives at inferior conjunction within about 2 days
before or after June 7 or December 9, the dates when the sun passes
the nodes of the planet's path. They are now coming in pairs

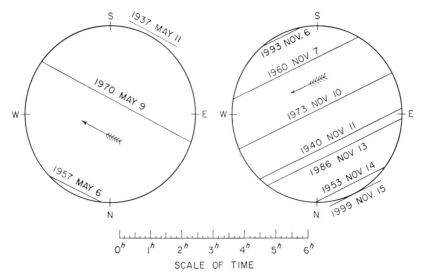

FIG. 8·5A. Transits of Mercury, 1937 to 1999. (*Diagram by Fletcher G.
Watson in* Sky and Telescope)

having a separation of 8 years. The latest transits occurred in 1874
and 1882; the next ones are scheduled for June 8, 2004, and June 6,
2012. Transits of Venus are visible without a telescope.

MARS, THE RED PLANET

Next in order beyond the earth, Mars revolves once in 687 days
at the average distance of 142 million miles from the sun, and
rotates on its axis once in $24^{\text{h}} 37^{\text{m}}$. Its diameter is 4200 miles, or
slightly more than half the earth's diameter. Its atmosphere is not
sufficiently extensive and clouded to hide its surface which exhibits
a variety of markings. The persistent idea that Mars contains
certain forms of life has made this planet an object of special interest, particularly at its closest approaches to the earth.

8·6. Oppositions of Mars with the sun recur at average intervals
of 780 days, or about 50 days longer than 2 years. They accordingly

come 50 days later in successive alternate years. Owing to the eccentricity of its orbit, Mars varies considerably in its distance from the earth at the different oppositions, from less than 35 million

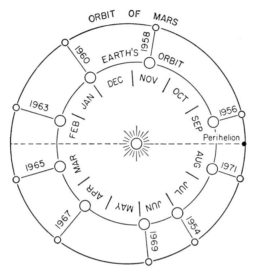

FIG. 8·6. Varying Distances of Mars at Oppositions from 1954 to 1971. The latest favorable opposition occurred in 1956. The next will come in 1971.

miles at perihelion to 63 million miles at aphelion. The dates of the oppositions from 1958 to 1965 and the constellations in which Mars is then situated are as follows:

Date of Opposition	Constellation
1958, Nov. 16	Taurus
1960, Dec. 30	Gemini
1963, Feb. 4	Cancer
1965, Mar. 9	Leo

Favorable oppositions occur when the planet is also near its perihelion. At these unusually close approaches, which are always in the late summer, Mars becomes the most brilliant starlike object in the heavens with the single exception of Venus, and also attracts attention then because of its red color. With a telescope magnifying only 75 times, its disk appears as large as does the moon's disk to the unaided eye. The latest favorable opposition of Mars occurred on September 10, 1956, after its perihelion passage on August 21. The planet was nearest the earth on September 7 at the distance of 35.1 million miles. The distance at opposition is now increasing (Fig. 8·6) until the most unfavorable opposition is reached on March 9, 1965. The next favorable opposition will come in early August in 1971.

8·7. The Seasons of Mars. Mars presents its poles alternately to the sun just as the earth does; its seasons resemble ours except that they are about twice as long. The winter solstice occurs near the time of perihelion, as in the case of the earth. Thus, as with us (3·16), the summer in the southern hemisphere begins when the planet is nearest the sun, and in the northern hemisphere when it is farthest from the sun. On the earth, as we have seen, the warmer summers and colder winters that might otherwise be expected in the southern hemisphere compared with the northern one are not appreciably so; the variation of our distance from the sun is relatively small, and our southern hemisphere has the more water to modify extreme temperatures.

The temperature difference is noticeable on Mars because of its more eccentric orbit, where the greatest distance from the sun exceeds the least by 20 per cent, or 26 million miles. The temperatures of the seasons are appreciably the more extreme in the Martian southern hemisphere. The snow cap around its south pole becomes larger in the winter season than does the north polar cap; and it completely disappears in the summer, which the other has not been observed to do. It is the south polar cap which is toward the earth at the favorable oppositions, and this is accordingly the one that more often appears in the photographs.

8·8. The Polar Caps; the Hazy Atmosphere. White caps, which appear alternately around the poles of Mars, are the most conspicuous features of the view with the telescope. Each snow cap expands rapidly as winter comes on in that hemisphere, and shrinks with the approach of summer. The southern cap has attained a diameter of 3700 miles, so that it then extended more than halfway from the pole to the equator. As the cap retreats toward the pole, the main body may leave behind for a time a small white spot, presumably on the summit or cooler slope of a hill.

The polar caps are more conspicuous in photographs in violet light, which reveal the areas of haze above them. The haze, as Kuiper has explained, may be caused by ice crystals similar to those in our cirrus clouds. Patches of haze also appear in the cooler air near the sunrise and sunset lines. Yellowish spots like clouds of dust are visible at times on various parts of the disk. Often the haze is widespread over the disk, making the view of the surface more difficult, and then it clears quite suddenly over large areas.

8·9. The Darker Markings appear through the telescope in a variety of shapes and sizes against the reddish background which

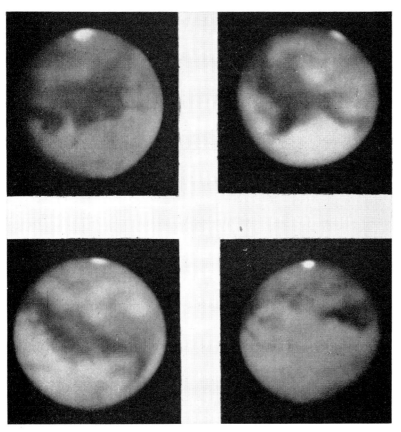

FIG. 8·9. Various Regions of Mars. South is at the top and east is at the right. In the *upper left* photograph, taken September 23, the dark central area is Mare Erythraeum. In the *lower left*, taken October 8, Mare Cimmerium is central, and in the *upper right*, taken 3½ hours later, Syrtis Major has come around to the center. The *lower right* photograph was taken October 19. Meanwhile the south polar cap has shrunk considerably. (*Photographed in 1941 by B. Lyot on the Pic du Midi, France*)

imparts its color to the light of the planet. The reddish areas themselves are often called "deserts." Dollfus, observing at Pic du Midi
in France, reports that their light resembles sunlight reflected from
pulverized yellow oxide of iron.

The larger dark areas are known by watery names which have
survived, like those of the lunar "seas," from the early maps.
Prominent among them are the Syrtis Major (Great Bog) and Solis

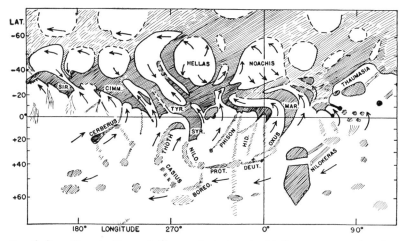

FIG. 8·9A. Sketch Map of Mars. It is based chiefly on a map by An-
toniadi. Wind arrows indicate the circulation during the Martian southern summer. (*Diagram by Dean B. McLaughlin*)

Lacus (Lake of the Sun). With the shrinking of each polar cap
the dark markings of that hemisphere are more distinct; they become green during the Martian spring, and then fade and turn
brown as winter approaches. Thus they might seem to behave as
areas of vegetation would do.

An alternate explanation of the dark markings is offered by
D. B. McLaughlin of the University of Michigan. He views them
as frequently renewed areas of volcanic ash guided by prevailing
winds into barlike and funnel-shaped forms which tend to termi-
nate in triangular estuaries. The dark areas are more abundant
in the southern hemisphere where the more extreme temperatures
promote higher winds. The Margaritifer Sinus, abbreviated to
Mar. in Fig. 8·9A, is illustrative. Notice how it changes direction
after crossing the equator as though influenced by the Coriolis
effect (2·1).

Changes in wind directions at certain seasons may bring in the red sands of the deserts to partly obliterate the darker markings. This interpretation would account for the variations in the forms and distinctness of the markings, and for the appearance of new ones, such as the new dark area "as large as Texas" reported by observers at the opposition of 1954.

8·10. The Canals of Mars. A complex network of fine dark lines known as the *canals* of Mars was first reported by the Italian astronomer Schiaparelli, who observed it with an 11-inch telescope and described the lines as like "the finest thread of spider's web drawn

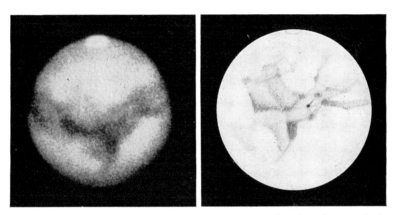

FIG. 8·10. Photograph and Drawing of Mars, Showing Some of the Larger Markings. The prominent marking below the center is Syrtis Major. (*Photograph by E. E. Barnard, Yerkes Observatory. Drawing by R. J. Trumpler, Lick Observatory*)

across the disk." He mapped the lines and gave them names, such as Nectar and Ambrosia. This careful observer found the canals less difficult to see in the hemisphere where the snow cap was melting, and was tempted to suppose that vegetation bordering them might add to the width of the strips.

Many observers have viewed the network since then, often with telescopes of moderate size. The impression has been that it appears only during rare instants of exceptionally steady seeing. Thus a continued succession of photographs with the very short exposures permitted by the largest telescopes might be expected to reveal the network eventually if it exists. Yet many other experienced observers have been unable to detect long narrow canals even visually, and have doubted their existence as such. Among these, Kuiper has recently remarked that the colors of the large dark markings themselves fade surprisingly in the best conditions.

8·11. The Climate of Mars. The atmosphere of Mars is rarer than ours, and is deficient in certain ingredients necessary for animal life. Free oxygen is not detected in the spectrum analysis of sunlight reflected from the planet; it must be less than 1 per cent as abundant there as in the earth's atmosphere. The chief constituent may be nitrogen, which is not revealed by this means. Water vapor is only a tenth of 1 per cent that of the earth, according to Kuiper, who has shown that carbon dioxide, however, is twice as abundant as in our atmosphere.

The average temperature of the surface of Mars is 40 degrees below zero Fahrenheit as compared with 60° above zero for the earth. The climate of Mars seems to be too severe for the flourishing of even the hardiest known vegetation in such profusion as to color the dark areas.

8·12. Mars Has Two Satellites. Their names are Phobos and Deimos. Both are very small, probably not exceeding 10 miles in diameter, and are so near the bright planet as to be invisible except with large telescopes at favorable times.

Phobos revolves from west to east at the distance of only 3700 miles from the surface of Mars, once around in $7^h 39^m$, or less than one third the period of the planet's rotation in the same direction. Viewed from Mars, therefore, Phobos rises in the west and sets in the east. No other known satellite in the solar system revolves in a shorter interval of time than the rotation period of its primary.

Deimos, the outer satellite, revolves eastward around Mars once in $30^h 18^m$. It is smaller than Phobos and only a third as bright. This satellite rises in the east in the Martian sky, but drops behind the rotating planet so slowly that it goes through its whole cycle of phases for an observer there before it sets.

THE ASTEROIDS

The *asteroids,* or *minor planets,* revolve around the sun mainly between the orbits of Mars and Jupiter. Invisible to the naked eye, with the occasional exception of Vesta, they are "starlike" in the sense that few of them show disks even through large telescopes. The majority have periods of revolution between $3\frac{1}{2}$ and 6 years.

8·13. Great Number of Asteroids. Toward the close of the 18th century, the German astronomer Bode invited his colleagues to share in a search for a planet between the orbits of Mars and Jupiter. He explained that a series of numbers, which later came to be known as Bode's law (7·19), represented the relative distances of the known planets from the sun with a single exception. No planet had been found corresponding to the number 2.8.

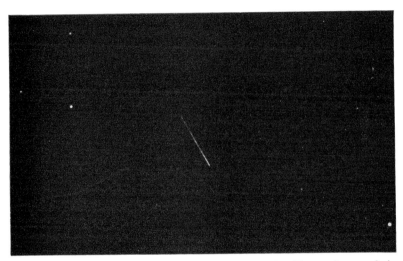

FIG. 8·13.   Long Trail of the Asteroid Eros Near Its Closest Approach in 1931. The exposure time was 1½ hours. (*Photographed by G. Van Biesbroeck, Yerkes Observatory*)

While the search was being organized, the missing planet was discovered incidentally by Piazzi in Sicily on the 1st of January, 1801, because of its motion among the stars. The mean distance of the new planet, which Piazzi named Ceres, proved to be almost exactly 2.8 times the earth's distance from the sun. There was greater surprise when other minor planets were presently discovered at about the same distance as Ceres.

Three other asteroids, Pallas, Juno, and Vesta, were picked up in the following few years. Many thousands have since been detected by the generally short trails they leave in photographs, owing to their motions among the stars during the exposures. More than 1600 have had their orbits determined, quite enough to inform us about their movements.

8·14. Motions of Asteroids. The asteroids are small as compared with the principal planets. Ceres, the largest one, is 480 miles in diameter. About a dozen have diameters exceeding 100 miles. Some are a mile or less across. All together they have not more than 5 per cent the mass of the moon.

The motions of asteroids depart considerably from the regularities we have noticed (7·21) in the movements of the larger planets. Although they all revolve from west to east, some have orbits so much inclined to the ecliptic that they venture far outside the zodiac. Some have rather highly eccentric orbits; one asteroid, Hidalgo, has its aphelion as far away as Saturn, and another, Icarus, comes at its perihelion nearer the sun than the orbit of Mercury.

The asteroids are not distributed at random through the zone they mainly frequent between the orbits of Mars and Jupiter. They avoid distances from the sun where the periods of revolution would be simple fractions, particularly one third, two fifths, and one half, of Jupiter's period. There they would be subject to frequent recurrences of the same types of disturbances by Jupiter. Where the periods are equal to Jupiter's, however, there are two regions in which asteroids congregate. The *Trojan asteroids* oscillate around two points near Jupiter's orbit, which are equidistant from that planet and the sun. They are named Achilles, Agamemnon, and so on after the Homeric heroes. Twelve are known, 7 of them east and 5 west of Jupiter.

8·15. Close Approaches of Asteroids. Several known asteroids come within the orbit of Mars and make closer approaches to the earth than do any of the principal planets. Among these is Eros which can come within 14 million miles, at which time this 15-mile object appears as bright as a star of the 7th magnitude. These favorable oppositions, when Eros is also near perihelion, occur rather infrequently; the latest one was in 1931, and the next one is scheduled for 1975. The large parallax on such occasions permits accurate measurements of the distance, which have been valuable for verifying the scale of the solar system (7·20).

Examples of asteroids that come even nearer us are Apollo and Adonis (Fig. 8·15). The perihelion distance of Adonis is only slightly greater than Mercury's mean distance from the sun; this asteroid passes a little more than a million miles from the earth's orbit and about the same distance from the orbits of Venus and

Mars. Another neighborly asteroid, Icarus, attracted Baade's attention in 1949 when it left a long trail on a photograph with the 48-inch Schmidt telescope. At perihelion its distance from the sun is less than 20 million miles.

Asteroids which have been observed within a few million miles of the earth are about a mile in diameter. At closest approach they

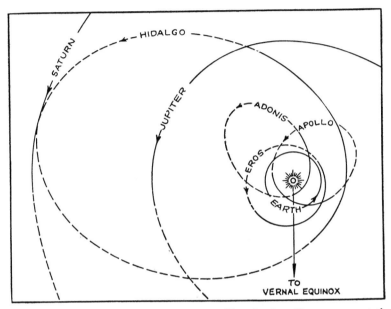

FIG. 8·15. Orbits of Four Unusual Asteroids. Broken lines represent the parts of the orbits below the plane of the earth's orbit. (*Adapted from a diagram by Dirk Brouwer*)

appear as faint stars moving so swiftly across the heavens that they can easily be missed. Most of them have vanished before their orbits could be reliably determined.

8·16. Asteroids as Fragments. The erratic orbits of some asteroids suggest that these are fragments which have been propelled in various directions by the collisions of larger bodies. This theory may account not only for the smaller asteroids that pass near us but also for the meteorites which fall on the earth and are occasionally large enough to blast out meteorite craters.

Many asteroids fluctuate periodically in brightness, as would be expected of rotating fragments having irregular shapes. Eros is an example. In its rotation once in $5^h 16^m$, this asteroid shaped roughly like a brick presents its larger sides and smaller ends to us in turn. Thus it becomes brighter and fainter out there in the sunlight twice in each period. The light variation is greatest when its equator is presented edgewise to us, and it becomes less in other parts of the orbit when a polar region is turned more nearly in our direction.

An extensive photoelectric study of the light variations of all asteroids as bright as the 10th magnitude at their oppositions, and of some fainter ones as well, has been begun by Kuiper and his associates at McDonald Observatory. Provisional reports on some two dozen asteroids have already been given. Except for the largest ones, the variations suggest the irregular shapes of the rotating bodies, but in some cases it is too early to distinguish between this cause and the spottedness of the surface which could also produce light variations. The periods range from 4 to 20 hours, and the axes are oriented at random. In one of them, Eunomia, the rotation is definitely from east to west.

JUPITER, THE GIANT PLANET

Jupiter is the largest planet. Its equatorial diameter, 88,600 miles, is 11 times as great as the earth's diameter. Its mass exceeds the combined mass of all the other planets. With the exceptions of Venus and occasionally Mars, this planet is the brightest star-like object in our skies. Even a small telescope shows its 4 bright satellites and cloud belts clearly. Jupiter has 12 known satellites, the greatest number attending a planet.

At the distance of almost 500 million miles from the sun, Jupiter revolves around the sun once in nearly 12 years, so that it advances one sign of the zodiac from year to year. The period of its rotation, about $9^h 50^m$, is the shortest among the principal planets.

8·17. Jupiter's Cloudy Atmosphere. The markings on the disk of the giant planet, which run parallel to its equator, are features of its atmosphere. Bright *zones* alternate with dark *belts.* The broad equatorial zone is bordered by the north and south tropical belts. Then come the north and south tropical zones, and beyond them a succession of dark and bright divisions extending to the polar regions. Bright and dark spots appear as well; they often change in form quite rapidly, as atmospheric markings might be expected to do. Yet some of them are of surprisingly long duration. The Great Red Spot (Fig. 8·17) is an extreme example; this oval spot 30,000 miles long, has been observed for at least a century; it behaves like a floating solid. The markings go around

FIG. 8·17. Jupiter, October 24, 1952, Showing the Great Red Spot. Photographed in blue light at the coudé focus of the Hale telescope. The 3rd satellite and its shadow appear near the top of the disk. (*Photographed at Mount Wilson and Palomar Observatories*)

in the rotation at different rates, owing to the unequal horizontal movements of the clouds themselves.

The atmosphere consists mainly of hydrogen and helium. Its refraction effect on the light of a star was recently observed by W. A. Baum and A. D. Code as the planet began to occult the star, and was interpreted by them to mean that Jupiter's outer atmosphere has a molecular weight of about 3. Methane and ammonia contaminate the atmosphere, as is indicated by the presence of their bands in the spectrum. At the temperature of $-200°$ F, methane is still gaseous, whereas ammonia is mainly frozen into crystals.

8·18. Structure of Jupiter. The bulging of Jupiter's equator, which is clearly shown in the figure, provides one clue to conditions in the interior. With its swift rotation the planet would be even more oblate if its mass were not highly concentrated toward its center. Other clues of what is hidden beneath the clouds are the low temperature and the low average density, about 1.3 times the density of water, of the whole planet, which requires very light material in the outer parts.

It is difficult to choose from among the different theoretical models that would justify the limited clues. As one extreme, Rupert Wildt of Yale University, about 20 years ago, designed a model in which the atmosphere is mainly of hydrogen and has a depth of 8000 miles. Beneath it there is a layer of ice 17,000 miles thick around a rocky core 38,000 miles in diameter; the core of the heavier elements is 6 times as dense as water, or somewhat more than the earth's average density. Hydrogen contributes 50 per cent of the mass of this model, an abundance now considered too low.

At the opposite extreme, W. H. Ramsey in England has proposed a model of the planet consisting entirely of hydrogen. Anything resembling an atmosphere in this model is only a few miles thick. Solid hydrogen begins at a depth of 2000 miles. Metallic hydrogen extends from a depth of 8000 miles to the center; it becomes highly compressed under the very great pressure, which increases to 32 million atmospheres at the center. Intermediate models have been discussed by these and other investigators. Whatever the choice may be, we conclude that Jupiter has little resemblance to the earth.

8·19. Jupiter's Twelve Satellites. Next to the moon the 4 bright satellites of Jupiter are the most conspicuous in our skies. They could be glimpsed with the naked eye if they were farther removed from the glare of the planet. They were discovered by Galileo early in 1610.

The bright satellites are numbered in order of distance from the planet; they have personal names as well, although these are not so often used. The 1st and 2nd satellites are about the size of the moon. The 3rd and 4th satellites are half again as great; they are the largest of all satellites and surpass even the planet Mercury in diameter. Like the moon they have equal periods of rotation and revolution.

These satellites revolve from west to east in nearly circular orbits which are nearly in the plane of the planet's equator and of its orbit around the sun. Because their paths are almost edgewise to the earth, the satellites seem to oscillate from one side of the

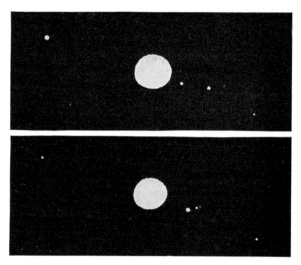

Fig. 8·19. Jupiter's Four Bright Satellites. The lower photograph was taken 3 hours later than the upper one. (*Photographed at Yerkes Observatory*)

planet to the other (Fig. 8·19). At times they disappear behind the planet's disk or into its shadow. At other times they pass in front of the planet; their transits across its disk are visible with telescopes of moderate size, and the shadows they cast upon it are visible as well.

The other satellites of Jupiter are too small and faint to be easily seen through the telescope. They are designated by numbers from 5 to 12 in order of their discovery. The 5th satellite is the nearest of all to the planet; in the small eccentricity and inclination of its orbit and in its direct revolution it resembles the bright satellites. The 7 outer satellites have orbits of considerable eccentricity and inclination to the ecliptic. They fall into two groups. The 6th, 7th, and 10th satellites revolve from west to east at mean distances of a little more than 7 million miles from the planet. The 8th, 9th, 11th, and 12th satellites revolve from east to west at distances about twice as great.

The data on the outer satellites in Table 7·III are as given by

Nicholson. The order of distance of the outermost four, as he
points out, has little significance, because disturbances of their
motions by the sun's attraction may change that order in a few
years. The diameters of the faint satellites, which do not appear

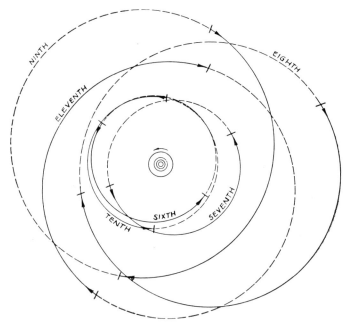

FIG. 8·19A. Orbits of Jupiter's Satellites. The outer satellites are in two
groups. The 6th, 7th, and 10th satellites revolve from west to east like
the inner ones. The 8th, 9th, 11th, and 12th revolve from east to west,
and their orbits vary considerably. The orbit of the 12th satellite is not
shown. (*Diagram by Seth B. Nicholson*)

as disks with the largest telescopes, are estimated from their brightness.

SATURN, THE RINGED PLANET

Saturn is the most remote of the bright planets and is, therefore,
the most leisurely in its movement among the constellations. It
revolves once in $29\frac{1}{2}$ years at the mean distance of 886 million
miles from the sun. A bright yellow star in our skies, it ranges from
equality with Altair to twice the brightness of Capella. This planet
ranks second to Jupiter in size and mass; its equatorial diameter
is 74,100 miles. It has the lowest average density, 0.7 times the

density of water, and the most prominent bulge at the equator of any of the planets. Its unique system of rings makes it one of the most impressive celestial sights with the telescope.

8·20. The Planet Itself. Saturn resembles Jupiter except for its smaller size, mass, and density. The core is relatively smaller in the model that assigns it a rocky core. Methane bands are stronger

| Ultraviolet | Violet | Yellow |

Fig. 8·20. Bright Spot on Saturn. (*Photographed through filters, August 7, 1933, by W. H. Wright, Lick Observatory*)

in its spectrum, and there is less evidence of ammonia, presumably because this ingredient is frozen out of its atmosphere at the lower temperature there of $-240°$ F.

From its broad, yellow, equatorial zone to its bluish polar caps, the cloud markings of Saturn show less detail than do those of Jupiter. A large bright spot which appeared in the equatorial zone in 1933 was exceptional; it was an oval spot 10,000 miles long at first, and quickly became longer. The rotation period derived from some spots in intermediate latitudes is around $10\frac{1}{2}$ hours, whereas the period from the Doppler effect in the spectrum at its equator is about half an hour less.

8·21. The Satellites of Saturn. Titan, the largest and brightest of Saturn's 9 known satellites, is considerably larger than the moon. It is the only satellite in the solar system known to have an atmosphere, although an atmosphere is now suspected in the case of Neptune's larger satellite. Titan's spectrum shows methane bands in Kuiper's photographs at McDonald Observatory. This satellite resembles Mars in its reddish color, probably because of similar action of the atmosphere on the surface rocks.

Four or five other satellites can be seen with telescopes of moderate size, appearing as faint stars in the vicinity of the ringed planet. All the satellites revolve from west to east around the planet with the exception of Phoebe, the most distant and the faintest one; Phoebe revolves from east to west like Jupiter's outer group of satellites. Some of the satellites vary in brightness in the periods of their revolutions; they evidently rotate and revolve in the same periods, and are either irregular in form or have surfaces of uneven reflecting power. The very high reflection from the inner satellites suggests to Kuiper that they have icy surfaces, and their low densities may mean that they are composed mainly of ice.

8·22. Saturn's Rings are invisible to the naked eye and were, therefore, unknown until after the invention of the telescope. When

FIG. 8·22.   Saturn in 1939.   (*Photographed by Hamilton M. Jeffers, Lick Observatory*)

Galileo began observing Saturn, in 1610, he glimpsed what seemed to be two smaller bodies in contact with the planet on opposite sides. The supposed appendages disappeared two years later and subsequently reappeared. This changing appearance of the planet remained a mystery until about half a century later, when the Dutch scientist Huygens, with a larger telescope, concluded that Saturn is encircled by a broad flat ring. In still later times it was found that there are 3 concentric rings instead of a single one.

The entire ring system is 171,000 miles across, but is scarcely more than 10 miles thick. The width of the *outer ring* is 10,000 miles. The middle or *bright ring* is 16,000 miles wide. It is separated from the outer ring by the 3000-mile *Cassini division*, named after its discoverer; this is the only real division in the rings. The inner or *crape ring*, which is continuous with the bright ring, is about 12,000 miles wide. Much fainter than the others and not very clearly shown in the figures, the crape ring is nevertheless rather easily visible with telescopes of moderate size, although it was not discovered until 1850.

FIG. 8·22A. Saturn in 1943. *(Photographed by George H. Herbig, Lick Observatory)*

8·23. Different Aspects of the Rings. Saturn's rings are inclined 27° to the plane of the planet's orbit, and they keep the same direction during its revolution. They accordingly present their northern

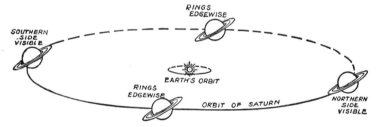

FIG. 8·23. Saturn's Rings at Different Angles. Twice in the course of Saturn's revolution its rings become edgewise to the sun. Each time the plane of the rings requires about a year to sweep across the earth's orbit.

and southern faces alternately to the sun, and also to the earth which is never more than 6° from the sun as viewed from Saturn. Twice during the sidereal period of 29½ years the plane of the rings passes through the sun's position (Fig. 8·23), requiring nearly a year each time to sweep across the earth's orbit. In that interval our own revolution brings the rings edgewise to us from 1 to 3 times, when they disappear through small telescopes and are only very narrow bright lines with larger ones.

The latest widest opening of the southern face of the rings occurred late in 1943, when the planet near the horns of Taurus appeared twice as bright as Capella; on such occasions the rings reflect 1.7 times as much sunlight as does the disk of Saturn itself. The rings became edgewise to the earth in 1950. Thereafter the northern face of the rings began to open. The widest opening is scheduled for 1958, when the planet will appear rather low in the south not far from the position of the winter solstice.

8·24. Texture of the Rings. Saturn's rings consist of solid particles which revolve like satellites around the planet in nearly circular

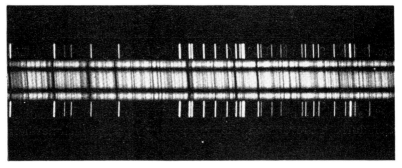

Fig. 8·24. Spectrum of Ball and Rings of Saturn. In the spectrum of the ball of the planet, in the middle, the lines slant because of the planet's rotation. In the spectrum of the rings, above and below, the lines have the opposite slant. This shows that the rings revolve more rapidly at their inner edges, proving their discrete nature. The bright "pickets" are comparison spectra. (*Photographed at Lowell Observatory*)

orbits in the plane of its equator and in the direction of its rotation. They are mainly icy particles, as Kuiper's study of the sunlight reflected from the rings suggests. The light from the separate pieces runs together at the great distance of Saturn to give the appearance of a continuous surface.

If the rings were really continuous, all parts would rotate in the same period, and the outside, having farther to go, would go around faster than the inside. The spectrum shows (Fig. 8·24), however, that the inside has the faster motion, as it should have in accordance with Kepler's harmonic law if the rings are composed of separate pieces.

The outer edge of the outer ring has the longest period of rotation, $14^h 27^m$. The inner edge of the bright ring rotates once in $7^h 46^m$, and the material of the crape ring must go around in still shorter time. Meanwhile the planet itself rotates in a period of about 10 hours. Thus the outer parts of the ring system move from east to west across the sky of Saturn, whereas the inner parts seem to go around from west to east, like Phobos in the sky of Mars.

URANUS AND NEPTUNE

8·25. Discoveries of Uranus and Neptune. The discovery of Uranus, in 1781, was accidental and unexpected. William Herschel in England was examining a region in the constellation Gemini when he noticed a greenish object which seemed to him somewhat larger than a star. The object eventually proved to be a planet more remote than Saturn, and it received the name Uranus. Forty years later, when this planet had gone nearly halfway around the sun, its orbit was calculated from many observed positions, with allowance for the disturbing effects of other known planets. The new planet, however, did not follow thereafter precisely the course it was expected to pursue. Astronomers finally concluded that its motion in the heavens was being altered by the attraction of a planet still more remote and as yet unseen.

Neptune was discovered by Leverrier, in France, in 1846. By comparing observed positions of Uranus during the preceding quarter of a century with the predicted ones, he was able to calculate the place at that time of the unseen disturber in the sky. An astronomer at the Berlin Observatory, where an accurate star map was available, directed the telescope toward the specified region in the constellation Aquarius and soon found Neptune within a degree of the place assigned it by Leverrier. The discovery was acclaimed as a triumph for the law of gravitation, on which the calculation was based.

8·26. Uranus, the first planet to be discovered, is nearly 30,000 miles in diameter; it revolves once in 84 years at 19 times the earth's distance from the sun. It rotates once in less than half a day, having its equator inclined nearly at right angles to the

FIG. 8·26. The Five Satellites of Uranus. The recently discovered satellite appears inside the halation ring at the left of the planet. (*Photographed by Gerard P. Kuiper at McDonald Observatory*)

ecliptic. Barely visible to the unaided eye, Uranus shows a small greenish disk through the telescope, on which the markings are not clearly discernible. The spectrum includes a dark band in the infrared observed by Kuiper and identified by Herzberg with molecular hydrogen, the first direct evidence of the presence of this element in the atmospheres of the major planets. Bands of the contaminating methane appear in the spectra of both Uranus and Neptune.

Five satellites revolve around Uranus in nearly circular orbits in the plane of its equator and therefore inclined nearly at right angles to the ecliptic. The orbits were presented flatwise to the earth in 1945, and will appear edgewise to us in 1966. The 5th satellite, discovered by Kuiper at McDonald Observatory in 1948, is the faintest and nearest to the planet.

8·27. Neptune, about the same size as Uranus, revolves once in 165 years. It rotates from west to east once in 15.8 hours, according to earlier spectroscopic measures. Using other means, however, O. Gruenther in Germany has recently reported a period of 12.7 hours.

Always invisible to the naked eye, Neptune appears with the telescope as a star of the 8th magnitude, and shows a small greenish disk on which markings have not been seen.   It seems to closely resemble Uranus.

Neptune has two known satellites.   The first, Triton, is somewhat larger than the moon and is slightly nearer the planet than the moon's distance from the earth; it is nearly twice as massive as the moon and perhaps has an atmosphere.   Triton revolves from east to west, contrary to the direction of the planet's rotation.   The

Fig. 8·27.   Neptune and Its Inner Satellite.   (*Photographed by Gerard P. Kuiper at McDonald Observatory*)

second satellite, discovered by Kuiper in 1949, is much the smaller and the more distant from the planet.   It revolves from west to east in an orbit having an eccentricity of 0.76, the greatest for any known satellite.

PLUTO, THE MOST REMOTE PLANET

8·28. The Discovery of Pluto was announced by Lowell Observatory on March 13, 1930, as the successful result of a long-continued search at that observatory for a planet beyond Neptune.   The planet was discovered by Clyde Tombaugh in his photographs taken in January of that year.   The search had been instituted by Percival Lowell, who had calculated the orbit of a transneptunian planet from slight discrepancies between the observed and predicted movements of Uranus, which seemed to remain after the discovery of Neptune.

Pluto is visible with the telescope as a star of the 15th visual magnitude. Its diameter is 3600 miles, as measured by Kuiper with a disk meter on the 200-inch telescope. Unless the density is greater than would be expected, its mass cannot exceed a tenth of the earth's mass. Pluto is thought to have a gritty snow-covered surface and perhaps an atmosphere that is considerably rarer than

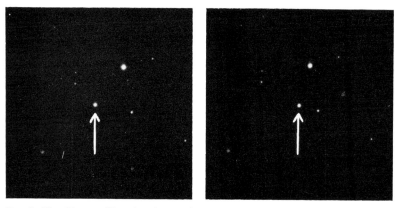

FIG. 8·28. Pluto. Showing its motion among the stars in one day. (*Photographed with the Hale telescope, Mount Wilson and Palomar Observatories*)

ours. Its period of rotation is 6.390 days, as determined by M. F. Walker and Robert Hardie from periodic fluctuations in its brightness.

8·29. The Orbit of Pluto. At its average distance the planet is $39\frac{1}{2}$ astronomical units, or 3670 million miles, from the sun. It revolves once in 248 years, which is half again as long as the period of Neptune's revolution. Its orbit is inclined 17° to the ecliptic, the highest inclination for any principal planet, so that Pluto ventures at times well beyond the borders of the zodiac.

The eccentricity, 0.25, of Pluto's orbit is the greatest for any principal planet. On this account and because of the great size of its orbit, its distance from the sun varies enormously. At aphelion it is 1800 million miles beyond Neptune's distance from the sun, whereas at perihelion it comes 35 million miles nearer the sun than the orbit of Neptune; yet in their present orbits the two planets cannot approach each other closer than 240 million miles. At the time of its discovery Pluto was near its ascending node (Fig.

7·21) and also near its mean distance from the sun. The distance will diminish until the planet reaches its perihelion in the year 1989. In the figure the part of the orbit south of the ecliptic is indicated by the broken line.

QUESTIONS ON CHAPTER 8

1. Name the principal planets in order of distance from the sun. State a unique feature of each.

2. Mention some points of resemblance between Mercury and the moon; Venus and the earth. What conditions on Venus seem to make that planet uninviting to life?

3. Why is Venus brightest at the crescent phase and not at the full phase, as in the case of the moon?

4. Mention some features of Mars which might suggest the presence of life, and some conditions which would seem discouraging to life.

5. Why is there some doubt as to the existence of a network of canals on Mars?

6. In what respects do some asteroids depart from the regularities (7·21) in the revolutions of the principal planets? Why might Pluto be considered not a principal planet?

7. The periodic fluctuations in the brightness of many asteroids inform us of their irregular shapes and possible origins. Explain.

8. Describe the telescopic view of Jupiter.

9. Jupiter's satellites are sharply divided into 3 groups. Explain.

10. Why are Saturn's rings presented to us at varying angles? Explain their edgewise presentation at intervals of 15 years.

11. What is the evidence that Saturn's rings have discrete constitution rather than continuous surfaces?

12. Describe the discoveries of Ceres, Uranus, Neptune, and Pluto.

REFERENCES

Kuiper, Gerard P., editor, *The Atmospheres of the Earth and Planets.* Revised edition. University of Chicago Press, 1951.

Richardson, Robert S., *Exploring Mars.* McGraw-Hill Book Company, New York, 1954.

Whipple, Fred L., *Earth, Moon and Planets.* Harvard University Press, Cambridge, 1941.

9

OTHER FEATURES OF
THE SOLAR SYSTEM

COMETS – METEORS AND METEOR STREAMS – METEOR-
ITES AND METEORITE CRATERS – THE ORIGIN OF THE
SYSTEM

Comets and meteors revolve around the sun in orbits which are
generally more eccentric than are those of the planets. Meteors
are assembled in streams associated with comets. Meteorites, which
seem to be allied more closely with asteroids, come through to the
ground, and very large ones produce meteorite craters. The chapter ends with the problem of the origin of the solar system.

COMETS

A conspicuous comet has a head and a tail. The head consists
of a hazy, globular *coma*, sometimes having a brighter *nucleus* near
its center. The luminous *tail* extends from the coma in the direction away from the sun and may reach far across the heavens. Most
comets, however, are never more than tailless telescopic objects.
Spectacular comets are infrequent; Halley's comet is a famous
example.

9·1. Halley's Comet is named in honor of the English astronomer
Edmund Halley, contemporary of Isaac Newton, who predicted its
return. Halley calculated the orbit of the bright comet of 1682,
and he was impressed by its resemblance to the orbits of comets of
1531 and 1607, which he had also determined from the records
of their observed places in the sky. Deciding that these three were
appearances of the same comet, Halley predicted that it would return to the sun's vicinity "about the year 1758." The comet was
sighted on Christmas night of that year, and reached perihelion
early in 1759. It came around again to perihelion in 1835 and in
1910, its latest appearance.

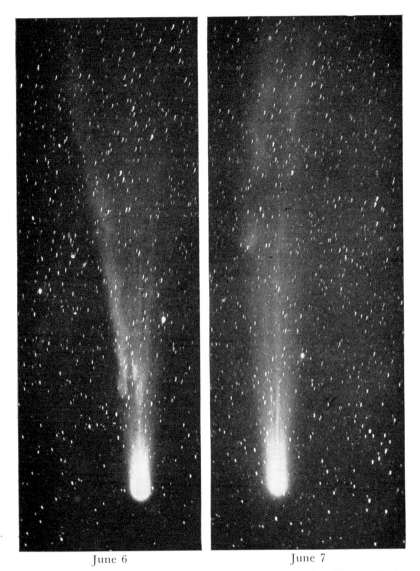

June 6   June 7

FIG. 9·1.   Halley's Comet at Its Latest Appearance, in 1910.   (*Photo-graphed at Lick Observatory*)

As many as 28 returns of this comet are identified from the records, as far back as 240 B.C. It was Halley's comet that appeared in the year 1066 at the time of the Norman conquest of England. The intervals between returns to perihelion have averaged 77 years, varying a few years because of disturbing effects of planets.

Halley's comet is not only the first periodic comet to be recognized, but it is also the only conspicuous one among the many periodic comets known today which return to view oftener than once in a century. It revolves from east to west around the sun

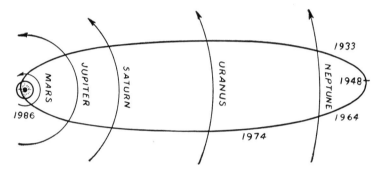

Fig. 9·1A.   Orbit of Halley's Comet.   The comet will return to perihelion in 1986.

in an elongated orbit (Fig. 9·1A) at distances from the sun which range from one half to more than 35 times the earth's distance. Invisible at present near its aphelion which is more remote than Neptune, it will return to perihelion in 1986.

9·2. Discoveries of Comets.   Anyone who searches the heavens persistently with a small telescope, particularly in the west after nightfall or in the east before dawn, may discover a comet. The newly discovered comet is likely to appear as a little fuzzy spot, and its gradual movement among the stars shows presently that it is not a faint star cluster or nebula.

Having discovered a comet, the observer would do well to transmit its position, direction of motion, and brightness to Harvard Observatory, which serves as a receiving and distributing station in this country for such astronomical news. As soon as 3 positions of the comet (its right ascensions and declinations) have been measured at intervals of several days, a preliminary orbit can be calculated.   An examination of the records then shows whether the comet is a new one or the return of one already known.

Five or six comets are picked up each year in the average, and two thirds of them have not been previously recorded.   Fourteen were discovered in each of the years 1947 and 1948, including two that became unusually conspicuous to the naked eye.   Comets are often known by the names of their discoverers; some such as Halley's comet bear the names of astronomers whose investigations entitle them by common consent to the distinction.

Fig. 9·2.   Motion of Mrkos' Comet in 22 Minutes.   (*Photographed, June 23, 1955, by Richard Fink and William Konig, Milwaukee Astronomical Society Observatory*)

9·3. The Orbits of Comets depart from the regularities we have noticed (7·21) in the case of the principal planets.   Most of the orbits are highly eccentric, and many are highly inclined to the ecliptic.   They are roughly divided into two classes.

The more numerous class consists of orbits that are nearly parabolas.   Although all are ellipses, they are so eccentric that they are not readily distinguished from parabolas in the small portions near the sun where the comets are visible.   These orbits extend far beyond the region of the planets, and the periods are so long that only one appearance of each comet is likely to be in the records.   The orbits are often highly inclined to the ecliptic.   About half of these comets revolve from west to east, and the other half from east to west.

The second class consists of definitely elliptical orbits of the "periodic comets," having periods which do not exceed a few hundred years.   The orbits follow more closely the general plan of the solar system. Although most of them are highly eccentric, they are more moderately inclined to the ecliptic. The revolutions of these comets are mainly from west to east; Halley's comet is one of the exceptions.

The Schwassmann-Wachmann comet and Oterma's comet, discovered respectively in 1927 and 1943, are unusual in having orbits not far from circles. The former revolves around the sun once in 16 years entirely between the orbits of Jupiter and Saturn. Normally of the 18th magnitude, it occasionally flares up surprisingly in brightness; in 1946 it became as bright as the 9th magnitude for a few days. The latter revolves in a period of nearly 8 years between the orbits of Mars and Jupiter. Both comets remain visible at their aphelions.

The bright comets of 1668, 1843, 1880, 1882, and 1887, which passed very close to the sun, have orbits that are nearly the same in the sun's vicinity. Presumably they are fragments of a comet that was disrupted at a previous close approach. Indeed, the comet of 1882 was itself observed to break into 4 parts which are expected to return as separate comets between the 25th and 28th centuries.

9·4. Jupiter's Family of Comets. Two dozen or more comets have periods around 6 years, or half of Jupiter's period. All their aphelions are fairly close to Jupiter's orbit, and the comets can

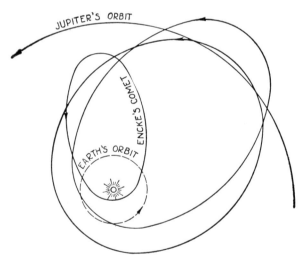

Fig. 9·4. Orbits of Three Comets of Jupiter's Family. Encke's comet has the smallest orbit of all.

make even closer approaches to the planet as they cross the ecliptic. They constitute *Jupiter's family of comets.*

It seems probable that Jupiter has assembled its family selectively from comets passing by in originally larger orbits. At successive encounters the planet's attraction has made these orbits smaller and smaller until the comets have become members of the family. The membership is unstable; further approaches of any one of these comets to the planet may occur in such a way that the orbit is enlarged, and the comet ceases to belong to the family. Three members of the family have been especially interesting.

Encke's comet has the smallest orbit and the shortest period of any known comet. Its aphelion point is a whole astronomical unit inside Jupiter's orbit, having gradually drawn in by that amount from its original place. Like other members of the family, Encke's comet never becomes at best more than faintly visible to the naked eye.

Biela's comet, having a period of $6\frac{1}{2}$ years, came to an end in a spectacular way. At its return in 1846 it was divided into two separate comets traveling side by side, and at the next return the separation had increased to $1\frac{1}{2}$ million miles. The comet was never seen again; but a stream of meteors, the Bielids or Andromedids, gave fine showers when it collided with the earth in 1872 and 1885. The Giacobini-Zinner comet, having a similar period, is associated with a stream which in 1933 and 1946 provided the finest meteor showers of recent times.

9·5. The Nature of a Comet. The middle of a comet's head is a mixture of frozen substances, chiefly methane, ammonia, and water, according to F. L. Whipple, having meteoric material embedded in it. The meteoric particles are stony and metallic, composed of such elements as iron, nickel, magnesium, silicon, and sodium. In this view the nucleus of the average comet does not exceed a mile or two in diameter. The mass of the entire comet is too small to disturb appreciably the motions of planets and satellites at close approaches, whereas the comet's orbit may be greatly altered.

Some of the ices evaporate at each approach of the comet to the sun. The gases issue explosively into the coma, carrying the solid fragments with them. The lighter material is then swept out from the coma through the tail by the pressure of sunlight and is dispersed into space in the direction opposite the sun. As the surface of ices that remain becomes increasingly gritty, the evaporation is retarded, so that the comet may return to the sun many times before its material is completely dissipated. The stony and metallic particles become a stream of meteors traveling in the comet's orbit.

FIG. 9·5.   Bright Comet of 1947.   (*Photographed by E. J. Casal, Montevideo Astronomical Observatory*)

The light of a comet is largely luminescence stimulated by the sunlight. Bright bands in its spectrum are identified with various diatomic combinations of carbon, nitrogen, hydrogen, and oxygen, such as cyanogen. A faint replica of the dark-line solar spectrum shows that a comèt shines partly by reflected sunlight. Bright lines of sodium, iron, and other metals appear when the comet is sufficiently heated by close approach to the sun.

METEORS AND METEOR STREAMS

The bright streaks of "shooting stars" across the starlit sky inform us of the flight of meteors through the air. *Meteors* are stony and metallic particles revolving around the sun either as individuals or in streams. Too small to be separately visible by reflected sunlight, they are seen only when they chance to plunge into our atmosphere. Impacts with the air molecules then heat them intensely. In the short intervals while they are being consumed, the meteors produce luminous *trails,* mainly between 60 and 40 miles from the ground. The brighter ones sometimes leave *trains,* streaks of phosphorescent gases which persist for a while after the meteors themselves have vanished.

9·6. The Frequency of Meteor Trails varies with the time of night. Twice as many trails are likely to be seen in an hour's watch before dawn as in the same interval after nightfall. In the morning we are on the forward side of the earth in its revolution around the sun, where we are most exposed to the incoming meteors. In the evening we are in the rear and are partly protected. The appearance of the trails also varies through the night. The morning meteors with which we collide head-on may enter the atmosphere as fast as 45 miles a second; they are heated so intensely that their trails are of shorter duration. The evening meteors which overtake us may arrive with speeds less than 10 miles a second; they are accordingly less intensely heated, so that their trails may be of greater length.

When no unusual displays of meteors are occurring, it has been estimated that a single observer can see an average of 10 meteor trails in the course of an hour on a clear, moonless night. Because the view of one person is limited to the region of the atmosphere over a hundred thousandth of the earth's surface, the trails bright enough to be visible to the unaided eye would accordingly appear at the rate of a million an hour over the entire earth; and the number visible with the telescope is much greater. Even where they are gathered into streams, however, the meteors are so widely separated in space that they are not expected to be a major hazard in any future interplanetary navigation.

9·7. Meteors Are Members of the Solar System. Where the same meteor trail is observed from two stations several miles apart, it

FIG. 9·6. Trail of a Brilliant Meteor. The meteor was brighter than the planet Venus. The left end of the trail is a little way south of Capella. The middle of the trail is nearly halfway between Algol and the Pleiades, and the right end is between Triangulum and the triangle of Aries. The Hyades appear in the lower left corner. (*Photographed at the Agassiz Station, Harvard Observatory*)

is possible to determine the velocity of the meteor and from this its orbit around the sun. Photographs with wide-angle cameras at two Harvard Observatory stations in New Mexico are providing the necessary data for many bright meteors. The cameras are directed toward the same place 50 miles above the ground, to record any bright meteor that enters the trap. They have rotating shutters to interrupt the trail at regular intervals, so as to facilitate the timing. All the individual meteors so observed have elliptical orbits similar to those of comets (9·3). Like the meteors in streams, they belong to the solar system and have not come in from outside the system.

The meteor's speed by itself is enough to determine the status of the meteor in this respect. If the speed, with allowance for the motion and attraction of the earth, is less than 26 miles a second—the velocity of escape from the sun at the earth's distance—the meteor was moving in a closed orbit around the sun. P. M. Millman and D. W. R. McKinley at Ottawa have determined the speeds of more than 10,000 meteors as faint as the 8th visual magnitude from their records of radio beams returned from the trails. Not one of these is certainly as great as the velocity of escape. Thus the fainter meteors as well as the brighter ones are members of the solar system.

9·8. Meteor Streams and Showers. Multitudes of meteors revolving together constitute a *meteor swarm*. Where the swarm is considerably strung out along its orbit, as is generally the case, it is also a *meteor stream*. *Sporadic meteors* are individuals which do not belong to a recognized stream. When a meteor stream crosses our orbit and finds the earth at the intersection, there is a *meteor shower*.

The trails of the meteors in a shower are directed away from a small area in the sky, the center of which is the *radiant* of the shower. The members of a stream have parallel paths, so that their bright trails through the air are parallel, except as the directions taken by individuals may be altered slightly by resistance of the air. These trails spread out over

FIG. 9·8. The Radiant of a Meteor Shower.

the sky (Fig. 9·8) just as the parallel rails of a track seem to diverge from a point in the distance. Showers of meteors and the streams that produce them are named from the positions of their radiants at the heights of the displays. Thus the trails of the Perseid meteors appear to diverge from their radiant in the constellation Perseus. The place of the radiant in the sky drifts from day to day during the progress of the shower as the earth changes the direction of its revolution.

The position of the radiant of a particular shower and the speed with which the meteors enter the air, after allowance is made for the earth's motion at that time, permit the calculation of the orbit of the stream around the sun. Several instances are known where a comet and a meteor stream have nearly identical orbits. An interesting case is the association of Halley's comet with the Eta Aquarid and the Orionid showers, which occur in May and October, respectively; these come from the same stream which crosses the earth's orbit twice.

Observers at the Jodrell Bank Station of the University of Manchester in England have made surveys of meteor activity in the daytime by means of radio echoes from the trails. They have not only determined radiants of showers conforming closely to those previously studied at night, but have also discovered radiants observable only in the daytime.

9·9. Noteworthy Showers of Meteors. In the course of a year the earth crosses the orbits of many meteor streams. Extended streams may give showers every year when they pass the intersections. Shorter streams produce showers at longer intervals when they and the earth arrive together at the crossings. Only infrequently have the showers been conspicuous enough to attract the attention of people who were not watching for them.

The chief showers in Table 9·I are from a list prepared by Millman. The positions of their radiants are given so that they may be located in the star maps. They include 3 daytime showers recorded by the English observers. The Perseids are the most conspicuous of the evening showers that appear every year. The Orionids and Geminids are also among the most faithful of the annual showers. The Leonids, which appear at intervals of about 33 years, gave remarkable displays in 1833 and 1866-67, but have not been spectacular in later returns. The Delta Aquarid stream is unique in its close approaches to the sun and Jupiter; its period of revolution is 4.2 years, the eccentricity of the orbit is 0.98, and the perihelion distance is less than 6 million miles.

The Giacobinids have been the most impressive in recent years. This stream revolves around the sun in the orbit of the Giacobini-Zinner comet, a member of Jupiter's family having a period of 6½ years. It gave a fine shower in western Europe in 1933 and another in America on the evening of October 9, 1946 (Fig. 9·9). At the height of the latter display a single observer counted as many as 100 trails a minute spreading from the head of Draco in a bright moonlit sky. An unexpected display of these meteors was recorded

FIG. 9·9. Giacobinid Meteors During the Shower of October 9, 1946. The camera was stationary during the 12-minute exposure, while the stars described small arcs of their daily circles around the pole. The meteor trails are straight, and diverge from the radiant in Draco. (*Photographed by Kenneth Spain, Vanderbilt University*)

by the English observers for 2 hours on the afternoon of October 9, 1952. Evidently an advance contingent of the stream was encountered by the earth half a year before the associated comet was scheduled to reach the vicinity of our orbit.

9·10. The Zodiacal Light. The triangular glow of the *zodiacal light* can be seen extending up from the west horizon after night-

TABLE 9·1.   NOTEWORTHY METEOR SHOWERS

| Shower | Maximum Display | Radiant at Max. | | Associated Comet |
		R.A.	Decl.	
Quadrantids	Jan. 3	15^h 24^m	$+50°$	
Lyrids	Apr. 21	18 12	$+34$	1861 I
Eta Aquarids	May 4	22 24	0	Halley
* Zeta Perseids	June 8	4 8	$+24$	Encke
* Arietids	June 8	2 56	$+23$	Encke
Draconids	June 28	14 40	$+58$	Pons-Winnecke
* Beta Taurids	June 29	5 44	$+18$	Encke
Delta Aquarids	July 30	22 40	-15	
Perseids	Aug. 11	3 4	$+57$	1862 III
Giacobinids	Oct. 9	17 28	$+54$	Giacobini-Zinner
Orionids	Oct. 20	6 20	$+15$	Halley
Taurids	Oct. 31	3 36	$+17$	Encke
Leonids	Nov. 16	10 8	$+22$	1866 I
Geminids	Dec. 13	7 32	$+32$	

* Shower in daytime.

FIG. 9·10. The Zodiacal Light. It is most conspicuous in the evening in middle northern latitudes around the beginning of spring, because the ecliptic is then most nearly vertical.

fall in the spring, and in the east before dawn in the autumn in our northern latitudes. Broadest and brightest near the horizon, it tapers upward, leaning toward the south. The glow is symmetrical with the ecliptic and is, accordingly, most conspicuous when the ecliptic is most nearly vertical.

Near the equator, where the ecliptic is always more nearly perpendicular to the horizon, the zodiacal light can be observed all year around. Here it is said to have been seen as a faint, narrow band circling the sky. The light is sunlight reflected by meteoric material and by dust grains of uncertain origin, which form a ring around the sun in the plane of the earth's orbit. Near the sun it is identified by a replica of sunlight in the spectrum of the outer corona.

Opposite the sun the zodiacal glow brightens a little and widens into the *gegenschein,* or *counterglow,* which is faintly visible to the naked eye in the best conditions as an oval spot 10° to 15° long. This spot is recorded effectively with the photoelectric cell, and it shows clearly in photographs with some of the new wide-angle cameras.

METEORITES AND METEORITE CRATERS

9·11. Stones from the Sky. Near noon one day in November, 1492, a month after Columbus first set foot in the New World, a number of stones came down in a field near Ensisheim, Alsace. The largest one, weighing 260 pounds, was placed in a church in that town; a smaller one is exhibited in the Chicago Natural History Museum. This is the oldest observed fall of meteorites on record, of which samples are still preserved.

The idea that stones fall from the sky goes back to very early times. There were stones preserved in some of the ancient temples, which were doubtless of celestial origin; these "stones from heaven" were objects of veneration. In later times, however, all reports of stones falling from the sky came to be regarded with suspicion. The stones seemed to choose remote places where there were no reliable observers. Doubtless, too, the accounts of terrified and perhaps highly superstitious spectators of some of the falls were so greatly exaggerated that no one could believe them.

Finally, in April, 1803, a shower of two or three thousand stones fell at L'Aigle, France, and many people saw it. Yet the news spread so slowly that when 300 pounds of meteorites came down near Weston, Connecticut, in December, 1807, the first observed fall on record in the United States, most people were reluctant to believe the report.

9·12. Falls of Meteorites. *Meteorites* are masses of stony or metallic material, and occasionally of both, which survive their flights through the air and fall to the ground. They arrive either singly or in many pieces. Several thousand individuals have come down in one fall, and in such cases are likely to be distributed over an elliptical area having its major axis several miles long in the direction of the flight. Although meteors are frequently associated with comets, many meteorites are believed to be fragments of asteroids (8·16).

Their speeds greatly reduced by air resistance, most meteorites cool before they reach the ground. In their brief flights through the air the heat has not gone far into their cold interiors, and the melted material has been swept away from their surfaces. They are usually cool enough to handle comfortably when they are picked up immediately after landing, and they do not penetrate far into the ground. Larger meteorites are less impeded by the air. Some enormous ones have struck at such high speeds that they have blasted out great craters in the earth (9·15).

9·13. The Meteorites Themselves are essentially of two kinds, the stones and the irons. There are gradations between them from stones containing flecks of nickel-iron to sponges of metal with stony fillings. Inside their varnish-like crusts the *stony meteorites* are often grayish, having a characteristic granular structure that serves to establish their celestial origin. The rounded granules are crystalline, chiefly silicates similar to those in igneous rocks. The largest known example, weighing at least a ton, fell on February 18, 1948, in Furnas County, Nebraska (Fig. 9·13). It is the largest meteorite of either kind where the fall was observed.

Iron meteorites are silvery under their blackened exteriors. They are composed mainly of alloys of iron and nickel, which are affected by acids in various degrees. Where they occur in crystal forms, a characteristic pattern of intersecting bands parallel to the faces of an octahedron may be etched with dilute acid on a polished section.

Individuals from nearly 1600 falls have been recovered. They

FIG. 9·13. The Furnas County, Nebraska, Meteorite. (*Official photograph of the Institute of Meteoritics, University of New Mexico*)

are generally named after the locality in which they were found; examples are the Canyon Diablo, Arizona, meteorites and the Willamette, Oregon, meteorite. Collections are exhibited in the Chicago Natural History Museum, the American Museum of Natural History, New York, and many other places.

9·14. The Great Iron Meteorites. About 35 individual meteorites weighing more than a ton are listed by F. C. Leonard of the University of California at Los Angeles. With the exceptions of the Furnas County stone and two stony irons, all are of nickel-iron and their falls were not observed. The two largest are the Hoba West meteorite and the "Ahnighito" meteorite.

The Hoba West meteorite lies partly buried in the ground in the Grootfontein district, Southwest Africa; its rectangular upper surface measures 9×10 feet. Its weight is unknown. The Ahnighito meteorite is the largest of four which the explorer R. E. Peary found near Cape York, Greenland, in 1894. It measures about $11 \times 6 \times 7$ feet, and weighs a little more than 34 tons

FIG. 9·14.   The Hoba West Meteorite.   (*Photographed by W. J. Luyten*)

FIG. 9·14A.   The Ahnighito Meteorite.   (*Courtesy of the American Museum of Natural History, New York*)

(68,085 pounds). This meteorite is exhibited in the Hayden Planetarium in New York City.

The Willamette meteorite, also in the Hayden Planetarium, weighs 15 tons. The largest meteorite found in the United States, this cone-shaped mass of nickel-iron was discovered, in 1902, some 10 miles south of Portland, Oregon. It evidently kept the same orientation in its flight and was fashioned by the rush of hot air. Some meteorites turned over and over as they fell, and were rounded.

Three great iron meteorites, each weighing more than 10 tons, were found in Mexico. They are the Bacubirito (29 tons), the Chupaderos (21 tons, in two pieces that fit together), and the Morito (11 tons). The last two may be seen in the School of Mines in Mexico City.

9·15. Two Siberian Falls of large meteorites in the present century have attracted attention. The first occurred on June 30, 1908, in a densely forested region of north central Siberia, completely devastating an area 20 or 30 miles in radius. The trees were felled without bark or branches and with their tops pointing away from the center of the area. Many craters were formed near the center, the largest one 150 feet in diameter. Not a trace has been found of the Tunguska meteorite itself, although its mass is estimated to have exceeded a million tons.

The second fall occurred on February 12, 1947, on western spurs of the Sikhorte-Alin mountain range near the Pacific Coast in southeastern Siberia. An object estimated to have had a mass of 1000 tons broke into many pieces before the fall and came down as an "iron rain" over a considerable area. The separate pieces produced a field of 200 small holes and larger craters, the largest one 90 feet in diameter. The field was strewn with many tons of meteoritic material.

9·16. Meteorite Crater in Arizona is a circular depression 4200 feet across and 570 feet deep. Its rim, which rises 130 feet above the surrounding plain, is composed of debris thrown out of the pit, from fine rock dust to blocks of limestone and sandstone weighing up to 7000 tons apiece.

This crater, near Canyon Diablo in northeastern Arizona, is a scar left by the fall of a great meteorite probably not less than 50,000 years ago. The meteorite is estimated at the minimum to have had a diameter of 250 feet and a weight of a million tons. So massive that it was only slightly retarded by the air, it struck the earth a mighty blow. The intense heat of the collision partly fused the meteorite and the rocks in contact with it; the gases expanded explosively, scattering what was left of the meteorite over the surrounding country and blasting out the crater. Several tons of meteoritic iron have been picked up within a radius of 6 miles around the crater.

FIG. 9·16.   Meteorite Crater in Arizona.   A great scar in the desert 20 miles west of Winslow, Arizona. (*Photographed by Clyde Fisher*)

Other craters and groups of craters in various parts of the world are recognized to be of meteoritic origin. The Wolf Creek crater in West Australia, having a diameter of 2800 feet at the bottom and a depth of 160 feet, is second in size. Among the very large circular depressions suspected of having meteoritic origin, but not as yet generally accepted as such, are the Ungava crater in northern Quebec, the Brent and Holleford craters in Ontario, and the Talemzane crater in southern Algeria.

THE ORIGIN OF THE SYSTEM

9·17. The Nature of the Problem.   Theories of the origin of the solar system are related to the problem of the beginning of the sun itself, and of the birth of the stars in general. According to current ideas, which we examine later (15·9), the stars evolved from contracting masses of cosmic dust and gas. We inquire now as to how a planetary system could have formed around a primitive star. Our question is specifically about the history of the solar system, because this is the only known system of its kind. How did the earth and its neighbors originate when the sun was being born? A successful answer must evidently conform to the rules of physics and must end with the system as it is known today.

The larger planets, we have seen, revolve around the sun from west to east in nearly circular orbits which are all in nearly the same plane; they generally rotate in this direction as well, with their equators moderately inclined to this plane. The larger satellites revolve around their planets and rotate on their axes in a similar manner. The less massive members of the system—the smaller satellites, the asteroids, and the comets and meteor streams —follow these regularities less faithfully, a fact which must also be accounted for.

Theories of the origin of the solar system have been devised during the past two centuries. Our knowledge of the system has increased in the meantime; the simpler accounts of earlier times do not completely represent the more complex system we recognize today. As prominent examples of the earliest and latest theories of its development, we consider the nebular hypothesis of Laplace and the protoplanet hypothesis of Kuiper.

9·18. The Nebular Hypothesis of the origin of the solar system was presented in 1796 by the French mathematician Laplace in his popular book *The System of the World*. It was the most famous although not the first of the early theories. The philosopher Kant had thought of a nebular origin of the system as early as 1755.

Laplace's account begins with a gaseous envelope surrounding the primitive sun and in slow rotation around it from west to east. As the envelope contracted toward the center, it rotated faster and accordingly bulged more at its equator. At length a critical stage was reached at which the rotation became fast enough to make the centrifugal effect at the equator as great as the attraction toward the center. The equatorial ring was then abandoned by the contracting envelope. Smaller gaseous rings were later left behind as often as the critical stage was repeated. Each ring gradually assembled (Fig. 9·18) into a gaseous globe having its circular orbit around the sun the same as the ring from which it was formed. Most of the globes developed satellites in a similar manner as they condensed into planets. The globe at the center, containing most of the original material of the system, became the sun.

This process was intended to produce a system having the orderly motions of its principal members, which were the only ones recog-

Fig. 9·18.   Nebular Hypothesis of Laplace.   Gaseous rings abandoned by a contracting, rotating solar nebula assembled to form the planets.   (*Courtesy of* Scientific American)

nized at the time. The rings of Saturn seemed to have remained to verify the correctness of the theory.

9·19. Value of the Nebular Hypothesis.   Because of its simplicity and the authority of Laplace in the mechanics of the solar system, the nebular hypothesis held a leading place among the scientific theories during the 19th century. It encouraged allied sciences to formulate accounts of orderly development in their fields. As its deficiencies were gradually recognized, they gave warning of situations to be avoided in later theories. These are chiefly as follows:

1. The tendency of gases to disperse would scarcely permit the rings to assemble into planets. If they did somehow so assemble, the planets would be more likely to rotate from east to west, as Laplace himself was aware.

2. The system developed by the hypothesis would have been unlike the present solar system in the total amount and distribution of *angular momentum;* this for each member is the product

of its mass, the square of its distance from the center of revolution, or the axis of rotation, and the rate of its angular motion around the center. A rule of mechanics states that the sum of these products for all members of an isolated system must always remain the same. Here we see why the envelope around the sun rotated faster as it contracted. Yet when Neptune was formed by the theory, the total had to be 200 times as great as the present total. In addition, the hypothesis requires that the greater part of the spin should now appear in the sun's rotation, where only 2 per cent is actually found.

3. Many exceptions have been discovered since Laplace's time to the regularities his hypothesis tried to represent. Moreover, the compositions of the planets and their atmospheres were not considered because they were quite unknown at that early time.

9·20. The Protoplanet Hypothesis is proposed by G. P. Kuiper of the Yerkes and McDonald Observatories. Like the early one it begins with a *solar nebula*, a flattened gaseous envelope rotating around the primitive sun. The nebula was composed like the sun itself mainly of hydrogen and helium with small percentages of heavier elements; and it contained from 5 to 10 per cent as much material as there was in the sun. Here the new theory differs sharply from the early one. The mass was so great that, with further contraction and flattening, the nebula became unstable under its own attraction and broke into large clouds of gas, the *protoplanets*.

The protoplanets were more massive where the nebula was denser, and they appeared at distances from the sun conforming to Bode's law (7·19), as the theory requires.

9·21. The Planets Formed. The heavier material of the protoplanets settled gradually to form solid cores. The lighter material, mainly hydrogen and helium, formed extensive atmospheres around the cores. At first, the primitive planets contained excessive amounts of material. The major planets had from 10 to 100 times their present masses. The proto-earth was 1000 times as massive as the present earth.

Meanwhile the sun, which was large and cold at its surface when the nebula was left behind, had become smaller and very hot. Its powerful radiations drove the remnants of the nebula and much of the protoplanets' atmospheres out of the system, just as the tails of comets are repelled from the sun today. Jupiter and Saturn with their strong attractions were able to retain a considerable part of their hydrogen. Uranus and Neptune retained more limited amounts. The inner planets were stripped to little more than their cores.

Thus we have the principal planets revolving from west to east, the original direction of rotation of the nebula, in orbits that are nearly circles and nearly in the plane of the flattened nebula's equator. At the start these planets were forced by solar tides raised in them to rotate from west to east in the same periods as those of their revolutions around the sun. Later, as they contracted further, all except Mercury slipped away from the tidal brakes and began to rotate in shorter periods but in the same direction.

9·22. The Satellites, as explained by Kuiper's theory, developed by a repetition of the planet-forming process. Each protoplanet of sufficient mass left behind in its contraction a flat disk of gas like a small-scale solar nebula rotating around it. Protosatellites were formed by the breaking up of each nebula. Influenced by the rotations of their planets, many of the resulting satellites conform to the regularities of the planets themselves. Relatively near the planets, these "regular" satellites have never succeeded in slipping away from the tide brakes. Thus they rotate in the same periods in which they revolve around their primaries. In keeping one face toward the earth, the moon is an example.

Although the moon in its motions is one of the "regular" satellites, it is unique among all the satellites in its near equality in mass with its primary. The earth and moon are more like a double planet and may have grown up together out of the solar nebula.

A dozen satellites are "irregular." Their orbits are more inclined to the ecliptic or are more eccentric, or both, than are the others. Half of them revolve from west to east and half from east to west. Kuiper explains that these and others withdrew from the control of their planets of diminishing masses and began to move independently in orbits like those of their planets. The 12 irregular satellites were later recaptured with the aid of the nebulae remaining around the planets. Other escaped satellites were not recaptured, but eventually returned close enough to be diverted into very different orbits. The suggestion is made that Hidalgo and the Trojan asteroids were originally satellites of Jupiter, and that Pluto may have belonged formerly to Neptune.

9·23. Asteroids and Comets. Between the distances of Mars and Jupiter from the sun there was not enough material in the solar nebula to form a large protoplanet. Instead, the material assembled into smaller bodies, the asteroids. At least two of the larger asteroids eventually collided and were shattered into many fragments having a variety of orbits. Some of these are asteroids which pass within the earth's orbit. Others are the meteorites.

Comets were formed, according to the theory, in the outer fringe of the solar nebula at something like Pluto's distance from the sun. About a mile in diameter, they numbered many million million. They were composed mainly of snows of water, methane, and ammonia, having stony and metallic grains embedded in them. The youthful comets were scattered by attractions of the planets inward and also outward as far as 100,000 times the earth's distance from the sun. Many comets have disintegrated into streams of meteors.

QUESTIONS ON CHAPTER 9

1. Give two reasons why Halley's comet is noteworthy. Name 3 other comets, and mention an interesting feature of each.

2. What is characteristic of the orbits of Jupiter's family of comets?

3. Describe and explain the changes in the appearance of some comets as they approach the sun.

4. Account for the association of meteor streams and comets. State one such association.

5. Explain the increasing frequency of the trails of sporadic meteors during the course of the night.

6. What is the evidence that meteors are members of the solar system and have not come in from outside it?

7. Explain the radiant of a meteor shower. How are the separate showers named? Give an example.

8. What times of year are the most favorable for viewing the zodiacal light in middle northern latitudes? Explain.

9. Distinguish between the two kinds of meteorites. Where is a very large meteorite to be seen?

10. Describe the nebular hypothesis of Laplace. Mention some features of the solar system which seem inconsistent with this hypothesis.

11. Discuss the origin of planets and satellites according to the protoplanet hypothesis of Kuiper.

12. Explain that the asteroids and satellites which do not conform to the regularities of the system may not be inconsistent with the protoplanet hypothesis.

REFERENCES

Leonard, Frederick C., *A Classification Catalog of the Meteoritic Falls of the World.* University of California Press, 1956.
Lovell, A. C. B., *Meteor Astronomy.* Oxford University Press, 1954.
Watson, Fletcher G., *Between the Planets.* Revised edition. Harvard University Press, Cambridge, 1956.

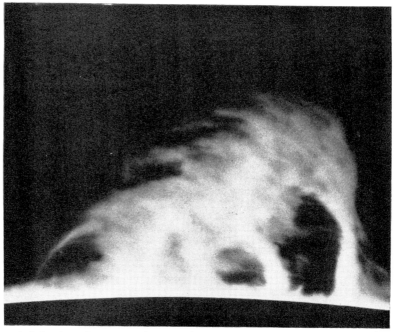

A Solar Prominence. *(Photographed by R. B. Dunn with the 15-inch Camera, Sacramento Peak Observatory)*

10

THE SUN WITH ITS SPOTS

THE PHOTOSPHERE; SUNSPOTS – THE SUN'S ATMOS-
PHERE – ECLIPSES OF THE SUN; THE CORONA

The sun is the only star near enough to us for its features to be examined in detail. Our account of the sun is accordingly associated both with the preceding descriptions of the solar system and with those of the stars in the following chapters.

10·1. Observing the Sun. The sun is too bright to be safely observed on a clear day without protection of the eye from its glare. Viewed through a dark glass it appears as a disk about as large as the full moon, and as a perfectly blank disk generally to the eye alone. With the telescope the disk is enlarged and its features are revealed. It would be unwise, of course, to look directly through the telescope at the sun without a device for diverting most of the light and heat which it concentrates at its focus. A convenient procedure is to let the telescope project the image on a smooth cardboard screen held back of the eyepiece. In this way many people can observe at the same time.

The astronomers' studies of the sun's surface and its surroundings are generally photographic. Fixed telescopes, into which the sunlight is directed by moving mirrors, permit the use of long-focus objectives which form large images of the sun. The longest of these is the 150-foot tower telescope of the Mount Wilson Observatory. Among the newer ones are the 50-foot and 70-foot towers of the McMath-Hulbert Observatory near Pontiac, Michigan. Special devices are employed in studies of the exterior features of the sun, which were formerly reserved for the rare moments of total solar eclipse. Radio telescopes are also recording activities of the sun.

10·2. The Structure of the Sun. In the ordinary view the sun is a gaseous globe 864,000 miles in diameter, or 109 times the earth's

Fig. 10·1. The McMath-Hulbert Observatory of the University of Michigan.

diameter. The sun is therefore 1⅓ million times as large as the earth; and since its mass is a third of a million times as great, it averages one fourth the earth's density, or 1.4 times the density of water. Its temperature increases from 10,000° F at its lowest visible level to many million degrees at the center.

The *photosphere,* the visible surface, is mottled with brighter granulations and faculae and is often marked with darker sunspots. The gases above the photosphere constitute the *sun's atmosphere.* The *chromosphere,* extending to the height of several thousand miles, is so named because of its color, which is imparted chiefly by the red glow of its hydrogen. It is normally the region where the spectacular solar flares are observed. The red *prominences* appear above the chromosphere, at times attaining heights of many hundred thousand miles. They are visible during total solar eclipses, and together with the inner corona are studied effectively with special devices at other times. The *corona,* the outermost solar envelope, appears as a filmy halo of intricate structure.

THE PHOTOSPHERE; SUNSPOTS

10·3. The Photosphere is as far into the sun as we can see. Here, where the pressure is only a hundredth of our air pressure at sea level, the gas becomes opaque. From this level the sunlight emerges, distributing energy equivalent to 5×10^{23} horsepower to light and heat the members of the planetary system. Each square yard contributes 70,000 horsepower. The sun has been pouring out energy at this great rate for at least a billion years, during all the geological ages, and is expected to continue to do so for several billion years in the future.

The temperature of the photosphere averages 5750° K, or about 10,000° F. It is somewhat higher near the center of the disk, where we look in directly, and is reduced to 8000° F near the edge, where our slanting view is obstructed at higher and cooler levels. Thus the sunlight from the edge is less bright and redder than from the center of the disk.

Through the telescope the photosphere presents a mottled appearance. Bright *granules* cover a third of the surface; averaging 700 miles in diameter, they are hotter spots in the seething furnace formed by gases coming from below. Each granule lasts only a few minutes before it cools to the temperature of its surroundings. Larger bright spots, the *faculae,* are often conspicuous against the less luminous background near the edge of the disk. Dark spots on the sun have held the greater interest.

10·4. Sunspots in Groups. *Sunspots* appear dark in contrast with the brighter general surface of the sun. They range in size from specks scarcely distinguishable from the spaces between the bright granules to the great spots visible without the telescope. They usually consist of two distinct parts: the *umbra,* the inner, darker part which is often divided; and the lighter *penumbra* around it.

Sunspots occur in groups; where a single spot is seen, it is likely

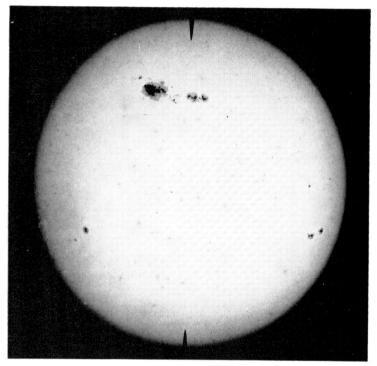

Fig. 10·3. The Sun, February 4, 1946. An exceptionally large group of sunspots appears above the center of the disk. (*Photographed at Mount Wilson Observatory*)

to be a survivor of a group. A normal group develops in about a week and then begins to decline. Two *principal spots* grow larger than the others which form mostly between them. The *preceding spot* in the direction of the sun's rotation frequently becomes the larger of the two. The *following spot* is the largest of the spots in the rear. It subdivides and vanishes along with the smaller spots, until only the preceding spot is left to shrink and disappear. There are exceptions to this pattern.

One of the largest groups ever recorded (Fig. 10·3) appeared early in 1946 and lasted more than 3 months, an exceptionally long duration. The group attained the length of 200,000 miles and the area of 5700 million square miles. Its largest spot, in this case the following spot, measured 90,000 by 60,000 miles. A slightly larger group (Fig. 10·5) appeared in 1947.

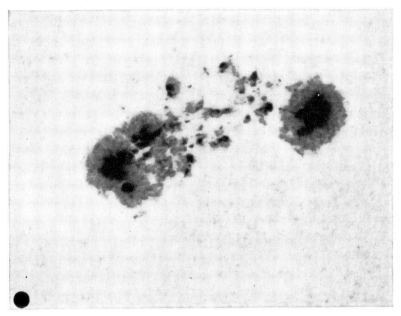

FIG. 10·4. A Large Sunspot Group. The direction of the sun's rotation is toward the right. The black disk in the corner represents the relative size of the earth. (*Photographed at Mount Wilson Observatory*)

10·5. The Sun's Rotation is shown by the gradual movement of sunspots across its disk. The spots come into view at the eastern edge, disappear two weeks later at the western edge if they last that long, and may reappear at the eastern edge after another two weeks. Because the sun's equator is inclined 7° to the plane of the earth's orbit, the paths of the spots across the disk are generally curved; the curve is greatest early in March, when the sun's south pole is toward us, and again early in September, when its north pole is toward us. The axis of the sun's rotation is directed toward a point in the heavens midway between Polaris and Vega.

Unlike the earth which rotates in the same period in all latitudes, the rotation period of the gaseous sun is longer as the distance from its equator is greater. Spots near the equator, which survive long enough, go completely around in 25 days, although they seem to us to require 4 weeks, because the earth has revolved partway around the sun in the meantime. At 35° from the equator, beyond which the sunspots are rarely seen, the true period is 27 days. In

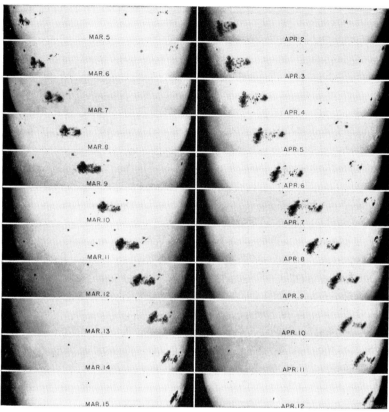

Fig. 10·5. Sunspots Show the Sun's Rotation. The large group of 1947 lasted for more than 3 months. (*Photographs by Mount Wilson and Palomar Observatories*)

solar latitude 75° the Doppler effect in the spectra of the approaching and receding edges shows that the period has increased to 35 days.

10·6. The Sunspot Number Cycle. In some years the sun's disk is seldom free from spots, whereas in other years it may remain unspotted for several days in succession. Sunspot groups vary in number in a roughly periodic manner, a variation first announced in 1843 by Schwabe, an amateur astronomer in Germany. The intervals between the times of maximum spottedness vary from 9 to 14 years, averaging 11.1 years, and the numbers of groups at the different maxima are not the same. The rise to maximum is faster than the decline.

The latest maximum occurred about 1948, the highest since 1778; the greatest number of groups was reported in 1947, but a

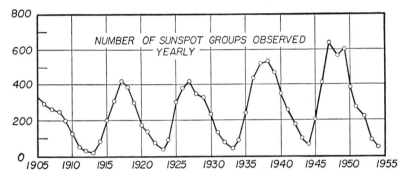

FIG. 10·6. The Sunspot Number Cycle. The point for each year represents the number of groups observed during the year. The curve shows the roughly periodic variation in the numbers. (*From data by Seth B. Nicholson, Mount Wilson Observatory*)

number nearly as great was recorded in 1949. The following minimum was reached in 1954. The next maximum would be expected in 1958.

10·7. The Shifting Sunspot Zones. Sunspots are confined mainly between latitudes 5° and 30° north and south of the sun's equator; only one has as yet been reported beyond 45°. At any particular time they are likely to appear in two rather narrow zones equidistant from the equator. As spots vanish and others appear, the zones shift toward the equator in cycles that parallel the sunspot number cycles.

Two or three years before sunspot minimum, small spots break out around latitudes 30°. Thereafter the two zones of spot activity draw in toward the equator, and when the next minimum is reached, a few surviving members of the fading cycle are seen around latitudes 5°. Meanwhile some spots of the new cycle have already become visible in the higher latitudes. Thus at the mini-

mum of 1954 the Mount Wilson observers recorded 15 groups near
the equator and 31 groups of the new cycle.

The cause of the one-way shifting of the spot zones, like the
cause of the number cycle and indeed of the spots themselves, is
not as yet known. Nor is it clearly understood why sunspots are
magnetic, and why their magnetism reverses with the beginning of
each new cycle.

10·8. Sunspots Are Magnetic. When the image of a sunspot is
focused on the slit of a spectroscope, the dark lines of the solar
spectrum appear split into two or more parts (Fig. 10·8). This

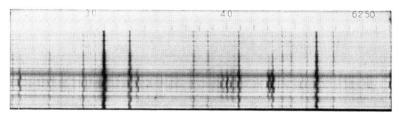

Fig. 10·8. Zeeman Effect in the Sunspot Spectrum. The slight splitting
of the dark lines is emphasized by a device which alternately suppresses
the violet and red components of the lines. Thus the lines have a zigzag
appearance. (*Photographed at Mount Wilson Observatory*)

Zeeman effect, known by the name of the Dutch physicist who discovered it in the laboratory, in 1896, is the splitting of the spectrum
lines where the source of the light is in the field of a strong magnet.
The effect in the sunspot spectrum shows that the spot is magnetic
and also reveals its *polarity*—whether the positive or negative pole
of the magnet is toward us.

Most sunspot groups are *bipolar;* their two principal spots have
opposite polarities which conform to the following rule: During a
particular cycle the preceding spots in the sun's northern hemisphere have their positive poles toward us, and the following spots
their negative poles. In the southern hemisphere the preceding
spots present their negative magnetic poles, and the following spots
their positive poles.

A remarkable feature of sunspot magnetism is the complete reversal of the pattern with the appearance of the groups of the next
cycle (Fig. 10·8A). The preceding spots in the northern hemisphere
now present their negative poles, and so on. First reported by

Mount Wilson astronomers around the sunspot minimum of 1913, this reversal of polarities has been observed at each succeeding minimum.

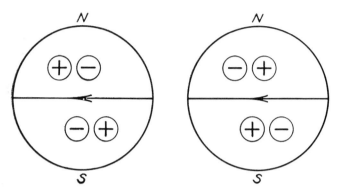

Fig. 10·8A.   Reversal of Polarities of Sunspots with the Beginning of a New Cycle.   The circles represent preceding and following spots of groups in the two hemispheres.

Sunspots are certainly refrigeration projects on a vast scale, and accordingly appear darker than the rest of the sun's surface.   Areas of the surface often much larger than the earth are kept for days far below the temperature of their surroundings.

THE SUN'S ATMOSPHERE

10·9. The Spectrum of Sunlight, as it is observed visually, is an array of colors from violet to red, which is interrupted by thousands of dark lines.   The lines are not seen in the rainbow or in the spectrum formed by the prism alone.   They require the selectivity given by the narrow slit before the prism and, accordingly, were not discovered until the slit was used.   The German optician Fraunhofer was the first, in 1814, to see them clearly; he mapped several hundred dark lines and labeled them with Roman letters beginning at the red end of the spectrum.   The lines are still known by the letters which he assigned them.

The dark lines are images of the slit of the spectroscope at the wave lengths that are darkened in the sunlight; these are abstracted from the continuous light of the photosphere mainly by gases of the different chemical elements in the sun's atmosphere.   The strongest solar lines are the Fraunhofer H and K of calcium near the

violet end of the visible spectrum.   There are also *telluric bands—*
groups of lines abstracted from the sunlight by molecules of the

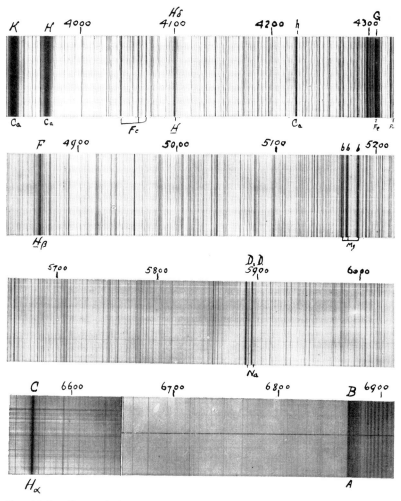

F<small>IG</small>. 10·9.   Parts of the Visible Solar Spectrum.   (*Photographed with the*
13-foot spectrograph, Mount Wilson and Palomar Observatories)

earth's atmosphere.   The B band formed by terrestrial oxygen
molecules is prominent in Fig. 10·9.   The separate lines of the
solar spectrum itself are produced by atoms of the different elements
in the sun's atmosphere, which cannot generally combine into
molecules at that high temperature.

The wave lengths of the lines are expressed in *angstroms,* abbreviated A; one angstrom is 10^{-8} centimeter. The visible region of the solar spectrum is between 3900 and 7600 A. Some conspicuous lines and bands are the following:

Fraunhofer Letter	Wave Length	Identification
A	7594 A	oxygen (telluric)
B	6867	oxygen (telluric)
C	6563	hydrogen
D	5893	sodium (double)
E	5270	iron
F	4861	hydrogen
H	3968	calcium
K	3934	calcium

The ultraviolet region can be photographed ordinarily as far as 2950 A, beyond which it is hidden by absorption of ozone and other constituents of our atmosphere. Features of the extreme ultraviolet are recorded in photographs of the spectrum from rockets above the absorbing levels. The infrared region is photographed as far as 13,500 A; its line patterns are clearly traced with the lead sulfide cell at the McMath-Hulbert Observatory to 24,500 A, and its coarser features are followed with heat-detecting apparatus beyond 200,000 A. Much of the infrared region is obscured by heavy bands absorbed by gases of our atmosphere, particularly oxygen, carbon dioxide, and water vapor.

10·10. Chemical Elements in the Sun. More than 60 chemical elements are recognized in the sun's atmosphere. They have been identified by comparing their laboratory spectra with the lines in the solar spectrum. Some unrecognized elements would not be expected to make much impression there, and some have not had their laboratory spectra determined well enough for dependable comparisons. Some inert gases and halogens have their strongest lines in the far ultraviolet which is cut off by absorption in the earth's atmosphere; these have not as yet been identified in the low-dispersion spectra photographed from rockets. We conclude that practically all the chemical elements are present in the sun.

The hot gases of the sun are generally composed of dissociated atoms. The molecules of 18 compounds are recognized as well by their dark bands in the spectrum. Examples are titanium oxide and the hydrides of calcium and magnesium, which occur in the cooler areas of sunspots. Only a few hardy compounds hold together above the unspotted regions.

Hydrogen is the most abundant element in the sun's atmosphere, and helium is second. These two elements also predominate in the sun's interior, in the stars, and in the universe generally. Hydrogen contributes about 55 per cent of the mass of the cosmic material, helium 44 per cent, and the heavier elements the remainder. Exceptions to these proportions occur in the earth and other smaller bodies from which most of the lighter gases have escaped.

10·11. The Chromosphere appears as a red fringe around the dark disk of the moon when it completely conceals the photosphere at

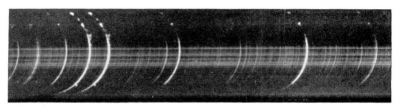

Fig. 10·11. The Spectrum of the Chromosphere. The pair of long crescents at the left are the H and K lines of calcium. Projections to the right of the crescents are prominences. Breaks in the crescents are caused by irregularities in the moon's surface. (*Photograph by Mount Wilson Observatory*)

the time of total solar eclipse. On these occasions the bright-line spectrum of the chromosphere can be observed; it is also known as the *flash spectrum,* because it flashes into view in the spectroscope near the beginning of the total eclipse, replacing the dark lines of the ordinary solar spectrum. The red Fraunhofer C line gives its color to the chromosphere and the prominences above it.

As it is photographed with a slitless spectroscope near the beginning or end of total solar eclipse, the flash spectrum (Fig. 10·11) appears as a succession of images of the narrow crescent of the chromosphere left uncovered by the moon. The different lengths of the crescents show that some of the chemical elements which produce them are effective to greater heights above the photosphere than are others. Hydrogen, calcium, and helium give the longest images.

The strong helium lines of the flash spectrum, by which this

useful element was discovered in the sun before it was recognized
on the earth, are almost entirely missing in the dark-line solar
spectrum. Aside from this and some other explainable exceptions,
the lines of the chromospheric and ordinary solar spectra are similar, illustrating the rule that a luminous gas emits the same pattern
of wave lengths that it absorbs from light passing through it.

10·12. The Chromosphere Outside Eclipse. Much of our knowledge of the exterior features of the sun is being obtained with
special apparatus when the sun is uneclipsed. Examples are the

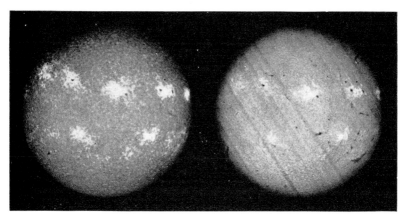

Fig. 10·12. The Sun in Calcium and Hydrogen Light. Spectroheliograms
taken with the K line of calcium (left) and the red hydrogen line (right).
(*Photographed at Mount Wilson Observatory*)

spectroheliograph and the coronagraph. The latter is effective at
high altitudes where purer and thinner air produces less glare
around the edge of the sun. Such instruments are in operation on
the Pic du Midi in the French Pyrenees and at several other mountain observatories, including the high altitude stations at Climax,
Colorado, and on Sacramento Peak in New Mexico.

The *spectroheliograph* is an attachment to the telescope employed
to record the chromosphere over the whole disk of the sun. An
adaptation of the spectroscope, it is a device for photographing the
sun in the light of a single line of the spectrum, and therefore of
the chemical element in the sun's atmosphere that produces the
chosen line. We will understand that the "dark" lines are dark
by contrast with the brighter background of the solar spectrum;

they contain the weaker light of the chromosphere, which is recorded in the photograph, or *spectroheliogram*.

The K line of calcium and the C line of hydrogen are the ones generally used for the purpose. The photographs (Fig. 10·12) with the first line show the bright calcium *flocculi*, which are especially conspicuous in sunspot regions. With the second line they show bright patches of hydrogen, also called flocculi, and the extended forms of higher and cooler prominences, which appear dark by contrast. The hydrogen markings are rather infrequently spun out in vortex structures in sunspot regions, giving the impression that the atmosphere above the spots is whirling down into them.

Monochromatic filters are also employed to transmit a very narrow range of wave length of the sunlight. The polarizing monochromator is an example; the filter here may be a succession of quartz crystal and polaroid sheets. Such devices are effective in photographing the solar prominences outside eclipse.

10·13. The Solar Prominences appear flame-like beyond the chromosphere during total solar eclipse, their vivid red in striking contrast with the white glow of the corona. In the photographs in

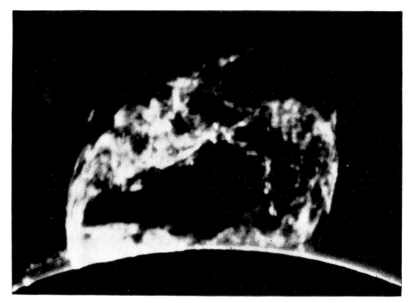

Fig. 10·13. Solar Prominence, June 28, 1945. (*Photographed by Walter Orr Roberts, High Altitude Observatory, Climax, Colorado*)

hydrogen light taken outside eclipse they often appear as long dark filaments against the brighter background of the chromosphere. Where they are carried beyond the disk by the sun's rotation, they appear bright against the sky. The prominences can be photographed in their hydrogen or calcium light, or can be viewed directly with the spectrohelioscope. Effective studies of their behavior have been made at the McMath-Hulbert Observatory and at high altitude stations in America and Europe in successions of photographs taken on motion picture film. The projections of the films give dramatic and very instructive portrayals of their activities.

Most prominences are of the *active* type; they originate high above the chromosphere and pour their streamers down into it. *Quiescent* prominences are the least active and have the longest lives; their most common form is the "haystack." *Eruptive* prominences are among the rarer types. These rise from active material above the chromosphere, attaining high speeds and great altitudes before they vanish. A prominence of 1938 reached the record speed of 450 miles a second. A prominence of June 4, 1946, rose to the distance of more than a million miles above the sun's surface.

10·14. Solar Flares are remarkable outbursts generally in the vicinities of large and active sunspot groups of irregular polarity. Viewed with the spectrohelioscope or monochromatic filter they appear as brilliant areas of the chromosphere. They vary from smaller flares of a few minutes' duration to more intense and rarer ones which require up to 15 minutes to attain their greatest brightness, and then disappear in an hour or more. They have been attributed to masses of glowing gas brought up from below the photosphere in the wakes of upheavals which cause the bursts observed with radio telescopes.

These hot gases emerge explosively and rise to considerable heights. The first report of their rapid ascent was given by Helen Dodson at the McMath-Hulbert Observatory from her photographs with a motion picture camera. The flare of May 8, 1951, at the edge of the disk rose in the first minute of its life at the rate of 450 miles a second, equaling the record speed for an eruptive prominence, and continued to the height of 40,000 miles.

10·15. The Radio Sun. The reception of noise from the sun was first reported, in 1942, by radar defense stations in Great Britain, where the source of the disturbance was traced to a large spot group

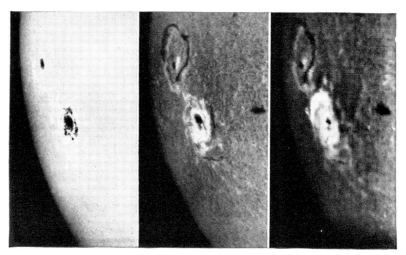

FIG. 10·14. A Solar Flare. Direct photograph and two hydrogen spectroheliograms of a sunspot group. The second spectroheliogram, taken 2½ hours later than the first, shows a solar flare. (*Photographed at Mount Wilson Observatory*)

near the central meridian of the sun. This accidental discovery provided a new means of studying the sun, which is being utilized with radio telescopes in various parts of the world. The radio emission is produced by the interactions of fast-moving electrified particles from below with the exterior gases; it is strongest at wave lengths of 1 to 10 meters, where it originates at different levels of the corona, and is weakest at centimeter ranges, from the lower chromosphere.

With the shorter wave lengths the Australian radio astronomers have devised apparatus for rapidly scanning the whole disk. They record bright spots which are generally associated with visible sunspot groups, but may last much longer than do the spots. From the *quiet sun,* in the years when sunspots are scarce, the radio emission has its least strength, which is fairly constant.

From the *active sun,* when sunspots are numerous, *bursts* of irregular and much greater strength are superposed. The explanations of how they occur and of their relation to the visible flares are still tentative. J. P. Wild in Australia suggests that the upheaval in the sun produces clouds of particles moving outward at a sixth the speed of light; when they reach the corona in seconds, they produce the radio *flashes* of a few seconds' duration. The following shock wave may carry great numbers of trapped particles into the corona at the rate of 1000 miles a second, where they cause a radio *outburst* lasting from 10 to 20 minutes.

10·16. Terrestrial Associations.   The appearance of an intense solar flare is likely to be soon followed by a deterioration of our radio communications in the higher frequencies.   Powerful ultraviolet radiations from the flare arrive with visible evidence of the flare itself, and the very swift particles which cause the radio flashes from the corona reach the earth less than an hour later.   These disrupt ionized layers of the upper atmosphere, which normally keep reflecting our own radio beams back to the ground (1·14).

Less swift electrified particles from the upheaval in the sun arrive here about a day after the solar flare was observed, and after the particles have produced the outburst of radio emission in their passage through the corona.   They then excite the gases of our upper atmosphere and set them glowing in an auroral display (1·19).   The appearance of the aurora is generally accompanied by unusual gyrations of the magnetic compass, which inform us that a *magnetic storm* is in progress.

ECLIPSES OF THE SUN; THE CORONA

10·17. The Moon's Shadow on the Earth.   An eclipse of the sun occurs when the moon passes directly between the sun and the earth, screening part or all of the sun's disk.   The earth is then partly darkened by the moon's shadow.

The average length of the umbra of the moon's shadow is 232,000 miles, which is 3000 miles less than the average distance of the moon from the earth's surface.   In the average the umbra does not reach the earth's surface; the fact that it often does reach is because of the eccentricity of the moon's orbit around the earth and of the earth's orbit around the sun.   When the moon is nearest the earth and the earth is also farthest from the sun, the conical umbra of the moon's shadow falls on the earth 18,000 miles inside its apex.

10·18. Total and Annular Eclipses.   A *total eclipse* of the sun occurs when the umbra of the moon's shadow extends to the earth's

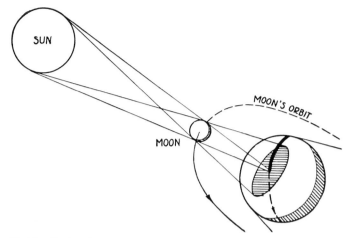

Fig. 10·17. Path of Total Solar Eclipse. The moon's shadow moves in an easterly direction over the earth's surface. The eclipse is total for an observer in the umbra, and is partial in the larger area of the penumbra.

surface. The area encompassed by the umbra rarely exceeds 150 miles in diameter when the sun is overhead, and is generally smaller. The observer within the area sees the dark circle of the moon completely hiding the sun's disk.

An *annular eclipse* occurs when the umbra is directed toward the earth but is too short to reach it. Within a small area of the earth's surface the moon is seen nearly centrally projected upon the disk of the sun, but the moon appears slightly the smaller of the two, so that a ring, or annulus, of the sun's disk remains uncovered.

Annular eclipses are 20 per cent more frequent than total eclipses.

Around the small area of the earth from which the eclipse appears total or annular is the larger area, some 2000 to 3000 miles in radius, which is covered by the penumbra of the shadow. Here a *partial eclipse* is visible, and the fraction of the sun that is hidden decreases as the observer's distance from the center is greater. Eclipses are entirely partial where the axis of the shadow

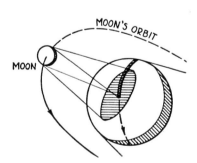

Fig. 10·18. Annular Eclipse of the Sun. The umbra of the moon's shadow does not reach the earth's surface.

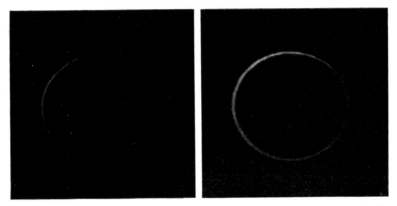

FIG. 10·18A. Annular Solar Eclipse, September 1, 1951. Immediately before (left) and after (right) the beginning of the annular phase. (Photographed by Luc Secretan at Philpott Dam, Virginia)

is directed slightly to one side of the earth. All total and annular eclipses are preceded and followed by partial phases.

10·19. The Path of the Moon's Shadow. The revolution of the moon causes its shadow to sweep eastward at the average rate of 2100 miles an hour. Because the earth is rotating toward the east at the rate of 1040 miles an hour at the equator, the speed of the shadow over the surface is 1060 miles an hour at the equator when the sun is overhead. The effective speed becomes greater with increasing distance from the equator, where the rotation is slower, and may reach as much as 5000 miles an hour when the sun is near the horizon.

Considering its high speed and small area, we see that the umbra can darken any part of its path for only a short time. The greatest possible duration of total solar eclipse at a particular place can scarcely exceed 7½ minutes, and that of annular eclipse can be only a little greater. The partial phase accompanying either type of eclipse may have a duration of more than 4 hours from beginning to end, but is usually much less.

The *path of total eclipse,* or of annular eclipse, is the narrow track of the darkest part of the shadow over the earth's surface, from the time it first touches the earth at sunrise until it departs at sunset. Meanwhile the penumbra moves over the larger surrounding region in which the eclipse is only partial. Occasionally the umbra is long enough to reach the earth at the middle of its

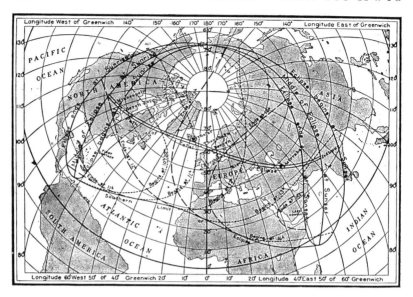

FIG. 10·19. Path of Total Solar Eclipse of June 30, 1954. The umbra of the moon's shadow touched the earth in Nebraska and left it in northern India. (*From* The American Ephemeris and Nautical Almanac)

path but at the beginning and end fails to extend to the surface. In this event the eclipse is total around the middle of the day and is otherwise annular.

10·20. Eclipse Seasons. In order to eclipse the sun, the moon must be almost directly between the sun and the earth. This condition is not fulfilled every time the moon arrives at its new phase, because the moon's path around the heavens is inclined 5° to the ecliptic. Thus the new moon is more likely to pass north or south of the sun.

Eclipses occur during two *eclipse seasons* around the times when the sun is passing the two opposite nodes of the moon's path. Owing to the rapid westward shifting of the nodes along the ecliptic (6·7), these seasons come about half a month earlier in the calendar from year to year; in 1955 they were around January and July. The length of the *eclipse year* is 346.6 days, which is the interval between two successive returns of the sun to the same node. Thus if the first season is early in the year, another season around the same node may begin before the end of the year.

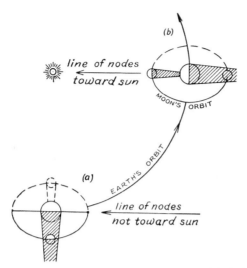

FIG. 10·20. Eclipse Seasons. Because the moon's orbit is inclined about 5° to the plane of the earth's orbit, eclipses can occur only at two opposite seasons, as at (b), when the sun is near the line of nodes of the moon's path. At other times in the year, as at (a), the moon does not pass between the earth and the sun or into the earth's shadow.

Each solar eclipse season lasts a little more than a month, or somewhat more than the month of the moon's phases. During each interval the moon becomes new at least once, and may do so twice. Two eclipses of the sun are accordingly inevitable each year, one near each node. Five may occur, two near each node and an additional eclipse if the sun comes around again to the first node before the year ends. Similarly, it can be shown that three umbral eclipses of the moon are possible in the course of the year, although a whole year may pass without a single one.

10·21. Predictions of Solar Eclipses. Accurate predictions of solar eclipses, of when they will occur and where they will be visible, are published in various astronomical almanacs a year or two in advance. Tracks of total solar eclipses for several years in advance are published in the U.S. Naval Observatory *Circulars.* The approximate times and places of eclipses from 1207 B.C. to A.D. 2161 can be found in Oppolzer's *Canon der Finsternisse,* which also contains maps showing the tracks of total and annular solar eclipses.

The predictions of eclipses are made possible by knowledge of

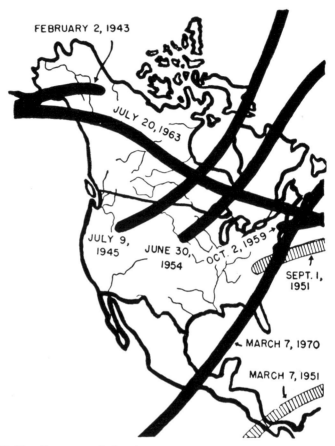

Fig. 10·21.   Recent and Coming Total and Annular Solar Eclipses in North America.   (*Diagram by Charles H. Smiley, Brown University*)

the motions of the earth and moon. They are facilitated by a relation between the occurrences of eclipses which has been known from very early times. The *saros* is the interval of 18 years 11⅓ days (or a day less or more, depending on the number of leap years included) in which eclipses of the same series are repeated. It is equal to 223 synodic months which contain 6585.32 days, and is nearly the same as 19 eclipse years having 6585.78 days. After this interval the relative positions of the sun, moon, and node are nearly the same as before. The sun is about one diameter west of its former position relative to the node; the paths of the eclipses of a series are accordingly displaced progressively in latitude, being shifted gradually from pole to pole until the shadow fails to touch the earth and the particular series is completed.

The third of a day in the saros period causes the path of each eclipse to be displaced in longitude a third of the way around the earth with respect to its predecessor. After 3 intervals, about 54 years and a month, the path returns to about the same region as before.

The dates, durations at noon, and land areas in which current total eclipses of the sun are visible are shown in the table; the paths of the eclipses that will be visible in North America until 1970 appear in Fig. 10·21. The eclipse of 1959 begins in southern New England. The path of the 1963 eclipse will pass near northern Maine, and that of the 1970 eclipse will follow along our Atlantic Coast.

TOTAL SOLAR ECLIPSES

Date	Duration (minutes)	Region
1957, Oct. 23	short	Antarctica
1958, Oct. 12	5	Chile, Argentina
1959, Oct. 2	3	North Africa
1961, Feb. 15	3	Europe, Siberia
1962, Feb. 5	4	East Indies
1963, July 20	2	Alaska, Canada
1965, May 30	5	New Zealand, Peru
1966, Nov. 12	2	South America, South Africa

10·22. The Sun in Total Eclipse is an impressive sight to be always remembered. The beginning of eclipse is manifested by the appearance of a dark notch at the sun's western edge. Gradually the sun's disk is hidden by the moon. When only a thin crescent remains uncovered, the sky and landscape have assumed a pale and unfamiliar aspect, because the light from the sun's rim is redder than ordinary sunlight.

The light fades rapidly as total eclipse approaches. There is a chill in the air; birds seem bewildered; some flowers begin to close. As soon as the last sliver of the sun breaks into brilliant beads and disappears, the filmy corona bursts into view. Red prominences are often seen close to the edge of the eclipsing moon; some planets and bright stars may appear. Totality ends as abruptly as it began; the sunlight returns and the corona vanishes.

The scientific value of total solar eclipse is owing to the availability on these rare occasions of features which are revealed less clearly or not at all at other times. Precise measurements of the positions of stars in the vicinity of the darkened sun have shown that they are apparently displaced slightly outward from the sun's edge, as they should be according to the theory of relativity. Many

FIG. 10·22. The Total Solar Eclipse of June 30, 1954. (*Photographed by John R. Winckler, University of Minnesota*)

features of the sun's corona, particularly the streamers of the outer corona, can be well observed only during total solar eclipse.

10·23. The Corona is the outer envelope of the sun and the chief contributor to the splendor of the total solar eclipse; its brightness is half that of the full moon. The corona is characterized by delicate streamers which vary in the sunspot cycle. Near sunspot maximum the form is roughly circular; petal-like streamers all around give the appearance that has been likened to that of a dahlia. Near sunspot minimum the corona is flattened in the polar regions (Fig. 10·23), where short, curved streamers are remindful of the lines of force around a bar magnet. Long streamers may reach out more than a million miles from the equatorial regions. The influence of the corona is far more extended than the photographs show. While the sun was passing near the Crab nebula in Taurus, a source of radio emission, the occulting effect of the corona was detected to a distance of more than 4 million miles from the sun's surface.

Fig. 10·23.   The Sun's Corona.   (*Photographed at the total eclipse of August 31, 1932, by Paul A. McNally, Georgetown College*)

The light of the corona is partly reflected sunlight, as the dark Fraunhofer lines in its spectrum show; it decreases slowly in intensity outward, and is ascribed mainly to the reflection by a portion of the dust ring that causes the zodiacal light (9·10).   The rest of the light, which gives a bright-line spectrum, comes from the luminous gases of the corona itself, and is stronger near the sun's equator than at its poles.   The bright lines in the spectrum of the corona were first identified, in 1941, by the Swedish physicist Edlén. They are emitted by shattered atoms of iron, nickel, calcium, and argon, which have been stripped of from 9 to 15 electrons.   Such disruption of the atoms would occur at a temperature of 2 million degrees F, whereas a temperature of less than 6000° F would normally be expected for material at that distance from the sun's radiating surface.

Fig. 10·23A.   An Artist's Conception of the Corona and Zodiacal Light Observed from Space.   (*Drawing by Charles A. Federer, Sr. for* Sky and Telescope)

Features of the inner corona around the uneclipsed sun were first photographed, in 1930, by the French astronomer B. Lyot with the coronagraph on the Pic du Midi. This type of telescope, having special precautions against bringing in direct sunlight to blot out the faint coronal light, is now in use at other high-altitude stations.

QUESTIONS ON CHAPTER 10

1. Suppose that the sun is represented by a ball 3¼ inches in diameter (about its diameter in Fig. 10·3). Show that the earth on this scale would be $\frac{1}{32}$ inch in diameter. Find a sunspot of this size in the photograph.

2. Explain the advantage of a long-focus telescope in photographing the sun.

3. Describe the growth and decline of a normal sunspot group.

4. Describe the sunspot number cycle and the shifting of the spot zones during the cycle.

5. Describe the magetism of sunspot groups in the two hemispheres and its change from cycle to cycle.

6. Associate each of the following definitions with the feature of the sun to which it applies:

(a) The surface that is ordinarily visible.
(b) The two principal members of a sunspot group.
(c) The darkest part of a sunspot.
(d) The red layer surrounding the visible surface.
(e) The outermost envelope of the sun.

7. Name: (a) four chemical elements which produce strong dark lines in the solar spectrum; (b) a fifth element producing prominent bright lines in the spectrum of the chromosphere.

8. Why do the prominences appear dark against the sun's disk and bright when they project beyond its edge? Account for their red color.

9. What is a solar flare? Distinguish between bursts and outbursts recorded with radio telescopes.

10. Mention some terrestrial effects which are frequently associated with solar flares.

11. Distinguish between total and annular eclipse of the sun as to cause and appearance.

12. Describe the changes in the appearance of the corona during the sunspot cycle.

REFERENCES

Abetti, Giorgio, *The Sun*. D. Van Nostrand Company, Princeton, 1938.
Dyson, Frank, and R. v. d. R. Woolley, *Eclipses of the Sun and Moon.* Oxford University Press, 1937.
Kuiper, Gerard P., editor, *The Sun*. University of Chicago Press, 1954.
Menzel, Donald H., *Our Sun*. Harvard University Press, Cambridge, 1949.
Mitchell, S. A., *Eclipses of the Sun*. Fifth edition. Columbia University Press, New York, 1951.

11

THE STARS IN THEIR SEASONS

THE CONSTELLATIONS – STARS OF SPRING – STARS OF
SUMMER – STARS OF AUTUMN – STARS OF WINTER –
THE SOUTHERN CONSTELLATIONS

THE CONSTELLATIONS

In the original sense the constellations are configurations of stars.
The brighter stars form patterns of dippers, crosses, and the like.
Some of the star-figures we recognize today were well known to the
people of Mesopotamia 5000 years ago, who had named them after
animals and representatives of occupations, such as the herdsman
and the hunter. The plan was later adopted by the Greeks who
renamed some of the characters after the animals and heroes of
their mythology.

11·1. The Original Constellations. Forty-eight constellations were
known to the early Greeks. Nearly all of these are described in
the *Phenomena*, which the poet Aratus wrote, about 270 B.C., and
which can be found in many libraries today. The popularity of
Aratus' poem did much to perpetuate the imagined starry creatures which he vividly described.

Interest in the celestial menagerie was also promoted by the publication of Ptolemy's *Almagest,* about A.D. 150, where the places of
the stars are designated by their positions in the mythological
figures. Then, too, famous artists of later times vied with one another to produce the liveliest pictures of the imagined creatures.

These creatures do not appear on modern maps and globes of the
heavens. They have nothing to do with the astronomy of today,
except the connection with which they began; their names are
still the names of constellations. Meanwhile, the constellations
have increased in number and have taken on a new significance,
although their oldest one as groups of stars survives as well.

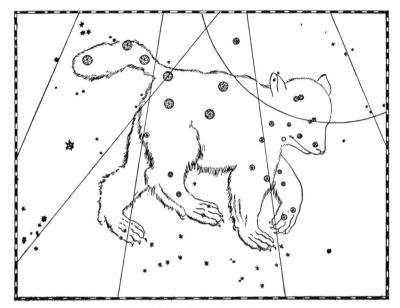

FIG. 11·1.   The Great Bear.

11·2. Constellations as Divisions of the Sky.   The original constellations did not cover the skies of the Greeks completely; they did not include the duller areas where there were no striking configurations of stars to claim attention.   At that time, only those stars within the imagined creatures belonged to constellations.   In addition, the part of the heavens around the south celestial pole that did not rise above the horizon of the Greeks remained uncharted.

Celestial map makers of later times filled the vacant spaces with new constellations which they named after scientific instruments, birds, and other things having no connection with the creatures of the legends.   Not all of them survived.   At present we recognize 88 constellations, which completely cover the sphere of the stars from pole to pole.   Seventy of them are visible, either wholly or in part, from the latitude of New York.

For the purposes of astronomy, the constellations are now definite divisions of the heavens marked off by boundary lines, just as the states are bounded.   The boundaries first appeared in the star maps at the beginning of the 19th century.   They are frequently irregular, making detours to avoid cutting across outstretched arms and paws of the legendary creatures. These devious dividing lines were straightened for most of the southern constellations by the American astronomer Gould, in 1877, and finally for all the constellations by decision of the International Astronomical Union, in 1928. The boundaries now run only from east to west and from north to south, although they zigzag considerably so as not to

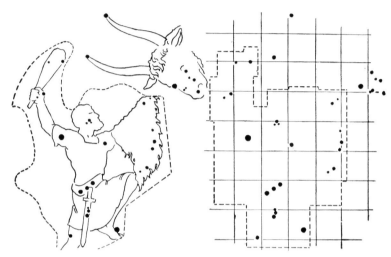

FIG. 11·2. Old and New Boundaries of Orion.

expatriate bright stars and variable stars from constellations with which they have long been associated.

11·3. Names of the Stars. The brightest stars and other especially famous ones are known to us by personal names which have been handed down through the ages. Some of these names are of Greek and Latin origin. Some are derived from the Arabic; names such as Algol, Altair (*al* is the Arabic definite article), and many others are survivals from earlier times when astronomy was a favorite study of the Mohammedan scholars. The stars were also named by shepherds, sailors, and nomads of the desert.

Procyon, meaning "before the dog," precedes the Great Dog Star in its rising. Aldebaran means "the follower"; it rises after the Pleiades. Antares is the "rival of Mars," owing to its red color. These are examples of how some of the stars were designated. Other star names have come to us in a different way.

In the earliest catalogs, such as Ptolemy's, the stars were distin-

guished by their positions in the imagined figures of heroes and
animals. One star was the "mouth of the Fish"; another was the
"tail of the Bird." Transcribed later into the Arabic, some of these
expressions finally degenerated into single words. Betelgeuse, the
name of the bright red star in Orion, was originally three words
meaning the "armpit of the Central One."

11·4. Designations of the Stars by Letters. The plan of designating the brighter stars by letters was introduced by Bayer, a Bavarian
attorney, in 1603. In a general way, the stars of each constellation
are denoted by small letters of the Greek alphabet in order of their
brightness, and the Roman alphabet is drawn upon for further
letters. Where there are several stars of nearly the same brightness
in the constellation, they are likely to be lettered in order from
head to foot of the legendary creature. The full name of a star in
the Bayer system is the letter followed by the possessive of the Latin
name of the constellation. Thus Capella, the brightest star in
Auriga, is α Aurigae. The letters for some of the brighter stars
are shown in the maps that follow.

Some of the fainter stars are known by their numbers according
to a plan of numbering the stars in each constellation in order of
right ascension. The star 61 Cygni is an example. Most faint
stars, however, are designated only by their running numbers in
one of the many catalogs to which the astronomer can turn for information as to their positions, brightness, and other features.

11·5. The Map of the Northern Sky. The six maps in this chapter
show all parts of the celestial sphere. They are designed particularly for an observer in latitude 40° N, but are useful anywhere
in middle northern latitudes. In order to avoid confusion, the
many stars only faintly visible to the naked eye are not included, the
names of inconspicuous constellations are generally omitted, and
the boundaries between the constellations do not appear in the
maps.

Map 1 shows the region of the heavens within 40° from the north
celestial pole. The pole is at the center, closely marked by Polaris
at the end of the Little Dipper's handle. Hour circles appear in
this projection as straight lines radiating from the center; they are
marked around the circumference of the map in hours of right
ascension. The concentric circles are circles of equal declination

at intervals of 10°; their declinations are shown on the vertical line.

This map is to be held toward the north. When it is turned so that the present month is at the top, the map represents the posi-

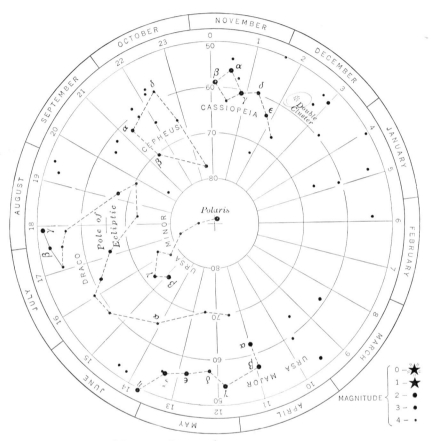

MAP 1. The Northern Constellations.

tions of the northern constellations at 9 o'clock in the evening, standard time, or, more exactly, local civil time if the correct part of the month is at the top. The hour circle that is then vertically under the date coincides with the celestial meridian at this time of night on this date. For a different time of night the map is to be turned from the 9 o'clock position through the proper number of hours, clockwise for an earlier time and counterclockwise for a later time.

If we wish, for example, to identify the northern constellations at 9 o'clock in the evening on August 7, the map should be turned so that this date is at the top (at about the 18-hour circle). The Great Dipper is now bowl-down in the northwest, Cassiopeia is opposite it in the northeast, and so on. These northern constellations appear again in the maps for the different seasons. On all the maps the brightness of the stars is indicated by symbols which represent their approximate magnitudes (12·11).

11·6. Directions in the Sky. North in the sky is toward the north celestial pole; south is toward the opposite pole. East to west is the direction in which the stars seem to circle daily. If these rules are remembered, there can be no confusion about directions in the sky.

The position of a star is clearly described when its directions from other stars are given in this way. Its position is also perfectly definite if we say how it is related to two or more other stars; perhaps the star completes an equal-sided triangle with two other stars already identified, or it may be in line with them. We have noticed how a line through the pointer stars of the Great Dipper leads to the pole star. Such directions remain unaltered through the day and year.

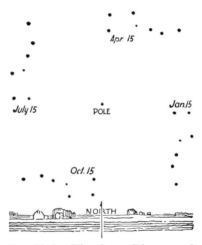

Fig. 11·6. The Great Dipper at 9 O'clock in the Evening at Different Seasons.

Directions relative to the horizon, however, change as the stars go around the pole. From a star above the pole, north is down and west is to the left; from a star below the pole, north is up and west is to the right. Notice how the Great Dipper changes its position relative to the horizon during the night or from night to night as the seasons progress (Fig. 11·6). Along in the winter this figure of 7 stars stands on its handle in the northeast at 9 o'clock. In spring it appears inverted above the pole. In summer the Dipper is seen descending bowl-down in the northwest, and in autumn it is right side up under the pole, where it may be lost to view for a time.

11·7. Star Maps for the Four Seasons. Maps 2, 3, 4, and 5 show the constellations which cross the meridian at 9 o'clock in the evening during each of the 4 seasons, all the way from the north celestial pole to the south horizon of latitude 40° N. The pole is near the top of each map. Hour circles radiating from the pole are marked in hours of right ascension near the bottom of the map, and circles of equal declination go around the pole.

We select the map for the present season and hold it toward the south. The hour circle above the date of observation is along the celestial meridian at 9 o'clock in the evening on that date. Accordingly, the central vertical line in each of the 4 maps represents successively the positions of the meridian at 9 o'clock on April 21, July 21, October 21, and January 21. Remembering that the daily motions of the stars are from left to right for these maps and that a star comes to the meridian 2 hours earlier from month to month, we can locate the meridian in the maps for other times and dates.

Thus the maps are arranged to show what stars are crossing the celestial meridian at a particular time of the day and year. Any one of these stars can be identified in the sky if its distance from the zenith is also known at that time. The rule for finding the zenith distance is derived from Fig. 2·13: The zenith distance of a star at upper transit equals the observer's latitude minus the star's declination. If the distance is positive, the star is south of the zenith; if it is negative, the star is north of the zenith.

The zenith at the place of observation is on the circle having the same declination as the latitude of the place. As we are facing south, it would be necessary to lean backwards to view the constellations in the upper parts of the maps. The northern constellations, however, are shown more conveniently in Map 1. They are repeated in the seasonal maps to display more clearly how they are related to the constellations farther south.

The following examples illustrate the use of the maps.

1. Read from Map 2 the right ascension and declination of the star Regulus.
   Answer: Right ascension $10^h 5^m$, declination 12° N.
2. On June 20, 1960, the planet Jupiter is in right ascension $17^h 55^m$, declination 24° S. What is its position among the stars (Map 3)?
   Answer: In Sagittarius, west of the handle of the Milk Dipper.
3. On what date does the star Antares (Map 3) cross the meridian at 9 o'clock in the evening, standard time? What is then its distance from the zenith as observed in latitude 40° N?
   Answer: July 12. The zenith distance is 66°, south.

4. On what date does Orion (Map 5) rise at 9 P.M.?

Answer: November 1. Because Orion is near the celestial equator, it rises 6 hours earlier than the time of its meridian crossing, which is 9 P.M. on February 1. Thus Orion rises at 3 P.M. on February 1, and at 9 P.M. on November 1.

STARS OF SPRING (MAP 2)

The star maps are useful for identifying the prominent constellations in the sky and also for reference during the reading of the book. Our brief inspection of the seasonal maps begins with the stars of spring, which are near the celestial meridian in the early evenings of this season.

11·8. Ursa Major. In the early evenings of spring the Great Dipper appears inverted above the pole. This figure of 7 bright stars is

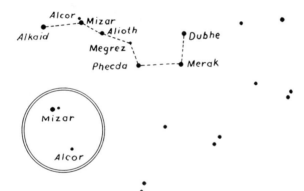

FIG. 11·8. Ursa Major. *Insert:* Mizar and Alcor viewed with an inverting telescope.

part of the large constellation Ursa Major, the Larger Bear, which extends for some distance to the west and south of the bowl of the Dipper; pairs of stars of nearly equal separations (Fig. 11·8) mark 3 paws of the ancient creature. Mizar, at the bend in the handle, has a fainter companion easily visible to the naked eye. With even a small telescope Mizar itself is revealed as a pair of stars.

Following the line of the Pointers northward we come to Polaris, the north star or pole star, less than 1° from the celestial pole. This useful star marks the end of the handle of the Little Dipper, the characteristic figure of Ursa Minor.

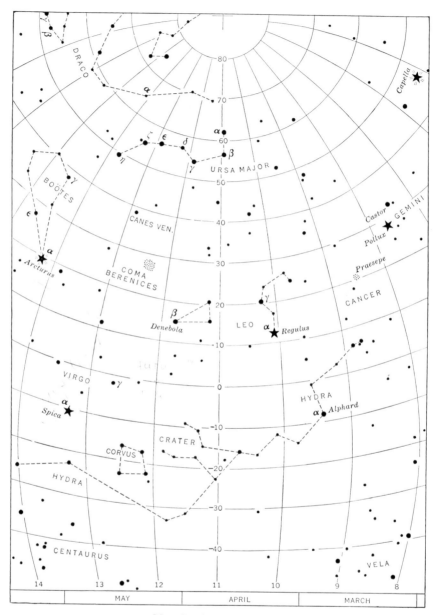

MAP 2. Stars of Spring.

11·9. Leo is peculiarly associated with the spring season. Its familiar Sickle appears in the east in the early evening as spring approaches, and it becomes the dominant figure in the south as this season advances. The bright star Regulus marks the end of the handle of the sickle-figure, which with the right triangle to the east is the distinguishing feature of this constellation of the zodiac.

To the east of Leo is the dim Cancer of the zodiac with its Praesepe star cluster. To the west is the larger zodiacal constella-

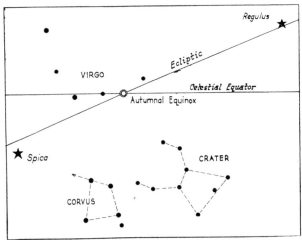

FIG. 11·9. The Position of the Autumnal Equinox.

tion Virgo containing the bright star Spica. The course of the ecliptic here is very nearly the line from the Praesepe cluster through Regulus and Spica. Three fifths of the way from Regulus to Spica it crosses the celestial equator at the autumnal equinox. The 4-sided figure of Corvus in this region is likely to attract attention. When Corvus is at upper transit, at 9 o'clock in the evening about the middle of May, the Southern Cross is on the meridian 40° to the south, where it is invisible from all except the extreme southern part of the United States.

STARS OF SUMMER (MAP 3)

A procession of familiar constellations, from Boötes to Cygnus, marches through the zenith in the evenings of summer in middle northern latitudes. A fine region of the Milky Way, which we

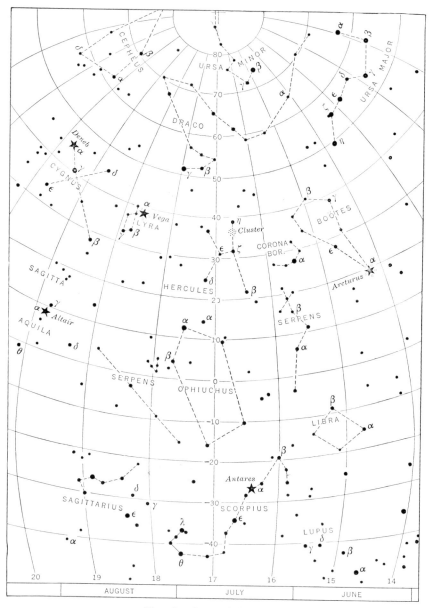

MAP 3.   Stars of Summer.

examine in a later chapter, extends from Cygnus past Aquila down
to Scorpius and Sagittarius in the south.

11·10. From Boötes to Lyra. Boötes is overhead when the stars
come out at the beginning of summer. Its stars outline the figure
of a large kite with the brilliant Arcturus at the point where the
tail is attached. This somewhat reddish star is pointed out by

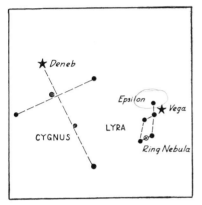

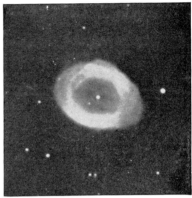

Fig. 11·10. Cygnus and Lyra. Showing the positions of the double-double Epsilon Lyrae and the Ring nebula.

Fig. 11·10A. Ring Nebula in Lyra. (*Photographed at the Dominion Astrophysical Observatory*)

following the curve of the Great Dipper's handle around past **its**
end. Arcturus' only peers in the whole northern celestial hemisphere are blue Vega and yellow Capella.

Eastward from the kite-figure and beyond the semicircle of
Corona Borealis, the Northern Crown, we find Hercules, which is
passing overhead at nightfall in midsummer. Some of its brighter
stars may seem to suggest the figure of a rather large butterfly that
is flying toward the west. The great cluster in Hercules, scarcely
visible to the naked eye, is situated two thirds of the way from the
imagined butterfly's head along the west edge of the northern wing.
Farther east on the line from the Crown through Hercules we come
to Lyra. The figure here is a small parallelogram with a triangle
attached at its northernmost point. Vega marks a vertex of the
triangle. The star at the north point of the triangle is the "double-
double" Epsilon Lyrae. It is visible as two stars to the unaided
eye, but is more easily seen with binoculars; each star is again

divided into two with the telescope. The Ring nebula in Lyra (Fig. 11·10), visible only with the telescope, is about midway between the two stars in the southern side of the parallelogram.

11·11. Scorpius and Sagittarius. The formidable figure of Scorpius, the Scorpion of the zodiac, dominates the southern sky at nightfall in early summer. Its bright Antares is a red supergiant star enormously larger than the sun.

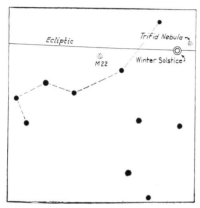

FIG. 11·11. Milk Dipper of Sagittarius. Showing the position of the winter solstice.

FIG. 11·11A. Trifid Nebula in Sagittarius. (*Photographed at Mount Wilson Observatory*)

Directly east of Antares, 6 stars of the zodiacal constellation Sagittarius outline the Milk Dipper, so named because it is in the Milky Way. In this direction we look toward the center of our galaxy. The great star cloud of Sagittarius is an outlying portion of the galactic central region that is mainly obscured by intervening heavy clouds of cosmic dust. The Trifid nebula and the globular star cluster M 22 are some of the other features of this spectacular tract of the heavens. The place of the winter solstice is also near the handle of the Milk Dipper.

STARS OF AUTUMN (MAP 4)

Cassiopeia comes up high in the north in autumn skies. The Northern Cross is overhead early in the season and, as it moves along, the Square of Pegasus becomes the dominant figure. Dim watery constellations spread across in the south, having only the

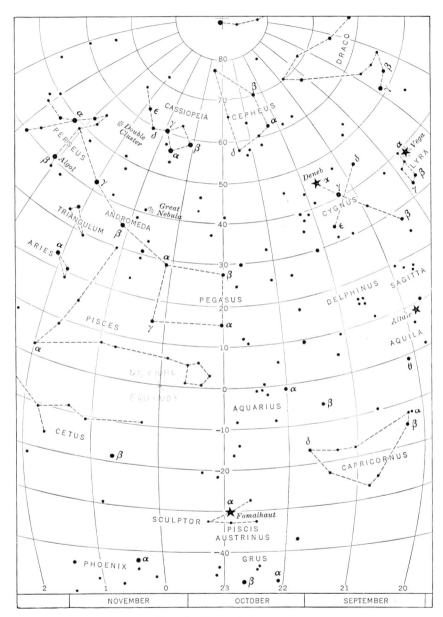

MAP 4. Stars of Autumn.

star Fomalhaut to attract attention except when bright planets
appear there as well.

11·12. The Northern Cross is overhead at nightfall in the early
autumn in middle northern latitudes. This attractive figure, set
in a fine region of the Milky Way (Fig. 11·12), is the characteristic
feature of Cygnus, the Swan. Its brightest star, Deneb, marks the

FIG. 11·12. The Northern Cross in the Milky Way. Beta Cygni at the
foot of the Cross is out of picture at the lower right. (*Photographed by
F. E. Ross, Yerkes Observatory*)

northern end of the longer axis of the Cross. Albireo (Beta Cygni) decorates the southern end of this axis; it appears double with even a small telescope, a reddish star with a fainter blue companion. The Northern Cross shows the direction toward which the sun with its planetary system is moving in the rotation of our galaxy.

11·13. The Square of Pegasus is peculiarly associated with our autumn skies. As this season approaches, we see it in the east in the early evening balanced on one corner. It crosses the meridian

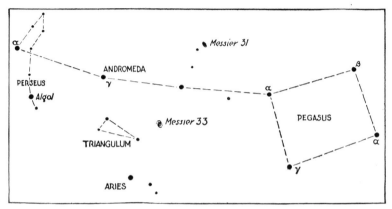

FIG. 11·13. Region of the Square of Pegasus. Showing the positions of the spiral galaxies M 31 and M 33.

at 9 o'clock about the 1st of November. Four rather bright stars mark the corners of the large square which is the characteristic figure of Pegasus; they are Alpha, Beta, and Gamma Pegasi, and in the northeast corner the Alpha star of Andromeda. If we imagine that the Square of Pegasus is the bowl of a very large dipper-figure, we find its handle extending toward the northeast (Fig. 11·13); its first three stars are the brightest of Andromeda. A feature of this constellation is Messier 31, which is only faintly visible to the naked eye but is actually a spiral galaxy larger than our own. It is denoted in Map 4 by its older name, the "Great Nebula" in Andromeda. Another galaxy is marked in the figure in the neighboring constellation Triangulum.

Southeast of the Square two streams of faint stars represent the ribbons with which the Fishes are tied. This dim constellation Pisces of the zodiac contains the zodiacal sign Aries, which has moved westward from its own constellation. Here we find the "first of Aries," or vernal equinox (Fig. 11·13A). The line of the eastern side of the Square prolonged as far again to the south leads

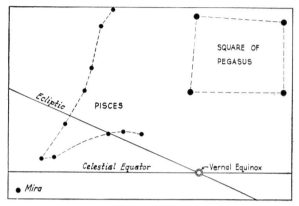

FIG. 11·13A. The Position of the Vernal Equinox.

to this important point of the celestial sphere. The red variable star Mira shown in this figure is in the adjoining constellation Cetus.

STARS OF WINTER (MAP 5)

The bright winter scene is grouped around Orion, its most conspicuous figure. The zodiac is farthest north here; Taurus and Gemini have between them the position of the summer solstice.

11·14. Taurus contains two bright star clusters. The Pleiades cluster looks something like a short-handled dipper (Fig. 11·14). Seven of its stars are clearly visible to the naked eye, and two or three others twinkle into view. The conspicuous feature of the larger, Hyades cluster is in the form of the letter V, which includes the bright star Aldebaran and represents the head of Taurus. At the tips of the horns are two fairly bright stars, the northern one of which is needed to complete the muffin-figure of Auriga; its brilliant Capella is near the zenith at 9 o'clock toward the end of January.

Gemini has an oblong figure. The heads of these Twins of the zodiac are marked by the bright stars Castor and Pollux. The position of the summer solstice (Fig. 11·14A) is between their feet and

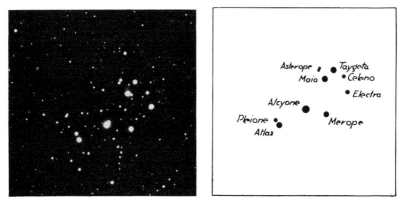

Fig. 11·14.   The Pleiades.   (*Photographed at Yerkes Observatory*

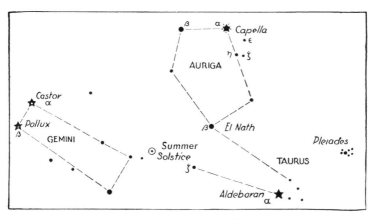

Fig. 11·14A.   Gemini, Auriga, and Taurus.   Showing the position of the
summer solstice.

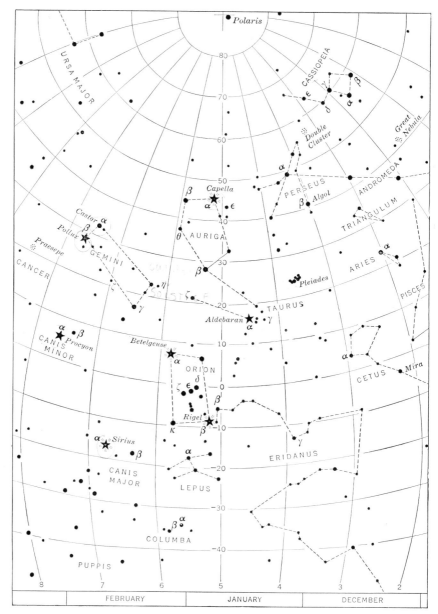

MAP 5.   Stars of Winter.

the horns of Taurus. The Milky Way sweeps down from Auriga and Taurus past the feet of the Twins and on to the south horizon.

11·15. Orion and His Dogs. Orion, the brightest constellation, is peculiarly associated with the winter. Its oblong figure rises in the early evening as winter approaches, appears in the south at

 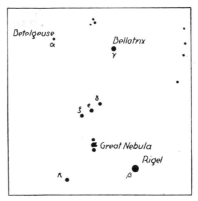

FIG. 11·15. Orion Tangled in Nebulae. Showing the position of the Great Nebula. (*Photographed at Mount Wilson Observatory*)

9 o'clock around the 1st of February, and is setting in the twilight as spring advances.

This bright region of the heavens inspired a lively scene in the old celestial picture book. Orion, a mighty hunter accompanied by his dogs, stands with uplifted club awaiting the charging Taurus. Red Betelgeuse glows below his shoulder. Blue Rigel diagonally across the figure is somewhat the brighter of the two. Three stars near the center of the rectangle mark Orion's belt, and three fainter ones in line to the south (Fig. 11·15) represent his sword. The middle star of the three appears through the telescope as a trapezium of stars surrounded by the foggy glow of the great nebula in Orion.

The stars of Orion's belt are useful pointers. The line joining them directs the eye northwestward to the Hyades and southeastward to Sirius, the "Dog Star," the brightest star in the heavens and one of the nearest. Sirius, Betelgeuse, and a third bright star across the Milky Way form a nearly equal-sided triangle. The third one is Procyon, the "Little Dog Star."

THE SOUTHERN CONSTELLATIONS (MAP 6)

11·16. The Region of the South Celestial Pole. Map 6 shows the part of the heavens that does not come up into view in latitude

MAP. 6. Region of the South Celestial Pole.

40° N. It contains the Southern Cross, the two Magellanic Clouds, a number of brilliant stars, and a fine region of the Milky Way.

Crux, the Southern Cross, is a small figure of 4 stars, which resembles a kite fully as much as a cross. It becomes entirely visible south of latitude 28° N. Its brightest star, Alpha Crucis, is about as bright as Aldebaran. The Magellanic Clouds, companions of our spiral galaxy, do not rise anywhere in the United States. From more southern latitudes they are clearly visible to the unaided eye. Canopus, almost directly south of Sirius, is second to it in brightness. Alpha Centauri is third in order of brightness among all the stars, and is nearest of all to the sun.

The south celestial pole is situated in the dim constellation Octans. There is not a star as bright as Polaris within 20° from this point. Sigma Octantis, a star barely visible to the naked eye, is 50' from the pole.

QUESTIONS ON CHAPTER 11

1. Define the term "constellation" in two ways. Take the constellation Orion as an example.

2. Three ways of designating individual stars are represented by the following examples: (a) Antares; (b) Alpha Tauri; (c) 61 Cygni. Explain.

3. Why are the names of the months placed as they are in Map 1? Notice that September 21 and right ascension 21 hours are together.

4. About what date is the bowl of the Little Dipper (Map 1) directly above the pole at 9 o'clock in the evening, standard time?

5. Precisely where would we look for the star Spica (Map 2) at 9 P.M. on May 25?

6. Describe the characteristic figures formed by the stars of Boötes; Leo; Cygnus; Pegasus; Orion.

7. Name the two brightest stars of the early evenings of summer; the four brightest stars of winter.

8. On what date does the great cluster in Hercules (Map 3) pass near the zenith at 9 P.M.?

9. Orion and Auriga (Map 5) cross the meridian at the same time. Do they also rise and set at the same time? Explain.

10. At the opposition of November 16, 1958, Mars is in right ascension $3^h 25^m$, declination $+19°$. How is it situated relative to the Pleiades and Hyades at that time?

11. For an observer in the southern hemisphere the south celestial pole is the elevated one. On what date does the Southern Cross appear directly above that pole?

12. Name the constellation containing: (a) the Milk Dipper; (b) the brightest star; (c) the Praesepe cluster; (d) the Ring nebula; (e) the eclipsing star Algol; (f) the star Canopus.

REFERENCES

Allen, Richard H., *Star-Names and Their Meanings*. Stechert, New York, 1899.

Baker, Robert H., *Introducing the Constellations*. Revised edition. The Viking Press, New York, 1957.

Baker, Robert H., *When the Stars Come Out.* Revised edition. The Viking Press, New York, 1954.

Norton, Arthur P., *A Star Atlas.* Twelfth edition. Gall and Inglis, Edinburgh, 1954.

Olcott, William T., *Field Book of Stars.* Revised by Newton Mayall and Margaret L. Mayall. G. P. Putnam's Sons, New York, 1954.

The 100-inch Reflecting Telescope, Mount Wilson Observatory.

12

THE STARS AROUND US

DISTANCES OF THE STARS – THE STARS IN MOTION –
SPECTRA OF THE STARS – BRIGHTNESS OF THE STARS
– TWO POPULATIONS OF STARS

The nearer stars show their distances from us by their slightly altered directions as the earth revolves around the sun, and their own motions by their progress against the background of the more remote stars. They include the brighter stars, which permit their spectra to be readily examined and classified. With such data of observation we compare the stars with one another and with the sun.

DISTANCES OF THE STARS

The distance of a celestial object is found by observing its parallax, which is defined (6·2) as the difference between the directions of the object when it is viewed from different places. From two particular places of observation the parallax becomes smaller as the distance of the object is greater, and for a particular object the parallax is made greater by sighting the object from places farther apart.

The moon's distance is known by measures of its parallax from widely separated stations on the earth. Parallaxes of the nearer planets observed in this way are large enough to show their distances reliably. The differences in the directions of even the nearest stars, however, observed from opposite sides of the earth are not greater than the width of a period on this page if it were viewed from the distance of a thousand miles. To detect the parallaxes of the stars we require the far greater separation of the points of observation afforded by the earth's revolution around the sun.

12·1. Parallaxes of the Stars. As the earth revolves around the sun, the nearer stars seem to oscillate slightly (Fig. 12·1). The extent of this displacement for a particular star is found by comparing

its positions in photographs taken 6 months apart with reference
to other stars in the photographs, which are likely to be too remote
to be considerably displaced.   Part of the observed displacement
may be caused by the movement of the star itself.   It is accordingly
necessary to repeat the photographs at half-year intervals until the

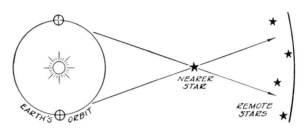

FIG. 12·1.   The Parallax of a Star.   Owing to the earth's revolution, the
nearer star appears to oscillate relative to the more remote stars.

annual parallax oscillation can be disentangled from the straight-
line motion of the star.

The *parallax* of a star, in the usual meaning of the term, is its
heliocentric parallax; it is the greatest difference in the star's directions from the earth and sun during the year, with slight correction
to bring the earth to its average distance from the sun.   It is very
nearly half the greatest parallax displacement that is observed for
the star.   When the parallax has been measured, in seconds of arc,
the distance can be calculated.

12·2. Distances in Parsecs and Light Years.   The *parsec* is the
distance at which a star would have a *par*allax of one *sec*ond.   One

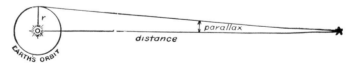

FIG. 12·2.   Heliocentric Parallax of a Star.

parsec equals 19.2 million million miles (19.2×10^{12} miles).   The
distance of a star in parsecs is the reciprocal of its parallax in
seconds.

The *light year* is the distance traversed by light in one year.   This
distance is found by multiplying the speed of light, 186,300 miles

a second, by about 31½ million, the number of seconds in a year. One light year equals 5.88 million million miles (5.88×10^{12} miles). One parsec equals 3.26 light years.

The relation between the distance and parallax of a star is accordingly:

Distance in parsecs = 1/parallax.
Distance in light years = 3.26/parallax.
Distance in miles = distance in parsecs × 19.2 million million.

As an example, consider the bright star Capella having the parallax of 0″.073. Its distance in parsecs is 1/0.073, or 13.7 parsecs. Its distance in light years is 3.26/0.073, or about 45 light years. Its distance in miles is 13.7 × 19.2 million million, or about 260 million million miles.

To find the sun's mean distance from the earth in terms of the speed of light, divide 92,900,000 miles by 186,300 miles a second; and we have 498½ light seconds, or 8.3 light minutes. The moon's distance from the earth is 1.3 light seconds; thus the echo of the radar pulse directed to the moon returns 2.6 seconds after the pulse is sent. The average distance of Pluto from the sun is 5½ light hours.

12·3. The Nearest Stars. The sun's nearest neighbor among the stars is the bright double star Alpha Centauri. The two stars have a distant and faint companion known as "Proxima" because it may be slightly nearer us than they are. The parallax of these stars is 0″.760, so that their distance is 4.3 light years, or about 26 million million miles. If the size of the sun is represented by a period on this page, Alpha Centauri would be shown on this scale by two similar dots 5 miles away. This is a fair sample of the wide separation of the stars around us.

More than two dozen stars are known to be within 12 light years of the sun. Although the bright stars Alpha Centauri, Sirius, and Procyon are included in this list, the majority of the nearest stars are too faint to be seen without the telescope. We conclude that the stars differ greatly in actual brightness, so that a bright star in our skies may not be nearer than a faint one.

The direct method of determining the distances of stars by observing their parallaxes is limited to the nearer ones. At the distance of 300 light years, which is only a step into space, the parallaxes become too small to be measured reliably. Ways of finding the distances of more remote stars will be mentioned later.

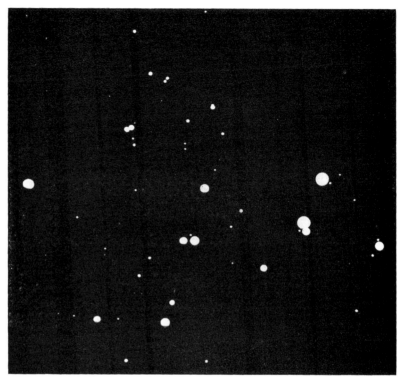

FIG. 12·3. Stars in the Sun's Neighborhood. Photograph of a model constructed at the University of Wisconsin by students in the elementary course. The sun is at the center. Alpha Centauri is below it, and Sirius and Procyon are the largest stars on the right. (*Photograph by Washburn Observatory*)

THE STARS IN MOTION

The motions of the stars in different directions relative to the sun are shown by the very gradual changes in their places in the heavens and by Doppler displacements of their spectrum lines. The sun is also moving among the stars around it. Like the sun, the stars are rotating on their axes.

12·4. Proper Motions of the Stars. Edmund Halley, whose name a famous comet bears, was the first, in 1718, to explain that the stars are not stationary. He observed that Sirius and some other bright stars had drifted as much as the apparent width of the full moon from the places assigned them in Ptolemy's ancient catalog. Meanwhile, the proper motions of all the lucid stars and of many fainter ones have become known by comparing the records of their places at different times suitably far apart.

The *proper motion* of a star is the angular change of its place in the heavens. This change in direction becomes so slow at greater distances that the more remote stars can serve as landmarks to show

August 23, 1894   May 30, 1916

FIG. 12·4. Barnard's Star Has the Largest Proper Motion. In the interval of 22 years between the two photographs, the star had moved an eighth of the apparent width of the full moon. (*Photographed at Yerkes Observatory*)

the progress of the nearer ones. Barnard's star (Fig. 12·4) has the swiftest proper motion. Named for the astronomer who first observed its rapid flight, this 10th-magnitude star in Ophiuchus moves among its neighbors in the sky at the rate of 10″.3 a year, or as far as the apparent width of the moon in 175 years. If all stars were moving as fast as this and at random, the forms of the constellations would be altered appreciably during a lifetime. W. J. Luyten reports that the known motions of only 329 stars exceed 1″ a year, and that the average for all naked-eye stars is not greater than 0″.1 a year. In the course of a century the positions of few stars change enough to be detected without a telescope.

12·5. Radial Velocities of the Stars. The proper motion of a star tells us nothing of its movement toward or away from us. The *radial velocity,* or the velocity in the line of sight, is revealed by the Doppler effect (5·14) in its spectrum. If the lines are displaced toward the violet end of the spectrum, the star is approaching us; if they are displaced toward the red end, the star is receding from us. The amount of the displacement is proportional to the speed of approach or recession.

The spectra of two stars are shown in Fig. 12·5 with the bright lines of the iron arc above and below them. Dark iron lines in the

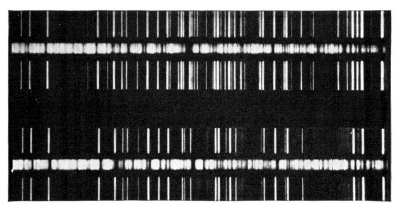

FIG. 12·5. Doppler Displacements in Stellar Spectra. In the upper spectrum the displacement of the dark lines to the violet (left) shows that the star is approaching the earth. In the lower spectrum the displacement to the red (right) shows that the star is receding from us. (*Photographed at David Dunlap Observatory*)

upper spectrum are displaced to the violet (left); the star is approaching at the rate of 58 miles a second. The same dark lines in the lower spectrum are displaced to the red (right); the star is receding at the rate of 62 miles a second. These are unusually swift motions. The radial velocities of most stars do not exceed 20 miles a second.

12·6. The Sun's Motion among the stars in our neighborhood is indicated by the common drift of these stars in addition to their individual motions. The stars are spreading out from the *apex of the sun's way* (Fig. 12·6), the point in the heavens toward which the sun's motion is directed, and are closing in toward the *antapex,* the opposite point. This effect is found by examining the proper motions of many stars in various parts of the heavens. It is also observed in the radial velocities, which have their greatest values of approach in the region of the apex and of recession around the antapex; these also show the speed of the solar motion.

Relative to the stars around it, the sun with its family of planets is moving at the rate of 12 miles a second toward a point in the constellation Hercules, in right ascension 18 hours and declination +30°, about 10° southwest of the bright star Vega. As fainter stars are observed, the apex shifts toward Cygnus, toward which the sun's motion is directed in the rotation of the galaxy (16·7).

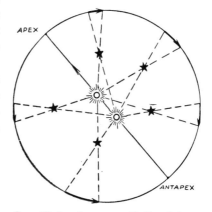

Fig. 12·6.   Apparent Drift of Stars Away from the Apex of the Sun's Way.

12·7. Rotations of the Stars.

Since the pioneer work of Struve and Elvey at Yerkes Observatory, about 1930, the rotations of stars on their axes have been extensively studied by means of the widening of their spectrum lines. Except where the axis of rotation is directed toward the earth, the starlight comes from a source that is partly approaching and partly receding from us. Thus the lines are widened by the Doppler effect by an amount which depends on the speed of the rotation and the direction of the axis.

Blue stars are likely to have high speeds of rotation, some of them as high as 200 miles a second at their equators. As an example, note the wide lines in the spectrum of Altair (Fig. 12·7); the period of rotation of this star is 6 hours, as compared with about a month in the case of the sun. The narrow lines in the spectrum of Vega, also a blue star, suggest that its axis is directed more nearly toward us. Yellow and red stars rotate much more slowly except where they belong to close binary systems, perhaps because some of their spin has been taken up in the forming of planetary systems. Our yellow sun has an equatorial speed of only 1¼ miles a second.

In some blue stars such as 78 Virginis, H. W. Babcock at Mount Wilson Observatory has discovered and studied intense magnetism comparable with the strongest fields in sunspots. The polarities oscillate from positive to negative and back in a few days. These effects are not associated in a simple manner with the rotations of

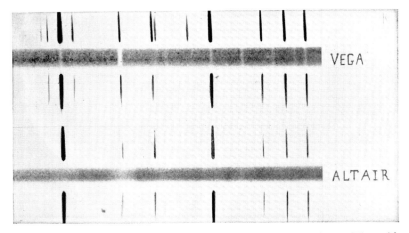

FIG. 12·7. Spectra of Vega and Altair. These are negatives. The widened lines in the spectrum of Altair show the rapid rotation of this star. (*Photographed at Yerkes Observatory*)

the stars. The exchanges in polarity are accompanied by the ebb and flow of certain gases between high and low latitudes in the atmospheres of these stars.

SPECTRA OF THE STARS

12·8. Photographs of Stellar Spectra are generally taken in two different ways. One method employs the *slit spectroscope* at the focus of the telescope. It permits a wider separation of the spectrum lines and the recording of a laboratory spectrum adjacent to the star's spectrum (Fig. 12·5). In the second method a large prism of small angle is placed in front of the telescope objective, so that the whole apparatus is a spectroscope without slit or collimator. This *objective prism* type is employed chiefly in qualitative studies of the spectra of many stars. A single photograph shows the spectra of all stars of suitable brightness in the field of the telescope (Fig. 12·8).

Studies of stellar spectra in objective prism photographs were in progress at Harvard Observatory as early as 1885. An important product of those studies is the *Henry Draper Catalogue,* mainly the work of Annie J. Cannon, which with its extensions lists the positions, magnitudes, and spectral classes of 400,000 stars. The spectral classes of the catalog are the basis of our present classification and interpretation of the spectra of the stars.

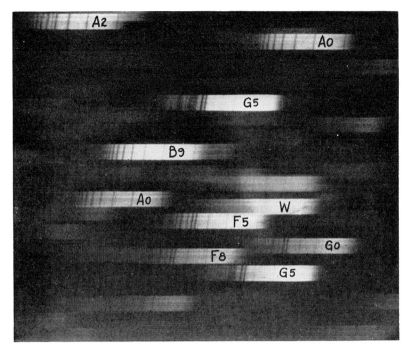

F<small>IG</small>. 12·8.   Objective Prism Spectra of Stars in a Region of Cepheus.
(*Photographed at Warner and Swasey Observatory*)

12·9. Classes of Stellar Spectra. The Harvard classification arrays the majority of the stars in a single continuous sequence with respect to the patterns of lines in their spectra. Six divisions of the sequence are the chief spectral classes, which are designated by the letters B, A, F, G, K, and M. Each class is divided into 10 parts. The spectra of class B, for example, are listed as B0, B1, B2, . . . , B9; and the next step is A0. Some features of the different classes, as they appear in the violet and blue regions, follow.

Class B. Helium lines are prominent in the spectra of these blue stars. Hydrogen lines increase in intensity through the subdivisions. Examples are Spica and Rigel.

Class A. Hydrogen lines attain their greatest intensity at A0, and then decline through the remainder of the sequence. Examples are Sirius and Vega.

Class F. Metallic lines become more intense, particularly the Fraunhofer H and K lines of calcium. These are yellowish stars, such as Canopus and Procyon.

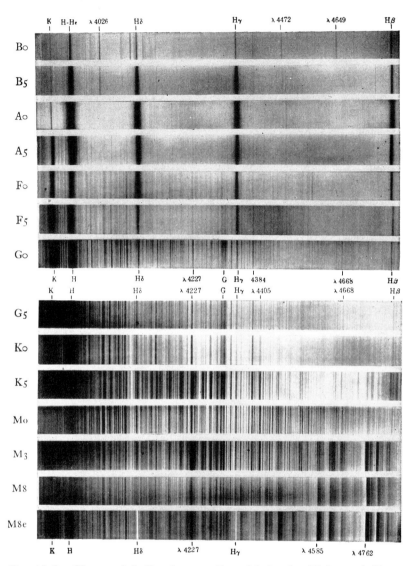

FIG. 12·9.   Classes of Stellar Spectra, B to M, in the Violet and Blue.
(*Photographed at the Observatory, University of Michigan*)

Class G. Metallic lines are numerous and conspicuous in the spectra of these yellow stars. The sun and Capella belong to this class.

Class K. Lines of the more active metals are prominent. Molecular bands are increasing. These stars are reddish. Examples are Arcturus and Aldebaran.

Class M. Bands of the titanium oxide spectrum are prominent. The violet end of the spectrum is weakened. These are red stars. Examples are Betelgeuse and Antares.

Stars which do not belong to the 6 most populous divisions form branching classes at the ends of the sequence. Preceding class B are O and W; the latter, having spectra characterized by broad bright lines, are known as Wolf-Rayet stars. The spectra of red stars of classes R and N contain carbon bands, and those of class S have bands produced by zirconium oxide.

12·10. The Sequence of Stellar Spectra. The progression in the line patterns along the sequence is not caused mainly by difference of chemical composition. Helium is not more abundant in the B stars, nor is hydrogen in the A stars. The sequence is in order of diminishing surface temperature and, therefore, of increasing redness of the stars. The temperatures of blue stars range from around 10,000° to more than 25,000° K, of yellow stars from 5000° to 6000° K, and of the reddest stars less than 3000° K, where K denotes absolute Centigrade. The dark lines of the different chemical elements become most intense at temperatures where their atoms in the stars' atmospheres are most active in absorbing light.

The compact helium atoms imprint their lines most effectively at high temperatures. Hydrogen atoms are most effective at more moderate temperatures, although the great abundance of this element in the stars makes their lines visible throughout the sequence. Neutral atoms of the metals are more easily disrupted and, accordingly, show their lines most conspicuously at still lower temperatures. Atoms assemble into molecules in the cooler atmospheres of the red stars, where they produce their characteristic bands in the spectra.

Difference of density in the stars adds variety in the sequence. The more luminous yellow and red stars have rarer and cooler atmospheres than the less luminous stars of the same spectral classes. This effect in included in the more recent and very useful classification of stellar spectra by W. W. Morgan and P. C. Keenan.

Nearly 2000 years ago, for the purpose of more easily identifying the stars in his catalog, Ptolemy divided the stars into 6 classes, or *magnitudes,* in order of their brightness. The brightest stars were assigned to the 1st magnitude. Somewhat less bright stars, such as the pole star, were of the 2nd magnitude. Each succeeding class contained stars fainter than the one before it, until the 6th magnitude remained for stars barely visible to the unaided eye on a clear moonless night.

12·11. Apparent Magnitudes. In modern practice the brightness and magnitudes of the stars are related by the rule: the logarithm of the ratio of brightness of two stars equals 0.4 times their difference of magnitude. By this rule a star of the 1st magnitude is $2\frac{1}{2}$ times as bright as one of the 2nd, more than 6 times as bright as one of the 3rd, and 100 times as bright as a 6th-magnitude star.

The earlier plan is extended to include stars visible only with telescopes. Stars down to the 19th magnitude can be seen with the 200-inch Palomar telescope, and stars as faint as the 24th magnitude can be photographed with it. There has been an upward revision of the range as well; the very brightest of the original 1st-magnitude stars are promoted to smaller-numbered classes by the requirement of the rule. Vega, which is about $2\frac{1}{2}$ times as bright as a standard 1st-magnitude star, is accordingly of the zero magnitude. Sirius, which is more than $2\frac{1}{2}$ times as bright as Vega, is of magnitude -1.6.

These *apparent magnitudes* denote the brightness of the stars as they appear in our skies, depending on their actual brightness and their distances from us. The magnitudes can be measured to hundredths in the photographs, and to thousandths by the more precise photoelectric methods. Along with the distances, motions, and spectra, the apparent magnitudes provide the basic data of observation for the studies of the stars.

12·12. Magnitudes in Different Colors. Where two stars differ in color, their difference in brightness is generally not the same in the blue-sensitive photographs as it is with the eye which is most sensitive to yellow light. Note, for example, how faint the red star Betelgeuse appears compared with the blue Rigel in the photograph of Orion (Fig. 11·15). As we see them in the sky, the red star averages scarcely more than half a magnitude the fainter of the two.

The magnitudes of stars in different colors of their light are measured in photographs with suitably stained plates exposed through color filters or photoelectrically through filters. They are generally observed in the ultraviolet, blue, visual, or yellow, and infrared, and are denoted respectively by the letters U, B, V, and I. The magnitudes of standard stars are being carefully determined

FIG. 12·12. A Red Star Appears Fainter in Blue (left) than in Yellow Light. (*Photographed at Yerkes Observatory*)

in the different colors, so that all investigators may keep to the same color systems.

The *color index* of a star is the difference of its magnitudes in any two selected colors. Its value is given most often as the difference, $B - V$, between the blue and visual magnitudes. The color index is then a useful numerical expression of the star's color. Taken as zero for stars of spectral class A0, it is accordingly negative for the bluest stars and reaches a positive value of 2 magnitudes or more for the reddest ones. In such determinations it is necessary to distinguish between the natural colors of the stars and any reddening of their light by intervening cosmic dust.

12·13. The Brightest Stars . The 20 stars listed in Table 12·I are brighter than apparent visual magnitude 1.5 and are often called "stars of the 1st magnitude," although they range through nearly 3 magnitudes. Fifteen of them can be seen in their seasons through-

TABLE 12·I. THE BRIGHTEST STARS

Name		Apparent Visual Magnitude	Spectrum	Parallax	Distance in Light Years	Absolute Visual Magnitude
α Canis Majoris	Sirius	−1.6 ^{d}	A0	0″.375	8.7	+1.3
* α Carinae	Canopus	−0.9	F0	.018	180	−4.6
* α Centauri		+0.1 ^{d}	G0	.760	4.3	+4.7
α Lyrae	Vega	0.1	A0	.123	26.5	+0.5
α Aurigae	Capella	0.2	G0	.073	45	−0.5
α Boötis	Arcturus	0.2	K0	.090	36	0.0
β Orionis	Rigel	0.3 ^{d}	B8	.005	650	−6.2
α Canis Minoris	Procyon	0.5 ^{d}	F5	.288	11.3	+2.8
* α Eridani	Achernar	0.6	B5	.023	140	−2.6
* β Centauri		0.9	B1	.016	200	−3.1
α Aquilae	Altair	0.9	A5	.198	16.5	+2.4
α Orionis	Betelgeuse	0.9 ^{v}	M2	.005	650	−5.6
* α Crucis		1.0 ^{d}	B1	.015	220	−2.7
α Tauri	Aldebaran	1.1 ^{d}	K5	.048	68	−0.5
β Geminorum	Pollux	1.2	K0	.093	35	+1.0
α Virginis	Spica	1.2	B2	.021	160	−2.2
α Scorpii	Antares	1.2 ^{d}	M1	.019	170	−2.4
α Piscis Austrini	Fomalhaut	1.3	A3	.144	23	+2.1
α Cygni	Deneb	1.3	A2	.006	540	−4.8
α Leonis	Regulus	1.3 ^{d}	B8	.039	84	−0.7

* Not visible in latitude 40° N.

^{d} Double star with telescope. The combined magnitude is given.

^{v} Light varies through a range of about a magnitude.

out the United States. The remaining 5 become visible south of the following north latitudes: Canopus, 38°; Achernar, 33°; Alpha and Beta Centauri, 30°; Alpha Crucis, 28°. It will be noticed that 3 of the southern stars have no personal names.

Betelgeuse and Antares are the reddest of the very bright stars, as is shown by their spectrum classes. Aldebaran, Arcturus, and Pollux are reddish. Capella and Alpha Centauri are yellow like the sun. Alpha Crucis and Spica are the bluest. The colors of even the brightest stars are pale compared with the red and green lights of an airplane flying against the background of the constellations, but they are readily distinguished with the naked eye.

The parallaxes in the table are taken from a list prepared by P. van de Kamp at Sproul Observatory. The brightest stars, as we see, have a considerable range of distance from us. Alpha Centauri, Sirius, and Procyon are among the nearest stars. Rigel, Betelgeuse, and Deneb are so remote that their distances are known less reliably; they are evidently very luminous to shine so brightly in our skies. The significance of the last column of the table is our next consideration.

12·14. Absolute Magnitudes. If the stars were all at the same distance from the earth, as the early scholars supposed they were, their apparent magnitudes would correctly represent their actual relative brightness, or *luminosity*. Where the distances are known, it is easy to calculate what the magnitudes would be if the stars were equally far away. Astronomers arbitrarily place the globe of their calculation at the distance around us where the stars would have the parallax of 0″.1.

The *absolute magnitudes* of the stars are the magnitudes they would have at the distance of 10 parsecs, or $32\frac{1}{2}$ light years. The relation is:

$$M = m + 5 - 5 \log r,$$

where M is the absolute magnitude, m is the apparent magnitude at the distance r in parsecs. The absolute magnitude has the same character as the apparent magnitude from which it is derived, whether visual or in some other color.

The sun's absolute visual magnitude is +4.8. At the moderate distance of $32\frac{1}{2}$ light years, the sun would therefore appear as a star only faintly visible to the unaided eye. Notice in the last column of the table that the apparently brightest stars are all more luminous than the sun.

TWO POPULATIONS OF STARS

Since its introduction by H. N. Russell at Princeton, in 1913, the diagram in which the absolute magnitudes of stars are arrayed with respect to their spectrum classes has played a leading part in directing the studies of the stars. More recently, in 1944, Baade at Mount Wilson Observatory explained that stars in various regions of the universe form two different arrays in the diagram, which he named the type I and type II populations. The first type is represented by stars in the sun's vicinity, the second by stars of the globular clusters. This broad spatial division does not take into account the evolutionary stages of stars as clearly as it originally seemed to do; but the manner of its possible division has not yet been formally decided.

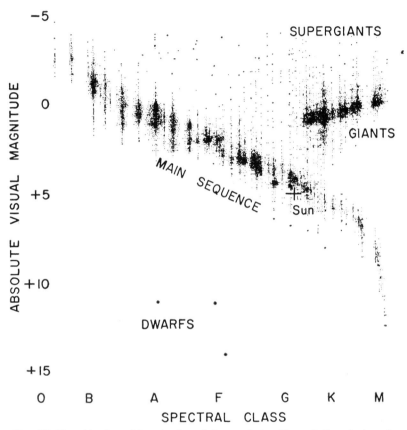

FIG. 12·15. Absolute Magnitudes of Stars of the Type I Population Arrayed with Respect to Their Spectral Classes. The point at magnitude +4.8 and class G2 represents the sun. (*Diagram by W. Gyllenberg, Lund Observatory*)

12·15. The Type I Population; the Main Sequence. When the absolute magnitudes of stars in our neighborhood are plotted with respect to their spectral classes, as in Fig. 12·15, the majority of the points appear in a band running diagonally across the diagram. This band is known as the *main sequence*. Its stars fainter than absolute magnitude +1 are often called dwarf stars.

The sun (absolute visual magnitude +4.8, class G2) belongs to the main sequence, as we see. Blue stars of the sequence are more luminous than the sun because they are hotter and somewhat larger. Red stars of the sequence are less luminous than the sun because they are cooler and somewhat smaller. Remembering that the sun at this standard distance of 32½ light years would appear as a star barely visible to the unaided eye, we understand why these red stars are generally invisible without the telescope.

12·16. Giant and Dwarf Stars. *Giant stars* are more luminous than are main-sequence stars of the same spectral class. They are giants in size as well. All stars of the same class have the same order of surface temperature, and therefore of surface brightness per square mile. If one class M star, for example, greatly surpasses another in luminosity, its surface must contain many more square miles; its diameter must be much the greater.

The dots near the top of Fig. 12·15 represent the *supergiants,* the most luminous stars. Those near the upper right corner denote the largest stars of all. The red supergiant Betelgeuse is one of these; its diameter is several hundred times that of the sun. The dots near the bottom of the diagram represent a few of the *white dwarfs.* Absolutely faint despite the fact that their surfaces are bluer and hotter than the sun's, these stars are not larger than some of the planets. An example is the companion of Sirius.

The type I population we are examining frequents dusty and gaseous regions, such as the spiral arms of our galaxy, in which the sun is situated.

12·17. The Type II Population of stars prevails in dust-free regions, and its combined light is redder than that of type I. Its giant sequence (Fig. 12·17) begins with K stars of absolute magnitude −2.4. On the downslope in the diagram it divides into two branches, one of which runs horizontally to the left at about magnitude zero. The second branch continues on down to join the main sequence at class F. Its extension toward the red along this sequence, based on recent studies of stars in globular clusters, is shown in Fig. 14·8.

The distribution of the two types of population in the galactic system and the exterior galaxies is described in later chapters.

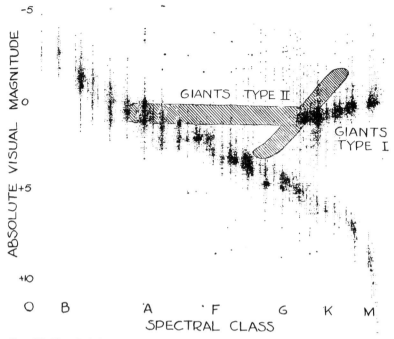

FIG. 12·17. Original Spectrum-Magnitude Diagram of the Type II Population. The points represent stars of type I, as in Fig. 12·15. The shaded strips represent type II giants. (*Adapted from a diagram by Walter Baade*)

QUESTIONS ON CHAPTER 12

1. Explain that the parallax method of measuring the distances of stars is more effective for the nearer stars.

2. The parallax of Altair is 0″.2. Show that the star's distance is 5 parsecs, 16 light years, or about 100 million million miles.

3. Distinguish between the proper motion and radial velocity of a star. Explain how each is determined.

4. How is the sun's motion relative to the stars around it revealed by the proper motions of these stars? by their radial velocities?

5. Stars with short periods of rotation have wide spectrum lines where their axes are not nearly in the line of sight. Explain.

6. State the class of stellar spectra in which: (a) hydrogen lines are most intense; (b) helium lines are most prominent; (c) lines of neutral metals are most conspicuous; (d) molecular bands appear. Account for the differences.

7. The apparent magnitude of a star is readily observed. Explain (12·14) that: (a) its absolute magnitude can be calculated if its distance is known, or (b) its distance can be calculated if its absolute magnitude is independently known.

8. Why is the color index of a red star greater than that of a blue star?

9. Explain that a giant star must be larger than a main-sequence star of the same spectral class.

10. Explain that the red supergiant stars are the largest stars. Name an example.

11. In what respects do the white dwarf stars differ from other stars? Name an example.

12. State the main differences between the two populations of stars.

REFERENCES

Hoyle, Fred, *Frontiers of Astronomy*. Harper and Brothers, New York, 1955.

Schlesinger, Frank, and Louise F. Jenkins, *Catalogue of Bright Stars*. "Containing all important data known in January, 1940, relating to all stars brighter than 6.5 visual magnitude and to some fainter ones." Second edition. Yale University Observatory, New Haven, 1940.

van de Kamp, Peter, *Basic Astronomy*. The Macmillan Company, New York, 1952.

Observer's Cage of 200-inch Hale Telescope.

13

DOUBLE AND VARIABLE STARS

BINARY STARS; ECLIPSING BINARIES — PULSATING STARS
— RED VARIABLE STARS — EXPLOSIVE STARS

Binary stars are physically associated pairs of stars. In some pairs the stars are far enough apart to be separated with the telescope; in others they can be observed only with the spectroscope. Some of the latter binaries mutually eclipse as they revolve, so that they vary in brightness.

Many single stars are variable in their light because they are pulsating. Irregular variations of large red stars are ascribed to their partial veiling by clouds rising high above them, and those of smaller stars seem to be caused by the influx of dust grains in their atmospheres or by local flares at their surfaces. Spectacular variations in light are exhibited by explosive stars.

BINARY STARS; ECLIPSING BINARIES

13·1. Visual Binary Stars are single stars to the naked eye, which are separated into physically connected pairs with the telescope.

| 1908 | 1915 | 1920 |

Fig. 13·1. Binary Star Krueger 60. Between 1908 and 1920 the double star, in the upper left corners, completed about a quarter of a revolution. See also Fig. 13·13. (*Photographed at Yerkes Observatory*)

Mizar, at the bend in the Great Dipper's handle (Fig. 11·8) was the first of these, in 1650, to be reported; the reference is not to

Mizar and its neighbor Alcor. Alpha Centauri and Castor are other early known examples. The stars of each pair are mutually revolving. More than 20,000 visual binaries are recognized, but not more than a tenth of these have made observable progress in their orbits and only a few have made complete revolutions since their discoveries. The majority are recognized only by their similar proper motions.

The orbits of somewhat more than 100 visual binaries are reliably determined. These are often the orbits of the fainter stars of the pairs relative to the brighter ones. The *apparent orbits* are observed in projection against the face of the sky, and are then turned by calculation into their actual planes. They are usually ellipses of considerable eccentricity. Among the many visual binaries we select Sirius and its companion as particularly interesting examples.

13·2. The Companion of Sirius. One of the nearest stars, the brilliant Dog Star drifts in the heavens three fourths the apparent width of the full moon in 1000 years. As early as 1844, Bessel at Königsberg discovered that it is pursuing a wavy course instead of having the uniform motion of a single star. He concluded that Sirius is mutually revolving with a traveling companion, and he derived its orbit around the center of mass with the unseen companion.

The companion was first seen, in 1862, by a telescope maker who was testing a new lens, now the objective of the 18-inch telescope at Dearborn Observatory. The companion revolves with the bright star in a period of 50 years and in an orbit of

Fig. 13·2. Sirius and Its Companion. The large dot in this negative is the image of Sirius. The small dot below it and to the left is the companion. (*Photographed at Leander McCormick Observatory*)

rather high eccentricity (Fig. 13·2A). Despite the glare of Sirius it is clearly visible with large telescopes except when the two stars are the least separated. The latest periastron passage occurred in 1944, and the widest separation will come in 1969. The companion of Sirius was the first to be known of the very dense white dwarf stars (12·16).

The companion of Procyon was likewise discovered by Bessel from its gravitational effect on the proper motion of the bright star and, eventually, was observed with the telescope. A recent case is the companion of the faint red star Ross 614, which was detected by Sarah L. Lippincott at Sproul Observatory and was later shown in a photograph by Baade with the 200-inch Palomar

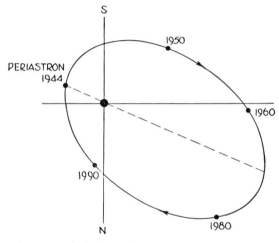

FIG. 13·2A.   Apparent Relative Orbit of the Companion of Sirius.   The stars were least separated in 1944.

telescope.   This companion has a mass that is only 8 per cent of the sun's mass and is one of the least massive stars thus far directly observed.   As yet unseen companions of other stars have been discovered by the variable proper motions of apparently single stars or by the irregularities in the revolutions of binary stars; examples are Barnard's star and the well-known binary star 61 Cygni.

13·3. Weighing the Stars.   Binary stars provide a means of determining the masses of the stars.   The rule is found in the general statement of Kepler's harmonic law (7·12).   Let one pair of mutually revolving bodies be a visual binary, and let the second pair be the sun and the earth.   Where the units of measurement are the sun's mass (the mass of the earth is negligible in comparison), the earth's mean distance from the sun, and the sidereal year, the law becomes:

The combined mass of the pair of stars equals the cube of their mean distance apart divided by the square of their period of revolution. By use of this relation, which requires a knowledge of the relative orbit and its distance from us, it is possible to "weigh" many pairs of stars.

13·4. Spectroscopic Binary Stars are mutually revolving pairs which are not separated with the telescope. They are recognized by the periodic oscillations of the lines of their spectra, the Doppler effect as the two stars alternately approach and recede from us in their revolutions. Capella and Spica are examples among the brightest stars.

The brighter star of Mizar's visual pair was the first spectroscopic binary to be detected. In the annals of double stars this one in

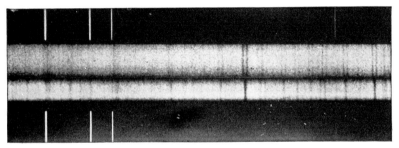

Fig. 13·4. Spectrum of Mizar. The dark lines in the spectra of the two components are separated in the upper spectrum and superposed in the lower one. (*Photographed at Mount Wilson Observatory*)

the Dipper's handle is doubly famous. In the early studies of stellar spectra at Harvard Observatory it was noticed, in 1889, that the dark lines in the spectrum of Mizar were double in some photographs and single in others (Fig. 13·4). Where the two stars of a binary differ considerably in brightness, however, only the shifting lines of the brighter one are visible in the spectrum.

Not all oscillating lines indicate revolving pairs. The effect is also observed in the spectra of pulsating single stars (13·10). In addition, the lines in the spectra of all stars oscillate during a year as the earth alternately approaches and recedes from them in its revolution around the sun.

13·5. Eclipsing Binary Stars have their orbits so nearly edgewise to the earth that the stars mutually eclipse twice in the course of

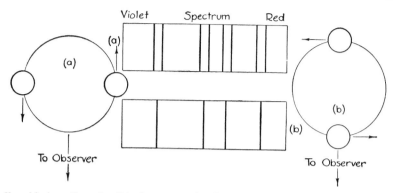

Fɪɢ. 13·4ᴀ. Doppler Displacements in the Spectrum of Mizar. (a) When one star approaches and the other recedes from us, the lines are double. (b) When both stars are moving across the line of sight, the lines are not displaced and are superposed.

each revolution. Through the telescope they appear as single stars which become fainter while the eclipses are in progress. The periods in which they revolve and fluctuate in light average 2 or 3 days, although many are only a few hours. The shortest known period of 4ʰ 39ᵐ is that of Nova Herculis, recently discovered to be an eclipsing star by M. F. Walker. In the very exceptional case of Epsilon Aurigae, the eclipses occur at intervals of 27 years and last about 2 years. Viewed from another part of our stellar system the stars that wink in this way for us might shine with constant light, while other close pairs of invariable brightness for us would undergo eclipses.

From their studies of eclipsing stars astronomers are deriving much information about features of stars in general. Analyses of the light and spectrum variations give remarkably clear pictures of these binary systems, showing the sizes and masses of their stars as well as the characteristics of their orbits. Studies of certain of these useful pairs by Otto Struve and others reveal that gas streams issue from their stars and swirl in the directions of their revolutions, seeming to represent prominence activity on a scale far surpassing that in the sun.

13·6. Algol, the "Demon Star," is among the most famous of the eclipsing stars. In the severed head of Medusa which Perseus carried in the old picture book of the skies, Algol (Beta Persei) winks in a way that might have seemed mysterious until the reason for its

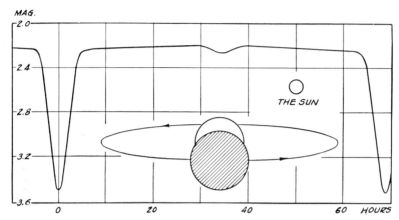

F_{IG}. 13·6. Light Variation and System of Algol. The size of the sun is shown on the same scale. (*Determined by Joel Stebbins*)

winking came to be understood. Algol revolves with a somewhat larger and considerably fainter companion in a period of 2 days and 21 hours (Fig. 13·6). Once in each revolution the companion passes in front of the brighter star, partially eclipsing it for nearly 10 hours. At the middle of this eclipse the light of the system is reduced to a third its normal brightness. The slight decrease in the light midway between the primary eclipses occurs when the companion is itself partially eclipsed.

The diameter of the brighter star is 3 times the sun's diameter. The centers of the two stars are 13 million miles apart, or slightly more than a third the mean distance of the planet Mercury from the sun. Their orbits are inclined 8° from the edgewise position.

PULSATING STARS

13·7. Variable Stars are stars that vary in brightness. Their fluctuations in light are discovered and studied by comparing them repeatedly with stars of constant brightness. The comparisons are often made in photographs taken at different times, or with the photoelectric cell where the highest precision is required. They are observed visually as well, especially where the variations are of large range. Amateur astronomers with small telescopes have found here an interesting and useful field.

The character of a particular variable star is recognized from the *light curve,* which shows how the star's magnitude varies with

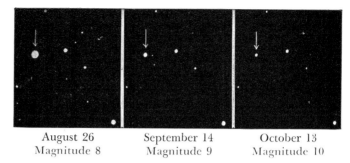

August 26	September 14	October 13
Magnitude 8	Magnitude 9	Magnitude 10

FIG. 13·7. Variation in Brightness of the Recurrent Nova RS Ophiuchi in 1933. (*Photographed by F. Quénisset*)

time. Where the fluctuation proceeds in regular cycles, the curve for a single cycle is representative; it is then described by giving the time of a selected phase, such as maximum brightness, and the period, or interval of time to the next similar phase. Each variable star is generally designated by a letter or two, or else by the letter V and a number, followed by the possessive of its constellation name. Examples are RR Lyrae and V335 Sagittarii.

Intrinsic variable stars are variable naturally and not because of their eclipses. They are mainly pulsating stars, irregular variable stars, and explosive stars.

13·8. Pulsating Stars. Many intrinsic variable stars fluctuate in brightness because they are rhythmically contracting and expanding. The stars become hotter as they contract, and cooler in turn as they expand. The process takes time to run out to the surfaces and into the atmospheres. Thus the stars are brightest to us not when they are most compressed but when their gases are moving outward fastest, and they are faintest when their gases are returning fastest. Such pulsations are held accountable directly or indirectly for the fluctuations in brightness of practically all supergiant and giant stars which have any semblance of regularity.

The periods of the variations in brightness become longer with diminishing density of the stars, from the blue to the red ones, according to a rule formulated by the English astronomer Eddington. The rule is that the period of the pulsation is inversely proportional to the square root of the star's density.

Pulsating stars are mainly of 4 types: RR Lyrae variables, cepheid variables, long-period variables, and other semiregular variables, which we examine in this order. A fifth type having only a dozen recognized members is being currently studied by Struve and his associates. Known as Beta Canis Majoris variables, they are highly luminous blue stars of early class B, having very small variations in periods of from $3\frac{1}{2}$ to 6 hours.

13·9. RR Lyrae Variables are named after one of their brightest examples. They are also known as cluster variables because they were first observed in the globular star clusters, although they are now recognized in greater numbers outside the clusters. They are blue giants of class A. They belong to the type II population and occupy a small domain all by themselves in the spectrum-luminosity diagram. Their fluctuations are in slightly irregular cycles of around half a day, and many of them rise very abruptly to their maxima.

All RR Lyrae variable stars have zero absolute *median magnitude,* the average of their greatest and least brightness. Thus their distances become known wherever their apparent magnitudes are observed. These useful stars have provided dependable distances of various features of the galactic system including the globular clusters, but they are too faint to be employed for measuring the distances of most exterior galaxies.

13·10. Cepheid Variable Stars take their name from one of their earliest recognized examples, Delta Cephei, in the little triangle that marks the southeast corner of the spire-like Cepheus (Map 1) in the northern sky. This star fluctuates with perfect regularity in cycles of 5 days and 9 hours, brightening more rapidly than it fades.

At their brightest the cepheids have the lines in their spectra displaced farthest to the violet, showing that the gases in front of the stars are moving toward us at greatest speed. At their faintest, the lines are displaced farthest to the red, showing that these gases are receding at greatest speed. While the stars are becoming fainter, their light also becomes redder and their spectra change to patterns of cooler stars.

Cepheid stars are yellow supergiants, of classes F and G. Their periods range from a day to several weeks, and are most frequent around 5 days. The more numerous *classical cepheids,* such as Delta Cephei, belong to the type I population, and those in our

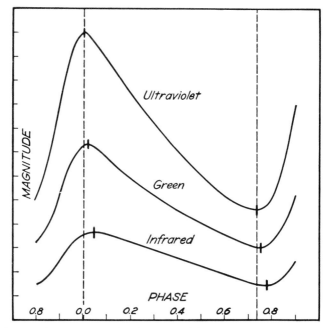

F<small>IG</small>. 13·10.   Light Curves of Delta Cephei in Three Colors.   The range of
the light variation is less and the times of maximum and minimum brightness are later in the longer wave lengths.   (*Determined photoelectrically
by Joel Stebbins*)

own galaxy accordingly congregate toward the Milky Way.   *Type
II cepheids* are associated with the second population and have
been recognized especially in the globular clusters.   Their light
curves are more nearly symmetrical and have broader maxima.
An example is W Virginis.

13·11. The Period-Luminosity Relation connects the periods and
absolute median photographic magnitudes of cepheid stars.   The
longer the period of the light variation, the more luminous is the
star.   Originally established by Shapley in 1917, the relation was
given its present form (Fig. 13·11) by Baade in 1952 as one of the
earliest achievements with the 200-inch Hale telescope.   The original curve for the classical cepheids is now raised 1.5 magnitudes in
the diagram, and it is replaced at the lower level by the curve for
the type II cepheids.   Classical cepheids accordingly have twice the
distances formerly assigned them.   Because these stars have set the

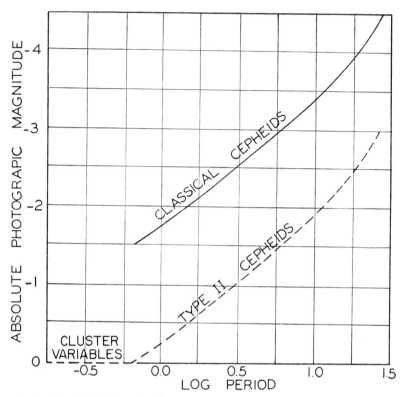

FIG. 13·11.   Period-Luminosity Curves for Cepheids.   From these curves the absolute median magnitude of a cepheid can be read when the period of the light variation is known.   The median magnitudes of all RR Lyrae (cluster) variables are zero.

scale of distances for most systems outside the Milky Way, the correction multiplies by the factor 2 the former distances and diameters of almost all exterior galaxies.   Other corrections, required by the new photoelectric magnitude standards, further magnify the original scale for these galaxies, as we see in Chapter 17.

When the period of a cepheid star is known, the absolute median magnitude, M, can be read from the appropriate curve.   Where the median apparent magnitude, m, is also observed, the distance, r, in parsecs is calculated by the formula: $\log r = (m - M + 5)/5$. In the case of an RR Lyrae variable the median absolute magnitude is zero regardless of the period.   All such distances require correction where cosmic dust intervenes.

13·12. Long-Period Variable Stars. Many red supergiant and giant stars, mainly of class M, are variable in brightness in semiregular manner. Their periods range from a few months to more than 2 years, being most frequent around 275 days. Their light variations range from 4 to nearly 10 visual magnitudes. They are often recognized by the bright lines which make their appearance in the spectra along with the characteristic dark lines and bands of the cooler stars (Fig. 12·9). The light variations of these stars are more complex than are those of cepheid stars, as indicated by the considerable departure from regularity in their periods and in their ranges in brightness from cycle to cycle.

Mira, in the constellation Cetus (Map 5), is the best known of the *long-period variables*. It was, in fact, the first variable star of any kind to be discovered, aside from a few "new" stars, and was accordingly called *stella mira*. This red supergiant has an average diameter several hundred times the sun's diameter, as measured with the interferometer; it is surrounded by extensive clouds of gases and perhaps of solid particles as well. Fluctuating in the average period of 330 days, the visual magnitude is around 3.5 at its brightest and 9 at its faintest, when it is accordingly invisible to the naked eye.

Certain variable stars of classes G and K, known as RV Tauri stars, from one of their well-known examples, are semiregular, forming a sort of connecting link between the cepheids and the red variables. Like the long-period variables, their regular pulsations seem to act as a trigger mechanism for less regular effects in their atmospheres.

RED VARIABLE STARS

13·13. Irregular Variable Stars. Red supergiant and giant stars frequently vary irregularly within rather narrow limits, seldom more than half a magnitude, because of effects in their atmospheres. Betelgeuse, having a visual range from magnitude 0.2 to 1.2, is the brightest of these *irregular variables*.

The behavior of the red supergiant Alpha Herculis has been clarified by the spectroscopic studies of A. J. Deutsch. This star varies unpredictably between magnitudes 3.0 and 4.0 in irregular cycles of several months' duration. Its distance is 500 light years and its diameter is 500 million miles as measured with the interferometer. It is surrounded by an expanding shell of patchy clouds which rise to heights above the star of at least 700 times the earth's distance from the sun. At very high levels they become clouds of solid particles, perhaps of soot, which disappear by dilution as they move outward and are replaced by others. Their partial veiling of the star is believed to be the cause of the irregular variability of Alpha Herculis and of other large red stars.

Some stars in dusty regions, generally red and yellow main-sequence stars, vary irregularly in brightness. Studied particularly by A. H. Joy at Mount Wilson Observatory, they are known as T Tauri stars. Their atmospheres are brightened irregularly by the influx of dust grains from the surrounding regions. Blue stars in the same neighborhoods do not show these effects, evidently because the dust grains are repelled by the strong radiations of the hot stars.

13·14. Flare Stars. Some red main-sequence stars are known as *flare stars*. They are subject to intense outbursts of very short

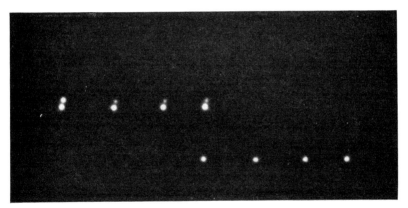

FIG. 13·14. Flare-Up of Krueger 60 B, July 26, 1939. The last of 4 successive exposures (left) on the binary and its distant optical companion shows the brightening of the fainter star of the pair. Note also by comparison with Fig. 13·1 that the binary, having a period of 44½ years, had made nearly three quarters of a revolution since 1908. (*Photographed at Sproul Observatory*)

duration remindful of the solar flares (10·14). Although the flares seem to be confined to rather small areas of the surfaces, their greater brightness than that of their dim surroundings much increases the total light of these stars. An example is the sudden and brief increase of 1½ magnitudes in the normally fainter star of the visual binary Krueger 60 (Fig. 13·14) reported by P. van de Kamp and S. L. Lippincott at Sproul Observatory.

13·15. Novae are stars which rise abruptly from relative obscurity and gradually decline to their former faintness. They are designated by the word Nova followed by the possessive of the constellation name and the year of the outburst, or else by letters as for other variable stars. Thus Nova Herculis 1934 is also known as DQ Herculis.

A nova as bright as Venus appeared in Cassiopeia in November, 1572, and was observed by Tycho Brahe until it became invisible to the naked eye in the spring of 1574. A nova in Taurus in 1054 and another in Ophiuchus in 1604 were said to have been as bright as Jupiter. These three were presumably of the especially spectacular type known as supernovae, which are described in Chapter 17. Nova Aquilae 1918, the brightest of the present century, rose to nearly the brilliance of Sirius. Such bright ones are exceptional. The majority of more than 100 recorded novae in our galaxy did not become visible without the telescope.

13·16. The Outbursts of Novae. Before its outburst a nova is smaller and denser than the sun. We think of it as a semidegenerate star of the type II population, which is collapsing to become a white dwarf. More energy is liberated by the contraction than the small surface can radiate. The star then blows off the excess

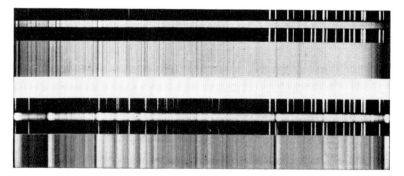

FIG. 13·16. Spectrum of Nova Herculis 1934. Before (above) and after (below) its greatest brightness. The widened spectrum appears below in each case. (*Photographed at Lick Observatory*)

energy along with a small fraction of its gaseous material in a succession of violent explosions. Clouds of gas emerge with speeds that have exceeded 3000 miles a second, as shown by the Doppler shifts of the spectrum lines. With the growing volume of these hot gases the star may rise 12 magnitudes, or about 60,000 times, in brightness.

The gas clouds are opaque at first, as D. B. McLaughlin has explained. The dark spectrum lines absorbed by the gases in front of the star are displaced strongly to the violet, giving the illusion that the whole star is swelling enormously. Soon after maximum light the spreading gas clouds become more nearly transparent. Bright undisplaced lines then appear in the spectrum (Fig. 13·16), much broadened because the light then comes both from parts of the star which are approaching us and parts which are receding from us in the expansion. The broad bright lines are bordered at their violet edges by narrow dark lines absorbed as before by the gases in front of the star.

When the surrounding gas clouds have become still more tenuous, the spectrum changes to the bright-line pattern of a fluorescent nebula. Meanwhile the brightness fades as the envelope is dissipated by its expansion, until the star returns to its original status. As an example, Nova Aquilae 1918 is now a faintly luminous white star a quarter as great and 70 times as dense as the sun.

13·17. Expanding Envelopes Around Novae. The gas clouds produced by the explosions of novae have sometimes grown large enough to be observed directly with the telescope. Nova Aquilae 1918 had a spherical envelope. It began to appear 4 months after the outburst and increased in radius at the rate of 1″ a year, which at its distance of 1200 light years means an increase of 1000 miles a second. In 1940, the vanishing envelope had a radius exceeding 5000 times the earth's distance from the sun. The envelope around Nova Herculis 1934 was ellipsoidal. All are likely to be composed of several shells representing successive explosions.

The envelopes around the novae have generally disappeared in a few years. Their short durations and rapid expansions differ from the long lives and slower expansions of the planetary nebulae (15·3), which they otherwise resemble. Yet the Crab nebula in Taurus (Fig. 13·17), now increasing in radius at the rate of 70 million miles a year, seems to have been spreading for more than 900 years from the site of a nova.

FIG. 13·17. Crab Nebula, M 1, in Taurus. The nebula is expanding from the site of a nova. (*Photographed with the Hale telescope, Mount Wilson and Palomar Observatories*)

13·18. Recurrent Novae, which have two or more recorded outbursts, seem to differ from normal novae only in their more moderate rise in brightness (around 7 magnitudes), and in their more rapid decline. Six recurrent novae are known. An example is RS Ophiuchi (Fig. 13·7), usually about the 12th magnitude, which rose abruptly to the 4th magnitude in 1898 and again in 1933.

There is also a group of variable stars having nova-like characteristics; SS Cygni is representative of this group. Normally around magnitude 15, they rise abruptly 5 magnitudes or less and decline more slowly, at irregular intervals which average from 2 or 3 weeks to several months. There is some indication that the intervals between the outbursts of nova-like stars increase with the extents of their rise in brightness. If the relation holds for normal novae, the intervals between their outbursts should be several thousand years, so that explosive stars such as Nova Aquilae 1918 might be expected to flare out again. Because it does not belong to this category of unstable stars, the sun is unlikely to be explosive, at least for several billion years to come.

QUESTIONS ON CHAPTER 13

1. The majority of visual binary stars have shown no evidence of mutual revolution. How is it known that they are physically connected?

2. Describe the discovery of the companion of Sirius before it was observed.

3. Why do the lines in the spectrum of Mizar (Fig. 13·4) appear double at times and single at other times?

4. Where the spectrum lines of a star are always single, how is it possible to decide whether it is an ordinary single star, a pulsating star, or a spectroscopic binary where the fainter spectrum is not visible?

5. The diagram of the system of Algol shown in Fig. 13·6 is derived from the accompanying light curve and the spectroscopic data. What features of the light curve show that:

(a) The eclipses are partial?
(b) The companion is much less luminous than the brighter star?
(c) The companion reflects some light of the brighter star?

6. Mention some differences between RR Lyrae stars, classical cepheids, and type II cepheids.

7. Explain the method of determining the distance of a classical cepheid variable star by means of the period-luminosity relation; the distance of an RR Lyrae variable star.

8. Show that the recent raising of the period-luminosity curve of the classical cepheids by 1½ magnitudes has doubled the former values of their distances.

9. Mention 3 types of intrinsic variable stars which are not pulsating stars.

10. Describe the outburst of a nova according to the view we have given here.

11. In what respects do recurrent novae differ from ordinary novae?

12. Does it seem likely that Nova Aquilae 1918 will flare out again? that the sun may soon become a nova? Explain.

REFERENCES

Aitken, Robert G., *The Binary Stars*. Second edition. McGraw-Hill Book Company, New York, 1935.

Campbell, Leon, and Luigi Jacchia, *The Story of Variable Stars*. Harvard University Press, Cambridge, 1941.

14

STAR CLUSTERS

14·1. Two Types of Clusters. Star clusters are assemblages of stars having their members less widely separated than are the stars around them. The stars of each group are moving together, so that the clusters maintain their identities for a long time. Because the members of a cluster are all practically at the same distance from us, they may be compared fairly one with another. The clusters are accordingly adding to our understanding of the different kinds of stars and their evolution. They are of two types: galactic clusters and globular clusters.

Galactic clusters are so named because those in our galaxy lie near its principal plane. They therefore appear close to the Milky Way except a few of the very nearest ones, notably the Coma Berenices cluster (Fig. 14·1). They are also known as *open clusters,* because they are loosely assembled and are not greatly concentrated toward their centers. Their stars are seen separately with the telescope, and the brightest stars of the nearest clusters are visible to the naked eye.

Globular clusters are spheroidal and are the larger and more compact of the two types. A familiar example is the great cluster in Hercules (Fig. 14·7). Globular clusters are visible at great distances from us. Instead of crowding toward the Milky Way, they form a nearly spherical halo around our galaxy.

The brighter clusters are often called by special names, such as the Praesepe and Pleiades clusters, or by the names of their constellations. More generally the clusters are designated by their running numbers on one of the two catalogs which also list many nebulae and exterior galaxies. Thus the Hercules cluster is known as M 13, or as NGC 6205. The first designation is the number in the catalog of 103 bright objects which the comet hunter Messier completed in 1784; a useful list of these objects and their positions in the sky is given by Owen Gingerich in *Sky and Telescope* for March, 1954. The second designation of the Hercules cluster is its number in Dreyer's *New General Catalogue.*

FIG. 14·1. Galactic Cluster in Coma Berenices. (*Photographed at Yerkes Observatory*)

FIG. 14·2. Praesepe Cluster in Cancer. (*Photographed by William Henry*)

14·2. Galactic Clusters. The Pleiades, or "Seven Sisters," in Taurus (Fig. 15·4) and the Hyades in the same constellation are familiar galactic clusters. Their brighter stars are plainly visible to the naked eye, and those of the Coma cluster are faintly visible. The Praesepe cluster in Cancer (Fig. 14·2), also known as the "Beehive," the double cluster in Perseus, and a few others are hazy spots to the eye alone, and are resolved into stars with binoculars. These and other clusters are fine objects for small telescopes. Galactic clusters are prominent in photographs of the Milky Way.

About 500 galactic clusters are recognized in our region of the galaxy. Their memberships generally range from about 20 to a few hundred stars, and exceed 1000 stars in the rich Perseus clusters. The known clusters are all within 20,000 light years from the sun. More remote ones are unnoticed against the bright background of the Milky Way or are concealed by heavy dust in these directions.

14·3. The Hyades Cluster offers an example of the common motions of cluster stars. It comprises the stars of the V-shaped group, except Aldebaran itself which has an independent motion not shown in the diagram (Fig. 14·3), and of the region some 15° in diameter around it. This cluster of at least 150 stars has its center 130 light years from the sun. It is moving toward the east and is also receding from us, so that the parallel paths of its stars are converging toward a point in the sky east of the present position

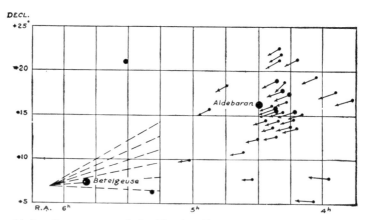

FIG. 14·3. Convergence of the Hyades Cluster. The stars of the cluster are converging toward a point in the sky east of the present position of Betelgeuse. The lengths of the arrows show the proper motions in 50,000 years.

of Betelgeuse. This cluster passed nearest the sun 800,000 years ago at half its present distance.

14·4. The Color-Magnitude Diagram. The size of a star cluster is so small compared with its distance from us that its stars may be considered to be all at the same distance. Thus the apparent magnitudes of these stars have the same relation as their absolute

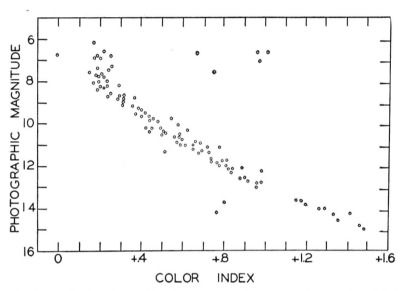

Fig. 14·4. Color-Magnitude Diagram of the Praesepe Cluster. (*Adapted from a diagram by Harold L. Johnson*)

magnitudes. The color-magnitude diagram of a cluster arrays the apparent magnitudes of its stars with respect to their color indexes.

Comparing our diagram for the Praesepe cluster with the standard spectrum-absolute magnitude diagram in Fig. 12·15 and remembering that color index has a known relation to spectrum class, we see how the distance of a cluster can be determined. The method is simply to match the apparent and absolute magnitudes for a particular part of the main sequence and then to calculate the distance of the cluster by the usual rule (13·11). In the case of the Praesepe cluster the distance is 575 light years.

Note that the top of the main sequence of the Praesepe cluster bends to the right, and that a few of the brightest stars are shown much farther to the right. According to a current theory of stellar evolution, the stars leave this sequence and become giants as they grow older, and the hotter stars do so sooner than the cooler ones. The shift from the main sequence is only for the hottest stars in

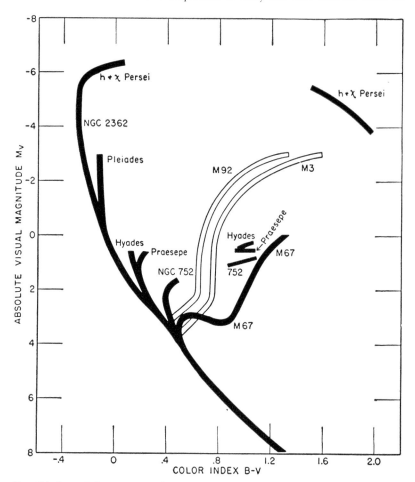

FIG. 14·4A.   Color-Magnitude Diagrams for Seven Galactic Clusters and Two Globular Clusters.   (*Diagram by Harold L. Johnson and Allan Sandage*)

the Perseus clusters (Fig. 14·4A). It extends to cooler stars in the Pleiades, still cooler ones in the Hyades and Praesepe, and so on. We seem to have here an important criterion of advancing ages of the galactic clusters, and we notice in the diagram a similar effect in the globular clusters M 92 and M 3.

An extreme effect of old age is seen for the galactic cluster M 67. This cluster is in Cancer not far from Praesepe in the sky. Both are at the unusual distance of 30° from the central line of the Milky Way. M 67 is 4½ times as far from us as is Praesepe, and it has the very unusual distance of 1450 light years from the principal plane of the galaxy. Away from the disturbing effects which tend to disrupt galactic clusters, it still contains 500 known stars and probably many fainter ones. In its old age its main sequence has retained only stars that are cooler and redder than the sun.

14·5. Lifetimes of Galactic Clusters. The common motions of the stars of a cluster indicates their common origin. The persistence of their nearly parallel motions shows that the cluster stars are not greatly affected by the field stars through which they pass. Yet at each encounter with a field star the cluster stars are attracted in different amounts, depending on how near the disturber they pass, so that their paths must be diverted slightly in different directions. Thus gradually loosened by the field stars, the clusters are prepared for eventual dispersal by other means. Galactic clusters, such as M 67, however, seem to have existed as long as anything else in our galaxy.

Some small groups of stars known as *associations* seem to be dispersing much more rapidly. The Dutch astronomer A. Blaauw reports that an aggregate of class B stars around Zeta Persei is spreading so swiftly that its stars were close together only 1.3 million years ago, having then presumably emerged from a turbulent dust cloud. The lives of other associations seem to be somewhat longer, but all are surprisingly short.

14·6. Globular Clusters are spheroidal assemblages often of many tens of thousands of stars. Some, such as the Omega Centauri cluster, shine with the brightness of a million suns. Over 100 globulars are recognized in the galactic system, and as many more are likely to be hiding behind its dust clouds. Scarce in space, not one of them has been seen within the distance of 20,000 light years from us, where all the known galactic clusters are observed. Their high luminosity makes them visible afar in our galaxy and around the nearer exterior galaxies.

The brightest globular clusters for us are Omega Centauri, near the northern edge of the Milky Way in the south polar region, and 47 Tucanae. They appear to the naked eye as slightly blurred stars of the 4th magnitude and were given designations as stars before their true character was recognized. These two are the nearest globulars, at the distance of 22,000 light years, and are among the richest ones. Messier 13 in Hercules is faintly visible to

Fig. 14·6. Globular Cluster Omega Centauri. (*Photographed with the 60-inch Reflector at the Southern Station of Harvard Observatory*)

the naked eye, as is M 22 in Sagittarius. Messier 5 in Serpens, M 55 in Sagittarius, and M 3 in Canes Venatici can be glimpsed without the telescope in favorable conditions.

14·7. The Hercules Cluster, M 13, at the distance of 30,000 light years is well known to observers in middle northern latitudes where it passes nearly overhead in the early evenings of summer. This cluster covers an area of the sky having two thirds the apparent diameter of the moon. Its linear diameter is 160 light years. More than 50,000 stars of the cluster are bright enough to be observed with present telescopes, although the stars in the central region are too crowded to be counted separately. The total membership may be 10 times as great. Like other globulars the Hercules cluster is an oblate spheroid; evidently it is flattened at the poles by slow rotation which is not otherwise detected.

The stars in the compact central region of the Hercules cluster have an average separation of 20,000 times the earth's distance from the sun, or about a twentieth of the spaces between the stars in the

Fig. 14·7. Globular Cluster M 13 in Hercules. (*Photographed with the Hale telescope, Mount Wilson and Palomar Observatories*)

sun's vicinity. For anyone living there the night sky would have a splendor quite unfamiliar to us. Probably a hundred times as many stars as we see in our skies would be visible to the naked eye from there, and the brightest ones would shine as brightly as the moon does for us.

14·8. The Type II Spectrum-Luminosity Diagram Extended. Baade's original diagram for the type II population (12·17) from his observations with the 100-inch telescope arrayed the giant stars chiefly, and it suggested the absence of the bluer stars of the main sequence. From their more recent photographs with the 200-inch telescope, Arp, Baum, and Sandage extended the diagram to fainter stars in the globular clusters M 3 and M 92 (Fig. 14·8). They showed that the type II main sequence begins at the end of the more nearly vertical giant branch and extends along down through the yellow stars to the limit of faintness that could be observed. They did not include the RR Lyrae stars in that survey, so that a gap appears in the horizontal branch of the giant sequence in the

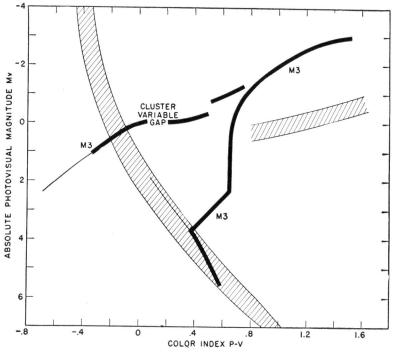

FIG. 14·8. Color-Magnitude Diagram of the Globular Cluster M 3. The type II array of the cluster stars is shown by the solid lines. The main sequence and red giants of the type I population not observed in the cluster are represented by the shaded areas. (*Diagram by H. C. Arp, W. A. Baum, and Allan Sandage, Mount Wilson and Palomar Observatories*)

diagram in the domain occupied only by those variable stars. The more luminous yellow and red stars of the cluster are represented near the upper right corner of the diagram. These include type II cepheids, semiregular variables, and some long-period variable stars.

14·9. The Array of Globular Clusters. More than 1300 variable stars are listed in globular clusters by Helen S. Hogg of the David

Dunlap Observatory. The majority are RR Lyrae stars, which have median absolute magnitude zero, so that their distances are known where their corresponding apparent magnitudes are observed.

Mainly by the use of these variable stars, Shapley, in 1917, measured the distances of the clusters and constructed a model of their arrangement in space. He considered it also a model of our galaxy in respect to its center and extent. This classical survey brought out clearly for the first time the separate status of the galaxy and the sun's eccentric place within it, and it prepared the way for the recognition of exterior galaxies. Shapley's survey of the clusters was made before astronomers were fully aware of the abundance of cosmic dust, which dims the stars and causes them to seem farther away than they are. The distances are now corrected for this effect, but still are not always as reliable as further studies can make them.

The globular clusters of our galaxy are mainly within a spherical halo around its flat disk, having its center about 30,000 light years from the sun in the direction of Sagittarius. A third of the clusters are found in the vicinity of this constellation.

QUESTIONS ON CHAPTER 14

1. Compare galactic and globular clusters with respect to size, appearance, and type of population. Name two examples of each kind.

2. State the reason for supposing that galactic clusters are far more numerous than the ones we observe.

3. How is it known that Aldebaran is not actually a member of the Hyades cluster?

4. Explain the method of determining the distances of galactic clusters by comparing the apparent and absolute magnitudes of their stars.

5. Show that the distances and linear sizes of the clusters are magnified by this method unless allowance is made for the dimming of their stars by intervening dust.

6. Explain that the relative ages of galactic clusters seem to be indicated by their color-magnitude diagrams.

7. Certain small aggregates of hot stars suggest that these stars may have been born a surprisingly short time ago. Explain.

8. Because globular clusters frequently contain RR Lyrae stars, their distances are reliably determined where suitable allowance is made for intervening dust. Explain.

9. Describe the Hercules cluster M 13.

10. Explain that a person within the Hercules cluster would observe a much more brilliant night sky than ours. Would he also see a milky way?

11. Compare the main sequence of the globular cluster stars with that of the stars around us.

12. Why are a third of the known globular clusters situated in the vicinity of the constellation Sagittarius?

15

COSMIC GAS AND DUST

BRIGHT AND DARK NEBULAE – THE INTERSTELLAR
MATERIAL – THE LIVES OF THE STARS

Nebulae are clouds of gas and dust; they are the more obvious
condensations of the interstellar material which is abundant in
the spiral arms of our galaxy and of the exterior galaxies as well.
Bright nebulae are made luminous by stars in their vicinities, either
by fluorescence or by reflection of the starlight. *Dark nebulae* do
not have stars near by to illuminate them. They are recognized
by optical means only as they obscure the stars behind them.

15·1. The Great Nebula in Orion is the most impressive of the
bright nebulae which are observed directly. Scarcely visible to the
naked eye, it surrounds the middle star of the three in Orion's
sword. With the telescope it appears as a luminous cloud around
the star, which itself is resolved into a group of very hot, class O
stars. In photographs with large telescopes it is spread over an area
nearly 4 times as large as the moon's apparent area. At its distance
of 1600 light years, the nebula shown in these photographs is 26
light years in diameter, as far as the distance of Vega from the sun.

Bright nebulae are made luminous by stars in their vicinities, a
relation first explained by Edwin Hubble. In the absence of involved or neighboring stars, the nebulae are generally optically
dark. Where the star is as hot as class B1, the nebular light gives
mainly a spectrum of bright lines. Where the star is cooler than
B1, the light is mainly reflected starlight. The Orion nebula is
an emission nebula.

15·2. Emission Nebulae. The extreme ultraviolet radiations of
very hot stars contain enough energy to remove electrons abun-
dantly from the atoms of the gas around them. When the ionized

atoms capture other electrons, the gas glows in wave lengths different from those radiated by the stimulating star. The glowing gas gives a bright-line spectrum which is much more conspicuous than the spectrum of the starlight reflected by the nebula.

Prominent in the spectra of such nebulae are "forbidden lines" of ionized oxygen and nitrogen, which are not observed in ordinary

Fig. 15·1. Great Nebula in Orion. It surrounds the middle star of the three visible to the naked eye in Orion's sword. (*Photographed by Edwin W. Dennison with the Curtis Memorial telescope of the Observatory, University of Michigan*)

laboratory conditions. Their source remained unknown until I. S. Bowen, in 1927, explained them theoretically. A pair of green lines of oxygen give the characteristic color to emission nebulae. Despite their better showing in the spectra, oxygen and nitrogen are far less abundant in these gases than are hydrogen and helium.

15·3. Planetary Nebulae are emission nebulae. All invisible to the naked eye, the nearer ones appear with the telescope as somewhat flattened disks surrounding very hot stars. The disks are brighter toward the circumference, so decidedly in some of them that they have the appearance of rings; a familiar example is the Ring nebula in Lyra (Fig. 11·10A). Some, such as the Dumbbell nebula (Fig. 15·3), are less luminous near the ends of their longer diameters.

Several hundred planetary nebulae are known. They range in apparent size from the helical nebula in Aquarius, having half the apparent diameter of the moon, to objects so reduced in the distance that they are distinguished from ordinary stars only by their

FIG. 15·3.   Dumbbell Nebula in Vulpecula.   (*Photographed by F. E. Ross at Mount Wilson Observatory*)

peculiar bright-line spectra. Their linear diameters are of the order of 20,000 times the earth's distance from the sun. Their masses, exclusive of the involved stars, are about a tenth the sun's mass.

Planetary nebulae bear some resemblance to the envelopes around novae. Their expansion, however, is relatively slow, about 12 miles a second in radius, and their lifetimes must be several tens of thousands of years; whereas the nova envelopes with their swift expansion have, with one exception, disappeared in only a few years.

15·4. Reflection Nebulae. The nebulae surrounding stars of the Pleiades are examples of *reflection nebulae*. They glow with starlight that is scattered by their dust. Reflection nebulae have the same spectra and nearly the same colors as have the stars which are responsible for their shining. In dusty regions they appear around the stars like the glows around street lamps on a foggy night.

FIG. 15·4. Nebulae Surrounding Stars of the Pleiades. (*Photographed by E. E. Barnard*)

15·5. Dark Nebulae are clouds of gas and dust which have no stars near enough to light them effectively. Their faint illumination by the general star fields can be detected only by measurements of high precision. Except where they are also lighted by supersonic collisions of their turbulent material, they make their presence known optically by obscuring whatever lies behind them. The rifts they imprint on the bright background of the Milky Way are conspicuous in the photographs. Some rifts are easily visible to the naked eye and have accordingly been known for a long time, but their interpretation as dark clouds rather than as vacancies in the Milky Way came fairly recently.

Where a large cosmic cloud contains one or more very hot stars, the hydrogen in the part of the cloud that is nearer the star is ionized by the star's ultraviolet radiations. Recombinations of the electrons and ions produce the fluorescent glow. A single class O star may ionize all hydrogen within a radius of 400 light years

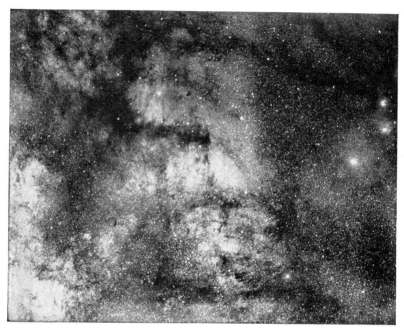

FIG. 15·5. Rifts in the Milky Way. Region of southern Ophiuchus and northern Scorpius. (*Photographed by F. E. Ross*)

around it. A class B0 star ionizes the gas to the distance of 80 light years. The dark envelope beyond such limiting distances is forced outward by the expansion of the hotter gases within, and may break into smaller clouds.

THE INTERSTELLAR MATERIAL

In addition to the obvious bright and dark nebulae, the arms of the galactic system contain an abundance of more tenuous gas and dust. The dust reddens and dims the starlight in various amounts. The gas imprints dark interstellar lines in the spectra of stars. Radiations from clouds of hydrogen gas, which are otherwise dark, are recorded with radio telescopes.

15·6. Reddening of Starlight. Interstellar dust scatters the light of stars behind it, so that less of the light comes through to us. Such stars are dimmed by amounts depending on the density and thickness of the intervening dust. Their distances are accordingly magnified and require corrections. These corrections are made easier to determine because the dust grains are so small, around a hundred thousandth of an inch in diameter, that they scatter the light in inverse proportion to the wave length, the violet more than

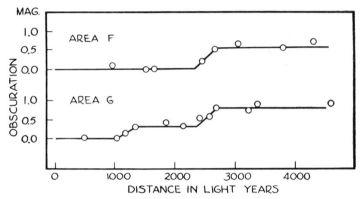

FIG. 15·6. Obscuration by Dust Clouds in Two Areas of Auriga. The separate points represent the averages of many stars measured in blue and red light.

the red. It is a corresponding effect that we see in the reddening of the light of the setting sun by particles of our atmosphere.

The *color excess* of a star is the amount in magnitudes that the star is made redder than the normal color for its particular class of spectrum. Multiplying its value by an appropriate factor, we have the whole obscuration for whatever type of receiver is employed. As an example, Fig. 15·6 shows the amounts of the dimming of stars observed photographically to distances of about 4000 light years in two arbitrarily lettered areas in Auriga.

15·7. Interstellar Lines in the spectra of stars reveal the presence of gas as well as dust. These dark lines are abstracted from the starlight by the gas through which it passes. They are generally narrower than the lines in the spectra of the stars themselves and have different Doppler displacements, showing the different motions

of the gas clouds. Among the chemical constituents of the interstellar gas indicated by these lines are atoms of sodium, potassium,
calcium, and iron, and molecules of cyanogen and hydrocarbon.

The division of the interstellar lines into two or more components was recognized some time ago, particularly by W. S. Adams
(Fig. 15·7), and was ascribed to the different motions of the separate intervening gas clouds. This division is given important inter-

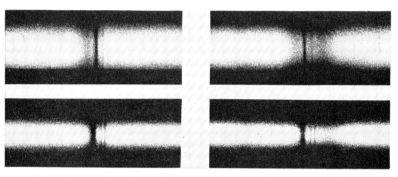

FIG. 15·7. Interstellar Lines in the Spectra of Two Stars. The Fraunhofer K line of calcium appears at the left and the H line at the right;
both are separated into components. The broad calcium lines of the stars
are shown as well. (*Photographed at Mount Wilson Observatory*)

pretation by the studies of Guido Münch at Mount Wilson and
Palomar Observatories. His photographs of the stellar spectra with
the 200-inch telescope show that the material in our galaxy which
causes the interstellar lines is situated in the spiral arms, like the
otherwise observed gas and dust.

15·8. Interstellar Hydrogen. Hydrogen is by far the most abundant chemical element in space, as it is in the stars themselves.
Although it does not by itself contribute optically to the dark
interstellar lines, it is prominent in the spectra of bright nebulae.
The recent discovery that hydrogen in the dark nebulae emits radiation which can be recorded with radio telescopes has greatly increased the importance of these telescopes in galactic exploration.

The radiation of neutral hydrogen at the wave length of 21 cm,
or about 8½ inches, was first observed, in 1951, by the Harvard
physicists E. M. Purcell and H. I. Ewen. The radiation occurs
wherever the single electron of the hydrogen atom at its lowest
level passes from a slightly higher energy state to a lower one. This

transition occurs very infrequently in any one atom, but supplies continued radiation from the combined atoms of a gas cloud.

THE LIVES OF THE STARS

The present account of stellar evolution resembles earlier ones in tracing the stars from their births in the nebulae to their final stages as the densest known stars. It differs markedly from earlier theories in the intermediate stages, mainly because of exciting new evidence from color-magnitude diagrams of star clusters. Stars are continuously being created, in the current idea. As their central temperatures increase enormously, they become cosmic crucibles in which all the heavier chemical elements are built up from lighter ones. They eventually return much of their more complex material to the cosmic clouds to enrich stars of succeeding generations.

15·9. From Nebulae to the Main Sequence. The first visible stage in the creation of stars from the cosmic clouds may be the dark "globules," to which B. J. Bok and others have drawn attention. Around a tenth or a hundredth of a light year in diameter, they appear as very small dark spots against the bright backgrounds in photographs of many regions of the Milky Way. Contracting under their own gravity, these "protostars" finally become hot enough to shine.

The youthful stars enter the type I diagram from the right and move horizontally across it, becoming smaller and hotter until they reach the main sequence. The interval of time from their births to their appearance in the main sequence is so brief that very few stars are likely to be detected in transit. This is especially true of the more massive ones. Aggregates of blue stars are observed spreading so swiftly from their places of origin (14·5) that they seem to have been born only a few million years ago.

The stars shine originally because they have become highly heated by contraction. When they have reached the main sequence, the temperatures in their interiors are so great that energy begins to be liberated by the transmutation of lighter elements into heavier ones. This becomes the main process that supplies the stars for the remainder of their lives. It begins with the building up of hydrogen into helium atoms, which for a time provides just as much energy as is released in the starlight. Contraction is halted at this stage. The stars change little in size, temperature, and brightness.

Here we find the reason why the majority of stars at a particular time are on the main sequence.

The transmutation of hydrogen to helium in the interiors of main-sequence stars is accomplished by the union of 4 hydrogen nuclei to form a helium nucleus. In this reaction some material is unused and is converted to energy by the relativity rule: the quantity of energy that is released equals the mass of the excess material times the square of the speed of light. This energy is passed along upward to the surfaces of the stars to keep them shining.

15·10. Evidence from the Star Clusters. When the supply of hydrogen in the core of the star approaches exhaustion, this core begins to contract again and to enlarge the region of the atomic reaction around it. The outer parts of the star expand. The star becomes brighter and moves upward into the giant section of the diagram. The blue stars, which consume their fuel faster in order to maintain their greater rate of shining, leave the sequence before the cooler and longer-lived red stars.

Allan Sandage has determined empirically (Fig. 15·11) the evolutionary progress in the globular cluster M 3 of the stars redder than class F5 in the interval of 5 billion years since they left the main sequence. The original F5 stars are now red supergiants. Stars bluer than F5 left the sequence earlier and are now presumably returning along the horizontal giant branch, where stars are found, or have already done so and have collapsed to become white dwarf stars.

We have also seen (14·4) that the main sequences of galactic clusters are bending over to the right more and more with advancing age of the clusters, and that their bluer parts are progressively disappearing.

15·11. Evolution from the Main Sequence. The evolution of stars considerably more massive than the sun is now believed to be swift and spectacular. As the core of the star contracts and grows hotter, the outer layers are blown out enormously, and share in the conversion from hydrogen to helium. The star becomes a giant and later a supergiant. When the central temperature reaches 150 million degrees, some of the helium in the core can build up into carbon, magnesium, and so on. At 5 billion degrees, iron atoms are

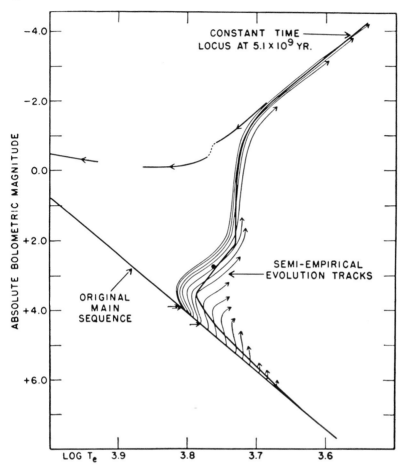

FIG. 15·11.   Semiempirical Evolution Tracks of Stars in the Globular Cluster M 3.   Values of log T_e correspond to the following spectral classes: 3.9 to A5, 3.8 to F5, 3.7 to K0 for the main sequence and G0 for giants, 3.6 for the main sequence and K0 for giants.   (*Diagram by Allan Sandage*)

appearing.   The release of neutrons in such processes can promote the forming of even the heaviest elements in small amounts.

At these extreme temperatures the star is likely to explode as a supernova, returning into space gaseous material up to twice the sun's mass.   In this and other ways the star must dispose of any original mass exceeding 1.4 times the sun's mass, as S. Chandrasekhar has shown, before it can complete its evolution along with normal stars.

In addition to the explosions of supernovae and ordinary novae, almost every type of star is returning gas to the interstellar medium. A. J. Deutsch estimates that the red supergiant Alpha Herculis alone is losing gas at the rate of one solar mass per 10 million years. He concludes that of the "dead stars" in the sun's vicinity, which have left the main sequence and have now completed their evolutions, half of their combined mass was returned to the cosmic clouds, and the other half is in the form of white dwarfs.

If the stars of the first generation condensed from gas that was entirely hydrogen, if they built up heavier chemical elements in their interiors and eventually returned much of the enriched gas to the cosmic clouds, then the second generation stars formed in these clouds would contain a percentage of heavier elements from the start. Third generation stars, such as the sun seems to be, would begin their evolutions with a still higher percentage than did the second generation. Variations in the metallic content of stars, as shown by their spectra, may be an important means of classifying the stars by generations.

15·12. The White Dwarf Stage is believed to be the final state of a star. When the star's supply of available fuel is almost exhausted, so that not enough energy is being released in its interior to keep it inflated, the star collapses. In this drastic experience it may explode repeatedly as a normal nova, until it settles down to shine feebly for an unknown length of time as a small and very dense white dwarf star.

QUESTIONS ON CHAPTER 15

1. Why are some nebulae luminous, whereas others are practically dark?

2. An emission nebula glows with a different kind of light from that of the hot stars involved in it. Explain.

3. Why is the light of nebulae around the cooler stars the same as the light of the stars themselves?

4. In what respects do planetary nebulae differ from the envelopes expanding around novae?

5. Name (a) an emission nebula; (b) a reflection nebula; (c) a planetary nebula; (d) a dark nebula.

6. How is it possible to decide whether a star that appears red is actually a red star or one that is reddened by interstellar dust? Define color excess.

7. Why are the interstellar lines in the spectra of stars divided into two or more components?

8. By what means has it become possible to record the optically dark hydrogen clouds with the radio telescope?

9. What is the possible connection of the dark "globules" of nebulosity with the birth of stars?

10. The relative weight of a hydrogen nucleus is 1.008, and that of a helium nucleus is 4.003. Where 4 hydrogens combine in a star to form a helium nucleus, explain the use of the remaining material.

11. Describe the probable evolution of stars after they have left the main sequence.

12. Account for the present idea that stars of successive generations contain increasing percentages of heavier chemical elements.

REFERENCES

Gaposchkin, C. P., *Stars in the Making*. Harvard University Press, Cambridge, 1952.

Goldberg, Leo, and Lawrence H. Aller, *Atoms, Stars and Nebulae*. Harvard University Press, Cambridge, 1943.

Struve, Otto, *Stellar Evolution*. Princeton University Press, 1950.

Nebula M8 in Sagittarius. (*Photographed by Otto Struve at McDonald Observatory*)

16

THE GALACTIC SYSTEM

THE MILKY WAY – SPIRAL STRUCTURE OF THE GALAXY

The *galactic system,* or the system of the Milky Way, is so named because this luminous girdle of the heavens is the most impressive feature of the spiral system as we look out from within it and see it projected on the face of the sky. The system is also known as *our galaxy.*

16·1. The Milky Way of Summer. The full splendor of the Milky Way is reserved for one who observes it on a clear moonless night from a place removed from artificial lights. The view with the naked eye or with a very wide-angle camera is the best for its general features. Photographs show its details more clearly than the eye can detect them. The Milky Way is formed by the combined light of stars which are not separately visible to the naked eye. Its central line is nearly a great circle of the celestial sphere, so highly inclined to the celestial equator that it takes quite different positions in the sky in the early evenings of the different seasons.

At nightfall in the late summer in middle northern latitudes the Milky Way arches overhead from the northeast to the southwest horizon. It extends upward through Perseus, Cassiopeia, and Cepheus to the fine region of the Northern Cross (Fig. 11·12). Here in Cygnus it is apparently divided by a succession of dust clouds of the Great Rift (Fig. 16·1) into parallel streams which go on down through Aquila into Sagittarius and Scorpius, and then out of sight for us. In this region we see the bright star clouds of Scutum and Sagittarius through partial openings in the dust; the latter is in the direction of the center of the galaxy.

16·2. The Milky Way of Winter. In the early evenings of late winter in our latitudes the Milky Way again arches overhead, now

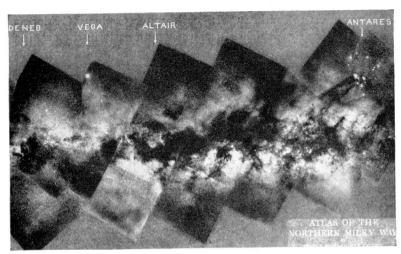

FIG. 16·1.   Great Rift in the Milky Way from Cygnus to Scorpius.   (*Mosaic from the* Atlas of the Northern Milky Way)

FIG. 16·2.   Region of the Southern Cross.   The Cross and the "coalsack" are near the center.   The bright stars at the extreme left are Alpha and Beta Centauri.   (*Photographed by Margaret Harwood at the Arequipa Station of Harvard Observatory*)

from northwest to southeast. It goes through Cepheus, Cassiopeia, Perseus, and Auriga which is near the zenith early in the evenings of February. Here it is narrowed by a succession of near-by dust clouds which angle from northern Cassiopeia through Auriga to southern Taurus. The Milky Way then goes on past Gemini and Orion, where it becomes broader and less noticeably obscured by dust.

The part of the Milky Way in the vicinity of the south celestial pole is either out of sight or else never rises high enough for favorable view anywhere in the United States. This region from Centaurus to Carina contains some fine star clouds, another long rift, and also the "coalsack" near the Southern Cross (Fig. 16·2).

16·3. Galactic Longitude and Latitude. In descriptions of our galaxy it is often convenient to denote positions in the heavens with reference to the Milky Way. For this purpose we define an additional system of circles of the celestial sphere. The north and south *galactic poles* are the two opposite points that are farthest from the central line of the Milky Way. The north galactic pole is in the constellation Coma Berenices, in right ascension $12^h 40^m$, declination $+28°$, referred to the equinox of 1900. The south galactic pole is in Sculptor to the east of the star Fomalhaut.

Halfway between these poles, the *galactic equator* is a great circle inclined $62°$ to the celestial equator, and crossing it in the constellation Aquila at a point in right ascension $18^h 40^m$. *Galactic longitude* is measured in degrees from this intersection toward the north along the galactic equator. *Galactic latitude* is measured in degrees perpendicularly from the galactic equator.

Thus the earth's equator is inclined $62°$ to the principal plane of the galaxy. The galactic equator runs about $1°$ north of the central line of the Milky Way, showing that the sun is situated somewhat north of the principal plane.

16·4. The Disk of the Galaxy. The Milky Way itself informs us of two features of the galaxy, as Shapley was the first to explain clearly, in 1918. First, the stars are assembled mainly in a thin disk around a thicker central region; second, the sun's place in the disk is far from its center.

The stars crowd toward the Milky Way. Stars visible to the naked eye are 3 or 4 times as numerous near the galactic equator as they are in a similar area around its poles. The increase exceeds

40-fold for telescopic stars, despite the heavy dust near the equator, and is fairly symmetrical in the two hemispheres. When we look toward the galactic equator, we are looking the longest way out through the disk and, therefore, at many more stars. The thin disk of the galaxy is 80,000 light years in diameter, and we are near its principal plane.

16·5. The Sun's Eccentric Position in the disk of the galaxy is indicated by the greater brightnesss and complexity of the Milky Way in the direction of Sagittarius than in the opposite direction. This is also the direction, as originally determined by Shapley, of the system of globular star clusters which form a spherical halo around the disk.

The distance of the center of the galaxy is nearly 30,000 light years from the sun. The position of the center is in galactic longitude 325°, latitude 0°; it is in right ascension 17^h 33′, declination −29°, which locates it in Map 3 between the star-figures of Sagittarius and Scorpius, and near the edge of the great Sagittarius star cloud. Some authorities have placed the center slightly southeast of this position.

16·6. The Central Region. The great Sagittarius star cloud is an exposed part of the central region of the galaxy. The remainder is hidden from ordinary observation by heavy dust clouds. This region has the type II population, which is also generally true of the halo of the galaxy and of its disk with the exception of its spiral arms. Starlight from the central region has been recorded through the dust by Stebbins and Whitford, who employed a photoelectric cell and infrared filter. They found the area of the most intense radiation extending 8° in galactic longitude, rather more than half as much in latitude, and centered in longitude 326°.5. Infrared photographs of this region have also been made. The radiation from a small nucleus of the region has been recorded with a radio telescope.

16·7. The Rotation of the Galaxy around an axis joining the galactic poles is indicated by its flattening at the poles and its wide extension at the equator. It is also clearly shown by the motions of the stars around us. They are moving in the rotation, like the revolution of the planets around the sun, more slowly as their distances from the galactic center are greater. Stars nearer the

FIG. 16·5. Toward the Center of the Galactic System. The great star cloud in Sagittarius is near the center. The Scutum star cloud is near the upper left corner. (*Photographed at Mount Wilson Observatory*)

center than the sun's distance are overtaking us and passing by, whereas stars farther from the center than the sun's distance keep falling behind us. This effect was first reported by the Dutch astronomer J. H. Oort, in 1927, in the radial velocities of stars in different parts of the Milky Way.

At equal distances from us the stars having galactic longitudes 45° and 225° greater than the longitude of the center are receding from us fastest, and those at 135° and 315° are approaching us fastest (Fig. 16·7). These differences in the radial velocities caused

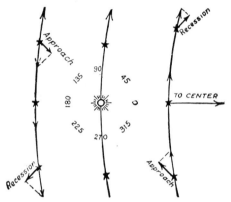

Fig. 16·7. Effect of Rotation of the Galactic System on the Radial Velocities of Stars. Stars nearer the center than the sun's distance are going around faster and are passing by the sun. Stars farther from the center are moving more slowly and are falling behind the sun. Thus stars around longitudes 45° and 225° greater than that of the center are receding from the sun, and stars around 135° and 315° are approaching the sun.

by the rotation of the galaxy increase in amount as the stars are farther from the sun. They are providing the means of tracing its spiral arms with radio telescopes (16·9).

SPIRAL STRUCTURE OF THE GALAXY

Features of the galactic system already described have generally been known for some time. Meanwhile, it had seemed increasingly probable that our system is a spiral resembling some of the exterior systems, and that the sun is situated in one of its arms. The definite tracing of the spiral arms began very recently and is now in active progress by at least three means: (1) by direct photography of bright nebulae and kinds of stars which are also found in the arms of exterior spirals; (2) by radio reception from the hydrogen in the dark gas clouds; (3) by studies of interstellar lines in the spectra of stars.

16·8. Spiral Arms Traced by Photography. The first definite evidence of spiral structure in our galaxy was obtained by Morgan,

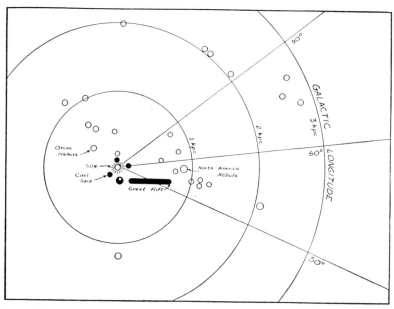

FIG. 16·8. Parts of Spiral Arms of the Galactic System. Traced by directions and distances of nebulae. (*Adapted from a model by W. W. Morgan, Stewart Sharpless, and Donald Osterbrock*)

Sharpless, and Osterbrock at Yerkes Observatory, in 1951. They employed as indicators of the arms the bright nebulae and blue stars associated with them. Their photographs were made with a Henyey-Greenstein wide-angle camera having a filter for transmitting the light of the red line of hydrogen.

Part of one arm traced at the time of their original report (Fig. 16·8) includes the North America nebula in Cygnus and the great nebula in Orion, and passes near the sun on the side away from the galactic center. Part of a second arm includes the double cluster in Perseus, and passes farther from the sun on that side as well. Evidence of a third arm on the side toward the center was

verified by further tracing by Bok and his associates with the
Schmidt telescope at the Boyden Station in South Africa.

16·9. Radio Surveys of the Arms.   Optically dark dust clouds,
which appear in the arms of exterior spiral galaxies, are also indi-

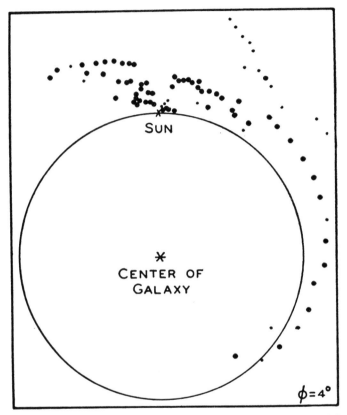

SUN

✳
CENTER OF
GALAXY

$\phi=4°$

Fig. 16·9.   Parts of Spiral Arms of the Galactic System.   Traced by the
Dutch radio astronomers.   The original values of the distances are slightly
   modified.   (*Diagram by Frank K. Edmondson, Indiana University*)

cators of the arms of our own galaxy.   They are being traced with
radio telescopes which record the radiation of their neutral hydrogen at the wave length of 21 cm (15·8).   To see how this is
done, consider a region of the Milky Way in longitude 120° greater
than that of the galactic center.   The gaseous material here is approaching the sun, as are the stars (16·7), in the rotation of the

galaxy. As its distance from us is greater, its speed of approach, and accordingly the Doppler shift in its spectrum, increases. Thus by tuning the radio telescope first to 21 cm and then to shorter wave lengths successively, the survey reaches to greater and greater distances in this direction. Where the signal becomes stronger, there is a spiral arm.

Radio surveys of the galaxy are in progress in the Netherlands, Australia, America, and elsewhere. The Dutch observers have swept from Sagittarius to the east halfway around the Milky Way. They have traced parts of two arms within the sun's distance from the center, and greater lengths of two arms beyond this distance. They have derived their distances from the shift of the 21-cm line by supposing that the gas is moving in circles around the center in the rotation. In the original diagram by Muller, van de Hulst, and Oort, the outermost arm seems to be circular instead of winding in toward the center, as it might be expected to do.

F. K. Edmondson of Indiana University has experimented with an alternate supposition that the motions of the gases are not in circles but are directed inward at an angle of 4° from the perpendicular to the radius. With the modified distances that result, the outermost arm in his diagram of the Dutch observations (Fig. 16·9) spirals in rather convincingly, and is then trailing in the rotation of the galaxy. Edmondson suggests that the arm coming in from the direction of Perseus may, after a single turn, join one of the short lengths traced by the Dutch observers between the sun and the center.

16·10. Evidence from Interstellar Lines. The gas which imprints interstellar lines in the spectra of stars (15·7) is situated in the spiral arms. This information is given by G. Münch of the Mount Wilson and Palomar Observatories from his studies of the spectra of stars in the northern Milky Way. He measured the violet Doppler displacements of strong divided interstellar lines in the spectra, and calculated the corresponding speeds with which the gases in two arms are approaching us there in the rotation of the galaxy. The relative speeds are the greatest near longitude 100°, or 135° different from that of the center, as we see in Fig. 16·7 that they should be.

The curves of Münch's diagram (Fig. 16·10), which show the rotation effect for the different longitudes at distances from us of 1300 and nearly 10,000 light years, respectively, represent the ob-

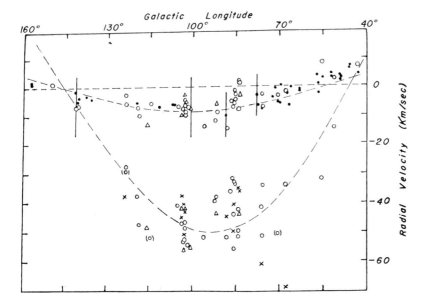

FIG. 16·10.   Interstellar Lines Caused by Gas in Two Spiral Arms.   Dif-
ferential radial velocities from interstellar lines in the spectra of stars in
the northern Milky Way.   (*Diagram by Guido Münch, Mount Wilson and
Palomar Observatories*)

served speeds as well as those that would be expected for the highly
turbulent gases.   The two arms shown by this inquiry are the two
outer arms also traced by direct photography and radio recordings.

16·11.   The Galactic System consists of a spheroidal region at the
center of a flat disk, in which two spiral arms are embedded and
surrounded by a spherical halo of star clusters and separate stars.
This system is smaller than the great spiral in Andromeda which
it otherwise resembles.

The central region of the galaxy is 25,000 light years in equatorial
diameter and a fourth as great in polar diameter; it has the type
II population and may be rotating all in the same period.   The
flat disk is 80,000 light years in diameter by Baade's measurement,
and its stars are mainly of type II.   The type I spiral arms contain
much gas and dust as well as stars; they coil in the same direction
as their rotation and join the central region at two opposite points.
The halo contains the globular clusters, which by a recent theory
revolve around the center in such highly elongated orbits that they

spend most of the time near their greatest distances from it. All together, the galaxy is estimated to contain 100 thousand million stars.

The sun is situated in or near one of the arms at the distance of

FIG. 16·11.   The Southern Milky Way from Sagittarius to Crux.   The total field is 140° in diameter and is centered on the star Antares.   (*Photographed by Arthur D. Code at Bloemfontein, South Africa, with a Henyey-Greenstein wide-angle camera*)

about 30,000 light years from the center.   From our place in the suburbs, the center is in the direction of Sagittarius.   Toward Auriga in the opposite direction we look the shortest way out along the disk.   In the rotation of the galaxy, which would be clockwise as viewed from its north pole, the sun is now moving toward the Northern Cross.   At the speed of 134 miles a second, as reported by the Dutch radio observers, the sun requires about 200 million years to go once around the center.

QUESTIONS ON CHAPTER 16

1. Why does the Milky Way have different positions in the early evening skies of different seasons? In what seasons does it pass nearly overhead at nightfall in middle northern latitudes?

2. Name 3 constellations in the part of the Milky Way visible in summer evenings; 3 constellations in the winter Milky Way; 2 in the part near the south celestial pole.

3. Define the terms: galactic poles; galactic equator; galactic longitude and latitude.

4. What is the evidence that the galactic system is mainly much flattened? State the direction of its center from us.

5. Describe the halo surrounding the main part of our galaxy.

6. What is the evidence that the outer parts of the galaxy are rotating more slowly as they are farther from the center?

7. Describe the sun's motion in the rotation of the galaxy.

8. Explain that objects in the Milky Way having galactic longitudes about 135° greater than that of the center are approaching us in the rotation; that they approach faster as their distances from us are greater.

9. Discuss the progress in tracing the arms of our galaxy by means of bright nebulae and associated stars.

10. Describe the radio method of tracing the arms by means of the optically dark hydrogen clouds.

11. Explain the meaning of the division of the interstellar lines in stellar spectra into two main components, and of the division of these again into several components.

12. Summarize the current information about the galactic system, with respect to its size, structure, rotation, and composition, and our position in it.

REFERENCES

Bok, Bart J., and Priscilla F. Bok, *The Milky Way*. Third edition. Harvard University Press, Cambridge, 1957.

Ross, Frank E., and Mary R. Calvert, *Atlas of the Northern Milky Way*. University of Chicago Press, 1936.

17

THE EXTERIOR GALAXIES

STRUCTURAL FEATURES OF GALAXIES – DISTRIBUTION
OF GALAXIES – THE MOTIONS OF GALAXIES

The galactic system is one of the many stellar systems which
constitute the major building blocks of the physical universe. The
galaxies are of three main types: spiral, elliptical, and irregular
systems. They are frequently assembled in clusters and in smaller
groups, such as the local group. The red shifts of their spectrum
lines, which increase as the distances of the galaxies are greater,
are the basis of the theories of the expanding universe.

STRUCTURAL FEATURES OF GALAXIES

17·1. The Great Spiral in Andromeda, Messier 31, is the brightest
and may also be the nearest of the exterior spiral systems. It is
visible to the naked eye as a hazy spot about as long and half as
wide as the moon's apparent diameter. Only the central region
appears to the eye alone and, for the most part, to the eye at the
telescope. Fainter surrounding parts come out in the photographs,
where the object is shown in its true character as a flat, double-
armed spiral inclined 15° from the edgewise position. In the
photograph in Fig. 17·1 the tilted spiral, which is actually nearly
circular, appears as an oval 3° long. Separate stars in the arms
were first observed, in 1924, by Edwin Hubble at Mount Wilson
Observatory. The cepheid variables among them served to determine the distance of the spiral and to show that it is situated far
beyond the Milky Way.

Current studies of the Andromeda spiral with the 200-inch Hale
telescope are giving new information about it and are guiding the
investigations of our own galaxy which has a similar structure.
The apparent diameter is increased to $4\frac{1}{2}°$ by Baade's observations
of the faint outskirts. At the revised distance of $1\frac{1}{2}$ million light
years, after tentative correction is made for the effect of intervening

FIG. 17·1. Great Spiral in Andromeda, M 31. One elliptical companion, M 32, appears directly above the central region; the other, NGC 205, is at the left of it. *(Photographed with the 48-inch Schmidt telescope, Mount Wilson and Palomar Observatories)*

dust, the linear diameter is 120,000 light years, or half again the diameter of the disk of the galactic system.

The type II population pervades the central region and extends through the disk beyond the conspicuous traces of the spiral pattern. Embedded in the disk are the spiral arms of the type I population, where we find about all the features we see in the Milky Way right around us. Dust clouds are localized in the arms. Gas clouds and associated highly luminous blue stars are also situated in the arms and are abundant in the outer regions, where they serve to trace the arms beyond their most noticeable parts. Several hundred globular star clusters surround the disk; they are similar to the globular clusters in the halo around the disk of the galactic system.

17·2. Spiral Galaxies are generally of two types: normal spirals and barred spirals. The detailed classification of these and other systems was first employed by Hubble.

Messier 81 in Ursa Major   Messier 51 in Canes Venatici

Fig. 17·2. Spiral Galaxies. (*Photographed at Mount Wilson Observatory*)

Normal spirals have lens-shaped central regions from which the two arms emerge and at once begin to coil in the same sense and the same plane. They are divided into three classes. *Class Sa* spirals have large central regions and thin, closely coiled arms; an example is NGC 4594 in Virgo. In *class Sb* the centers are smaller, and the arms are larger and wider open; examples are M 31 and the galactic system. Both classes are mainly of the type II population, except that their arms are type I. In *class Sc* the centers are smallest, and the arms are largest and most loosely coiled. These

Fig. 17·2A.   Barred Spiral NGC 1300 in Eridanus. (*Photographed with the Hale telescope, Mount Wilson and Palomar Observatories*)

systems are more generally type I; an example is the "pinwheel" M 33 in Triangulum (Fig. 17·9).

Barred spirals have their two coils starting abruptly from the ends of a bright bar which projects from opposite sides of the central region. They are classified in the series *SBa, SBb,* and *SBc,* paralleling the normal spirals. As the series progresses, the central region diminishes while the arms build up and unwind. A third and less familiar type of spiral has its arms beginning in a bright ring around the center.

17·3. Spirals at Different Angles. These flat spirals are presented to us in a variety of ways. Turned flatwise to the earth, they ap-

pear nearly circular. Messier 51, the "whirlpool" (Fig. 17·2), is
an example; it has an irregular companion projected near the end
of one arm. Where they are moderately inclined, as in the cases of
M 31 and M 81, another giant, they appear elliptical. In the edgewise view they are reduced to bright streaks having lens-shaped
central regions. Characteristic of spirals seen on edge is the dark
band that sometimes seems to cut them completely in two. NGC
4594, the "sombrero" (Fig. 17·3), is a fine example. Just as the

Fig. 17·3.   Spiral Galaxy Viewed Nearly Edgewise.   NGC 4594 in Virgo.
(Photographed at Mount Wilson Observatory)

dust clouds of the galactic system obstruct our view along its
equator, so the dust of the edgewise spirals obscures their equatorial
regions.

17·4. Elliptical Galaxies bear some resemblance to the central
regions of spirals. They are designated by the letter E followed
by a number which is 10 times the value of the ellipticity. The
series runs from the circular *class E0* to the most flattened *E7*,
where the object resembles a convex lens viewed on edge. The
extreme classes are represented in Fig. 17·4. M 32, one of the
companions of the Andromeda spiral, is an example of the slightly
elliptical class E2; and the other companion, NGC 205, is of class
E5.

These are systems of stars, generally dust-free and of the type
II population. Individual stars of the nearer ones are observed
in photographs with the largest telescopes.

FIG. 17·4.   Extreme Types of Elliptical Systems.   NGC 4278 (left) has a nearly circular disk.   NGC 3115 (right) is among the most flattened of the elliptical systems.   (*Photographed with the Hale telescope, Mount Wilson and Palomar Observatories*)

17·5. Sequence of Regular Galaxies.   The separate series of elliptical and spiral galaxies are joined in Hubble's diagram (Fig. 17·5) into a sequence of all regular systems.   *Regular galaxies* are those having rotational symmetry.   The sequence begins at the left with the spherical forms.   These become more and more extended at their equators, until spiral structures begin to appear around them.

The appearance of the spirals is preceded by the division of the sequence into two intermediate classes, *S0* and *SB0*.   They differ from the E7 lenses in the distribution of brightness in their disks and sometimes in their greater flattening, and in the second class in having a wide bar through the lens.   From these the normal and barred spirals continue in parallel branches in the figure.   The spiral patterns unwind as the central regions become less prominent.

This sequence has served as a convenient basis for the thinking about the evolution of galaxies.   The progression from left to right suggests that material emerging from the most flattened elliptical systems built up the disks and arms of the spirals.   A very different view of the figure is that it arrays the original "fossil" forms of the galaxies.   Here the thought is that the turbulent material of a primitive expanding universe may have separated into many large eddies, each one having a quantity of spin that permanently deter-

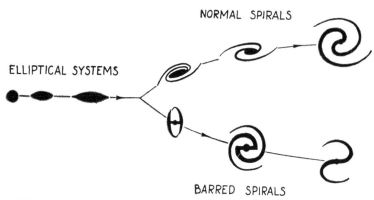

NORMAL SPIRALS

ELLIPTICAL SYSTEMS

BARRED SPIRALS

FIG. 17·5. Sequence of Regular Galaxies. Near the division into two branches are the intermediate classes S0 and SB0. (*Adapted from a diagram by Edwin Hubble*)

FIG. 17·6. Large Magellanic Cloud. (*Photographed by Karl Henize with the Mount Wilson 10-inch refractor at Bloemfontein, South Africa*)

mined the form of that galaxy. This major problem of cosmic evolution is evidently as yet unsolved.

17·6. The Magellanic Clouds, named in honor of the celebrated navigator, are the two satellites of the galactic system. Plainly visible to the naked eye, they are too close to the south celestial pole (Map 6) to be seen north of the tropical zone. They have nearly the same distance of 150,000 light years. As they generally appear in the photographs the Clouds have apparent diameters of 12° and 8°, so that their linear diameters are 30,000 and 20,000 light years. However, the neutral hydrogen of both Clouds extends out much farther than do the stars and almost runs together, as the Australian radio astronomers have reported.

The Clouds have been hitherto classed among the irregular galaxies, which seem to lack rotational symmetry. Yet the Australian radio astronomers have now observed their rotations, and G. de Vaucouleurs' photographs with a small camera at Mount Stromlo seem to show that the Clouds are flat, one-armed, barred spirals having larger dimensions than were previously assigned them. The Large Cloud is nearly flatwise to us, and the Small Cloud is inclined 30° from the edgewise presentation, acording to this observer. These and perhaps other irregular galaxies may be degenerate spirals, as Hubble suggested in tentatively placing the irregulars at the end of his sequence (17·5).

DISTRIBUTION OF GALAXIES

17·7. Their Arrangement in the Sky. The apparent distribution of the exterior systems over the face of the sky is shown in Fig. 17·7. This diagram represents a survey of the brighter galaxies by Shapley and Adelaide Ames at Harvard Observatory. Few such systems are visible within 10° of the galactic equator, which is marked by the heavy curved line in the figure; here they are generally concealed behind the dust clouds of our own system. Their numbers increase toward the galactic poles, where there is the least amount of intervening dust. The increase is fairly symmetrical in the two hemispheres except for the presence of the conspicuous Virgo cluster of galaxies represented at the left. It was because of their seeming avoidance of the Milky Way that the galaxies were called "extragalactic nebulae" before their true nature was understood.

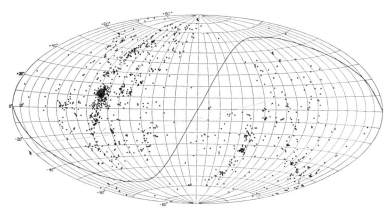

FIG. 17·7. Distribution of the Brighter Exterior Galaxies. The entire celestial sphere is represented with the north celestial pole at the top. The heavy curved line is the galactic equator. (*From Harvard Observatory Annals, Vol. 88*)

FIG. 17·8. A Vista of Galaxies in a Region in Pisces. (*Photographed at Mount Wilson Observatory*)

The fainter systems are similarly arranged in the sky, as was shown by Hubble's more extensive survey at Mount Wilson. If the dust were not present, the galaxies would presumably be about equally numerous in all directions.

17·8. The Distances of the Galaxies are required before we can describe their distribution in space. For the nearer systems, where their separate stars are shown in photographs with the largest telescopes, the distances are best derived from observations of their cepheid variables and other stars of high luminosity. Their RR Lyrae stars would be equally useful, but they are too faint to be seen in these photographs except in a few systems nearer us than the distance of the Andromeda spiral. For the remote galaxies where separate stars are invisible, the distances are estimated by comparing the observed brightness of entire systems with the absolute brightness assigned to these particular types.

The distances of the galaxies are now derived more reliably than before for two main reasons. First, the recent correction to the luminosities of the classical cepheids (13·11) has doubled the former values of the distances. Second, the more precise photo-electric scale of magnitudes is revising the distances still further. For the present, the former values of the distances beyond the local group are multiplied by about the factor 3. The diameters of the systems are of course increased in the same proportion. Further studies are needed, however, before we have a completely accept-able model of the universe of galaxies within the range of the Hale telescope.

17·9. The Local Group. The galactic system is a member of a group of at least 17 galaxies which occupy an ellipsoidal volume of space 2 million light years in its longest dimension. Our sys-tem is near one end of this diameter, and the Andromeda spiral is near the other end. These and M 33 in Triangulum are the normal spiral members. The less regular members are the Magel-lanic Clouds and two smaller ones. The remaining 10 are elliptical galaxies, of which 6 are of the less populous and fainter *Sculptor type*. The first known examples of these dwarf ellipticals were dis-covered at Harvard Observatory in the constellations Sculptor and Fornax; the other four, two in Leo and one apiece in Draco and Ursa Minor, were found more recently in photographs with the Palomar 48-inch Schmidt telescope.

The members of the local group are listed in Table 17·I. The Andromeda spiral is the largest of these, and the galactic system is the second in size. Because many of them are near enough to the Milky Way so that the amounts of their obscuration by dust are less reliably determined, the distances and diameters are given tentatively. It may be that some other members of the group are concealed behind the dust clouds.

TABLE 17·I.   THE LOCAL GROUP

Designation	Type	Distance (light years)	Apparent Diameter	Linear Diameter (light years)
Galactic system	Sb	. . . .	. . . .	80 ,000
Large Mag. Cloud	I	150 ,000	12°	30 ,000
Small Mag. Cloud	I	150 ,000	8°	20 ,000
Draco system	E	200 ,000	31′	2 ,000
Ursa Minor system	E	200 ,000	55′	3 ,000
Sculptor system	E	230 ,000	45′	3 ,000
Fornax system	E	460 ,000	50′	7 ,000
Leo II system	E	800 ,000	10′	2 ,000
NGC 6822	I	950 ,000	20′	6 ,000
NGC 185	E	1 ,100 ,000	14′.5	5 ,000
NGC 147	E	1 ,100 ,000	14′.1	5 ,000
Leo I system	E	1 ,200 ,000	10′	3 ,000
IC 1613	I	1 ,500 ,000	17′	7 ,000
M 31	Sb	1 ,500 ,000	4°.5	120 ,000
M 32	E2	1 ,500 ,000	12′	5 ,000
NGC 205	E5	1 ,500 ,000	15′.8	7 ,000
M 33	Sc	1 ,500 ,000	62′	30 ,000

17·10. Galaxies in Clusters.   The larger assemblages of galaxies contain from 50 to 500 members. They are designated by the names of the constellations in which they appear. The Virgo cluster is an example. At the distance of 20 million light years, it is the nearest and most conspicuous of all. Its members are spread over an area of the sky 10° in diameter, having its center in right ascension 12ʰ 24ᵐ, declination +12°. Spirals are exceptionally numerous here as compared with the memberships of the clusters generally, and the brightest stars in these member spirals

Fig. 17·9. Spiral Galaxy M 33 in Triangulum. A member of the local group. *(Photographed at Mount Wilson Observatory)*

are observed in photographs with the largest telescopes. The Coma cluster (Fig. 17·10) is another example. At the distance of 120 million light years, its apparent diameter is less than 2°.

The more compact clusters, especially near their centers, are largely composed of class S0 galaxies. The frequency of such systems in the more crowded regions has been taken to mean that the arms of former spirals were removed by collisions of the galaxies. The dust and gas of the arms would be swept out of the systems, whereas the widely separated stars would be less disturbed. The clusters are regions from which very strong radio emissions would be expected where collisions of galaxies occur. They are also promising hunting grounds for the outbursts of supernovae.

17·11. Novae in the Galaxies. Novae flare out in the exterior systems as they do in our own. They are of two general types, depending on the brilliance of their outbursts. *Normal novae* resemble the usual ones of the galactic system (13·14) in their abundance and in their luminosities at maxima. It is estimated

FIG. 17·10.   Part of Cluster of Galaxies in Coma Berenices.   *(Photographed with the Hale telescope, Mount Wilson and Palomar Observatories)*

that 25 or 30 of these appear yearly in the Andromeda spiral. *Supernovae* are far more spectacular; at maxima they sometimes have considerable fractions of the brightness of the galaxies in which they appear.   Although they are rare in any particular system, averaging one in 400 years, they may be discovered rather frequently in a cluster having several hundred members.

The brightest supernovae at their maxima are of the order of 200 million times as luminous as the sun.   Placed at the standard distance of $32\frac{1}{2}$ light years, where the sun would be barely visible to the naked eye, such supernovae would appear to us 14 times as bright as the full moon.   The first on record in the exterior systems flared out, in 1885, in the Andromeda spiral and became as bright as the 7th magnitude.   Three recorded novae in the galactic system are supposed to have been supernovae; they were the nova associated with the Crab nebula and the remarkably bright novae of 1572 and 1604.

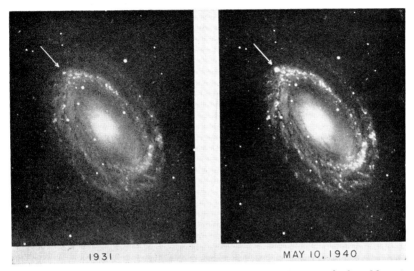

FIG. 17·11. Supernova in the Spiral NGC 4725. (*Photographed at Mount Wilson Observatory*)

17·12. Discrete Radio Sources, formerly called "radio stars," are small-area sources of emission in the radio wave lengths. A few are identified with familiar optical objects, but hundreds await such identifications; indeed some of these have been suspected of being beyond the reach of optical telescopes. Because their positions in the sky show no special dependence on the Milky Way, the majority of the sources might seem to be outside our system. They have been variously ascribed to normal galaxies including the Andromeda spiral, to galaxies in collision, and to supernovae. Radio power of spectacular amount, of the order of 10^{33} kilowatts, is reported from two galaxies colliding head-on in Cygnus. Some sources, however, are assigned to nebulae in the galactic system, such as the Crab nebula and a bright nebulosity in Cassiopeia, and one of them to the nucleus of our system itself or else to a place in front of the nucleus. Accounts of new developments in this active field are likely to be found in current periodicals.

THE MOTIONS OF GALAXIES

17·13. Rotations Shown by the Spectra. The flattened forms of regular galaxies suggest that they are rotating. The character of the rotations is clearly revealed in the spectra of spirals presented to us nearly edgewise. When the slit of the spectroscope is placed along the major axis of the tilted spiral, the spectrum lines are slanting (Fig. 17·13). It is the same Doppler effect which shows the rotation of a planet (Fig. 8·24). The central region of a spiral rotates all in the same period. In the disk the period becomes

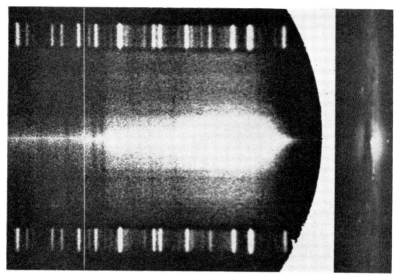

Fig. 17·13. Spectrum of Edgewise Spiral NGC 4565. The violet end of the spectrum is at the left. The slanting dark lines show that the upper part of the spiral is approaching and the lower part is receding from us in the rotation. (*Photographed by N. U. Mayall, Lick Observatory*)

longer with increasing distance from the center, like the planetary type of rotation of the galactic system in the sun's vicinity.

Hubble's general rule that the arms of spirals are trailing in the rotations is verified in all cases where the evidence is available. Thus M 33 (Fig. 17·9) rotates in the clockwise direction.

17·14. The Red Shifts. The relation between the displacements of their spectrum lines toward the red and the distances of the galaxies was announced by Hubble in 1929. Having corrected the observed shifts of the lines for Doppler effects of the sun's motion in the rotation of the galactic system, Hubble showed that the red shifts increase linearly as the distances of the galaxies are greater.

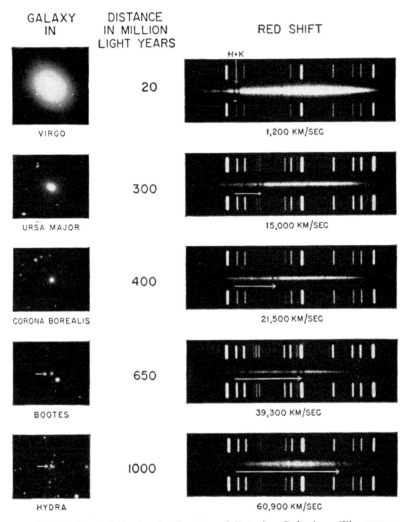

FIG. 17·14. Red Shifts in the Spectra of Exterior Galaxies. The arrows
show the shifts of the H and K lines of calcium. The former values of
the distances are multiplied tentatively by about the factor 3. (*Photographs by Mount Wilson and Palomar Observatories*)

More extensive investigations of this relation were reported in 1956 by Humason, Mayall, and Sandage.

The red shifts have now been observed in the spectra of galaxies in 26 clusters, from the Virgo cluster at the distance of 20 million light years to the Hydra cluster at a billion light years, and in hundreds of field galaxies as well. In this range the velocities of recession of the galaxies from us increase from 700 to 38,000 miles a second, or one fifth the speed of light. Although the Hydra cluster approaches the present limit of spectroscopic measures with the Hale telescope, it is hoped that such observations may eventually be extended with this telescope to 2 billion light years, which at the present rate of increase would produce a velocity of recession somewhat greater than a third the speed of light.

With the revised scale of distances, the increase in the velocity of recession of the galaxies is 180 km/sec per 1 million parsecs, or about 35 miles a second per 1 million light years. These investigators find an apparently significant increase in the rate at the greater distances, but they consider it a preliminary result. There is still uncertainty in the distances, caused partly by possible effects of evolution on the brightness of galaxies. As it stands, the result shows that the rate of recession of the galaxies has been diminishing during the past billion years.

17·15. The Expanding Universe. The red shifts in the spectra of galaxies are now generally regarded as Doppler effects. The universe is accordingly expanding; the galaxies are separating. The systematic red shifts do not operate, however, within the individual galaxies themselves or within their groups and clusters. The preliminary observations for the more remote galaxies suggest that the rate of the recession is diminishing with time.

The decrease in the rate of the recession might be expected to continue until the expansion ceases and contraction under gravity sets in; and when the material has contracted to excessive density, it might begin to expand again. Thus the universe would oscillate in cycles of perhaps some 15 billion years. It would be finite in space and of infinite duration.

Among other interpretations of the expanding universe we mention two which have potential interest, although they do not now seem to be justified by the observed red shifts. George Gamow describes an infinite universe in which the galaxies are separating at speeds exceeding their mutual velocities of escape. This could occur if the average density of the material is less than the critical value required to prevent escape. The expansion would then go on indefinitely, and it may have been preceded by contraction for an indefinite time.

In the steady-state theory described by Fred Hoyle, new material is continuously created, and the universe keeps expanding accordingly so as to maintain the average density at a constant value forever. This is a universe infinite in space and, like the other two, may have neither any beginning nor any end in finite time.

QUESTIONS ON CHAPTER 17

1. Describe the 3 chief types of galaxies, naming an example of each.

2. State several points of resemblance between the great spiral in Andromeda and the galactic system. Explain that the former has now proved to be considerably the larger of the two.

3. Distinguish between normal and barred spiral galaxies. Explain the division of each type into 3 classes.

4. What is the significance of the dark bands across spirals presented edgewise to us?

5. Describe the division of elliptical galaxies into several classes.

6. Describe the sequence of regular galaxies and its possible relation to their evolution.

7. The recent revision of the period-luminosity relation for the classical cepheids has doubled the former values of the distances of most exterior galaxies. Yet the astronomers are now multiplying the former distances by 3 instead of 2. Why?

8. Describe the local group of galaxies. Name several members of the group.

9. Name the nearest cluster of galaxies and one cluster that is more remote. Why are the photographs of clusters especially useful for the discovery of supernovae?

10. Describe the method of studying the rotations of galaxies.

11. If the observed acceleration in the recession of galaxies is greater at the greater distances, explain that the more recent rate of expansion is slower than it was a billion years ago.

12. Explain that the universe may be considered to have infinite duration in all three interpretations (17·15) of its expansion.

REFERENCES

Gamow, George, *The Creation of the Universe*. The Viking Press, New York, 1952.

Hubble, Edwin P., *The Observational Approach to Cosmology*. Oxford University Press, 1937.

Hubble, Edwin P., *The Realm of the Nebulae.* Yale University Press, 1936.

Shapley, Harlow, *Galaxies.* Harvard University Press, Cambridge, 1943.

Current contributions to the literature of astronomy appear in periodicals, such as:

The Astronomical Journal. Published by the American Astronomical Society. Yale University Observatory, New Haven 11.

The Astrophysical Journal. An International Review of Spectroscopy and Astronomical Physics. Published bimonthly. The University of Chicago Press, Chicago 37.

The Journal of the British Astronomical Association. Published 10 times a year. 303 Bath Road, Hounsley West, Middlesex, England.

The Journal of the Royal Astronomical Society of Canada. Published bimonthly. 252 College Street, Toronto, Ontario. The Society also publishes for each year *The Observer's Handbook,* a useful reference for astronomical data and events of the ensuing year.

Monthly Notices of the Royal Astronomical Society. Published monthly. Burlington House, London, W. 1.

The Observatory. A Review of Astronomy. Published monthly. The Editors, Royal Greenwich Observatory, Herstmonceux Castle, Hailsham, Sussex, England.

Publications of the Astronomical Society of the Pacific. Published bimonthly by the Society. 675 Eighteenth Avenue, San Francisco 21. The Society also publishes monthly *Leaflets* written in popular style by various astronomers.

Scientific American. Contains frequent articles on astronomy and allied sciences. Published monthly by Scientific American, Inc., 2 West 45th Street, New York 36.

Sky and Telescope. Published monthly. Sky Publishing Corporation, Harvard Observatory, Cambridge 38, Massachusetts. Monthly articles by Otto Struve on subjects of current interest are outstanding features of this useful periodical.

APPENDIX

THE AMATEUR ASTRONOMERS

These final pages are for the readers who have found the introductory course in astronomy a pleasant experience and have acquired an interest in the subject which has not terminated with the ending of the course. The interest may lead to the reading of other books and of articles in current periodicals about new developments in astronomy, to the frequent renewal of acquaintance with familiar sights in the heavens, and perhaps to the ownership of a telescope. Opportunity for exchange of information and ideas with others having a similar interest may be afforded by membership in an amateur astronomical society in the neighborhood.

For those who may wish to go somewhat further and to examine the possibility of a career in astronomy, Freeman D. Miller of the University of Michigan has written a useful pamphlet published by the Bellman Publishing Company, Cambridge 38, Massachusetts (32 pages, paper bound, $1.00). The pamphlet describes among other things the branches of astronomy, the operation of a typical observatory, and the academic training and scientific background required to qualify for the relatively few available positions in astronomy.

The Local Amateur Societies. There are many amateur astronomical societies in various parts of the country. A large number of these are listed occasionally in the periodical *Sky and Telescope*, including the places and times of their meetings and the addresses to which communications may be sent. As an example, we find in the list that the Milwaukee Astronomical Society meets in the Library on the 3rd Friday of each month. Like some others, this Society maintains an observatory having an excellent telescope; the comet photographs in our Fig. 9·2 were taken there in order to supply positions from which the comet's orbit could be calculated.

The societies meet in observatories, planetariums, museums,

321

libraries, college and other buildings, and private homes. They welcome new members and often require for admission only that the applicant be interested in astronomy. Many groups are member societies of one of the two larger associations.

The Larger Associations. The *Astronomical League,* formerly organized in 1947, has a membership of more than 80 amateur astronomical societies in different parts of the country. It also includes individuals not within reach of any local society, and groups of junior amateur astronomers under 18 years of age. In a booklet describing its purposes and activities, the objectives of the League are stated as follows: (a) to promote the science of astronomy; (b) to encourage and coordinate activities of amateur astronomical societies; (c) to foster observational and computational work and craftsmanship in the various fields of astronomy; (d) to coordinate amateur activities with professional research.

The member organizations are divided geographically into 8 groups. Each regional group holds a convention once every year or two, and there is an annual convention for all groups. Features of the conventions are sessions for talks by amateurs and professionals, star parties to which members bring their telescopes, and visits to observatories. The League issues its *Bulletin* five times a year for exchange of ideas and for news from the different branches. The annual *Proceedings* describes the activities of the general conventions. Communications to the League are addressed to one of the member societies or to the executive secretary.

The *Western Amateur Astronomers,* organized in 1949, is an association of more than 20 local amateur societies in California, Nevada, Arizona, and New Mexico. Its purpose is primarily to insure an annual convention. During the 3-day convention there are papers by amateurs and addresses by professional astronomers; there are symposiums on various subjects, including the making of telescopes, a star party, and normally a visit to a large observatory. This organization is affiliated with the Astronomical Society of the Pacific. Communications are addressed to one of the member societies.

Three other larger associations in the United States, Canada, and Mexico include both amateurs and professionals in their memberships. The *Astronomical Society of the Pacific* has for its purpose to promote the science of astronomy and to spread astronomical information through its publications, popular lectures, excursions, and meetings. The bimonthly *Publications* keep the members of the Society in touch with current astronomical research. Nontechnical articles on astronomy also appear in the *Publications* and in the 8-page monthly *Leaflets*. Membership in the Society is open to anyone. Members receive the publications and are entitled to the benefits of the lectures, excursions, and meetings. The address of the Society is 675 Eighteenth Avenue, San Francisco 21, California.

The *Royal Astronomical Society of Canada,* organized in 1903, has 1600 Canadian members and 400 others scattered over the globe. It is divided into 13 Centers across the country, each having its own meetings. The national headquarters of the Society are in its building at 252 College Street in Toronto. Subscription to the bimonthly *Journal* is included in the membership fee.

The *Astronomical Society of Mexico* was founded in 1901 by Luis G. Leon. Some of the men he initiated into astronomy reorganized the Society in 1938 to its present active state, and they were also mainly responsible for the founding of the National Observatory at Tonanzintla, south of Puebla. The Society's building is situated in a public park in Mexico City. The observatory on the third floor contains a 12-inch telescope, with which groups of people may observe at scheduled times. The lecture room and classroom on the lower floors are used for popular lectures and for short courses in elementary astronomy. The Society issues the periodical *El Universo.* The address is P.O. Box 9647, Mexico City.

Examples of large amateur organizations in other countries are the British Astronomical Association and the Astronomical Society of France.

The More Specialized Groups. *The Amateur Telescope Makers* are among the most numerous and active of the amateurs. They have no formal general organization, but either have local societies of their own or are members of astronomical societies. They have workshops in planetariums and other places where they make telescopes and discuss the problems of their craft.

Russell W. Porter is generally regarded as the founder of the modern guild. Porter made a small reflecting telescope as early as 1911, and he acquired an interest in telescope making that continued through his lifetime. Presently his advice was asked by Albert G. Ingalls, then of the *Scientific American,* who was making a telescope mirror. The result of this contact was Ingalls' *Amateur*

Telescope Making, now in three volumes, which has been the text-book of the amateurs ever since.

A group of men under Porter's direction began to make tele-scopes for their own enjoyment in the machine shop of Governor James Hartness in Springfield, Vermont. This was the beginning of the Amateur Telescope Makers of Springfield, the parent society. Stellafane, the turreted "House of Stars" with its 16-inch reflecting telescope on the mountain at Springfield, is the mecca of amateur telescope makers who assemble there every summer, bringing their own telescopes for the star parties.

Many of the amateurs employ their telescopes for general pur-poses or for certain systematic observations. Others derive their chief pleasure in the making of the telescopes and in demonstrat-ing the degree of optical and mechanical perfection that they have achieved. There is a fascination itself, as Porter remarked, in the shaping of glass with one's own hands so perfectly as to show the stars clearly. In his later years Porter's skill in design proved valuable in the construction of the Hale telescope on Palomar Mountain.

The *American Association of Variable Star Observers,* founded in 1911, has several hundred members in this and other countries. Any person who has attained age 16 and is interested in the work of the Association is eligible for membership. The members em-ploy telescopes of small or moderate size for observing the magni-tudes of selected variable stars. Leon Campbell at Harvard Ob-servatory served for many years as Recorder. Under his efficient guidance the number of individual observations reached the million mark, giving the histories of several hundred variables over periods up to a third of a century.

The records of the observations are now reported to the Recorder, Margaret W. Mayall, at the A.A.V.S.O. headquarters, 4 Brattle Street, Cambridge 38, Massachusetts. The *Variable Star Notes* of the Association are published in the *Journal* of the Royal Astro-nomical Society of Canada.

The *American Meteor Society* has a membership composed of amateurs and some professional astronomers. Its purpose is to encourage the observation of meteor trails and also to promote general interest in astronomy. Communications are addressed to the acting president, Charles P. Olivier, 521 Wynnewood Avenue, Narbeth, Pennsylvania. Reports of the Society are published in *Meteoritics,* the Journal of the Meteoritical Society.

The *Meteoritical Society* is primarily for professional scientists, but also welcomes to membership others who are interested in meteorites and are in sympathy with the purpose of the Society. Its purpose is to promote the discovery, collection, investigation, and preservation of meteorites, and to forward the observation and study of meteors. For the latter purpose it includes a Meteor Section. The secretary is John A. Russell, Department of Astronomy, University of Southern California, Los Angeles 7, California.

The *Association of Lunar and Planetary Observers* has more than 400 members. Walter H. Haas, the director, publishes *The Strolling Astronomer* 5 or 6 times a year. The subscribers to this publication are deemed members of the Association, and conversely. The secretary is David P. Barcroft, 1203 North Alameda Blvd., Las Cruces, New Mexico.

The Planetariums. The larger planetariums are frequent gathering places for amateur astronomers, not only for the sky demonstrations and exhibits, but also for other services that are provided there. Some are the meeting places of amateur societies, and some afford facilities for amateur telescope making. Many planeteriums have telescopes which are employed for frequent observing.

Planetariums in increasing numbers in various parts of the country and abroad offer impressive views of the heavens and of the movements of the celestial bodies. They show replicas of the skies more clearly than many city dwellers are likely to see the real sky. By speeding up the celestial movements, they make these motions easier to see and to comprehend. They can take the audience quickly to other latitudes where constellations not visible at home are displayed. The planetarium, as an astronomer has remarked, "is a school, a theater, and a cinema in one; a schoolroom under the vault of heaven, a drama with the celestial bodies as actors." The word "planetarium" is applied either to the projection apparatus or to the building which houses it.

There are six large Zeiss planetariums in the United States. These are the Adler Planetarium in Chicago, the Fels Planetarium in Philadelphia, the Griffith Observatory in Los Angeles, the Hayden Planetarium in New York, the Buhl Planetarium in Pittsburgh, and the Morehead Planetarium at the University of North Carolina. The Morrison Planetarium in San Francisco has a somewhat similar apparatus. The domes which represent the sky are around 60 to 80 feet in diameter. The complex projection apparatus in the middle of the floor shows the changing celestial scene to an audience of several hundred people at once. The lectures are given at scheduled times, and the topics are varied through the year.

The first planetarium of a different type was designed by F. D. Korhosz for the Museum of Natural History in Springfield, Massachusetts, and was opened to the public in 1937. More than 100 smaller and less costly Spitz planetariums are in operation in colleges and museums in America, and there are many others in other parts of the world. The first of these was produced in 1947 by its inventor, Armand N. Spitz. The first large Spitz planetarium, model B, comparable in size and effectiveness with the Zeiss projector, is at the Municipal Center in Montevideo, Uruguay. The second is for the U.S. Air Force Academy, Colorado Springs, Colorado.

INDEX